BILL KNOX

Modern Precision-Built Display Cases—Striking Examples of Cabinetmaking Skill—Are Fixtures of Distinction in the Campus Camera Shop of Westwood Village, California

Courtesy of Grand Rapids Store Equipment Co., Los Angeles Factory

Cabinetmaking

AND Millwork

TOOLS · MATERIALS
CONSTRUCTION · LAYOUT

ALF DAHL
Head, Building Trades Department
Los Angeles Trade-Technical Junior College
(Formerly Frank Wiggins Trade School)

J. DOUGLAS WILSON
Formerly Curriculum Supervisor
Trades and Industries
Los Angeles City Schools

AMERICAN TECHNICAL SOCIETY
CHICAGO, U. S. A.

PREFACE

Before the introduction of power-driven machinery the cabinet-maker did all the cutting, shaping, and assembling of articles made from wood. Power-driven woodworking machines opened the way for a new occupational specialist, the millman. This group is primarily concerned with setting up and operating the various woodworking machines.

The millman is also responsible for grinding and shaping cutter knives to produce a variety of wood products which are assembled by other workers.

The cabinetmaker, in contrast to the millman, generally does all of the work of fitting and assembling. However, in many cases the cabinetmaker assembles the parts that are prepared by the millman.

Today the work of the cabinetmaker and the millman are so similar that no distinction can be drawn to fit all areas. The information in this book covers the work of both the cabinetmaker and the millman. Therefore, it can be used in all areas.

Since a modern cabinetmaker and millman must be able to analyze drawings, plan operations, make out stock bills, select lumber, and perform a variety of operations, this book stresses related information and basic skills. The worker who knows the related information of his trade and can plan and lay out work is going to advance more rapidly than the worker who lacks this knowledge.

To become a foreman or supervisor, it is necessary to master as much information about your job as possible. To become a really skilled craftsman, it is also necessary to know standards of construction and design as well as standards for wood and other materials. A thorough knowledge of construction standards and material standards simplifies the work of the cabinetmaker and increases the chances for promotion.

The revised Second Edition of this book contains six additional chapters on important aspects of cabinetmaking and millwork, with special emphasis on the problems of layout and construction.

The information found in this book will be valuable for anyone who wants to advance in the field of cabinetmaking or millworking or for those who want to progress at their present job.

THE PUBLISHERS

CONTENTS

The Cabinetmaker's Work

QUESTIONS CHAPTER I WILL ANSWER FOR YOU

1. *What is cabinetmaking?*
2. *What specialized work is associated with cabinetmaking?*
3. *Where are cabinetmakers employed?*
4. *What materials are used by the cabinetmaker?*
5. *What are some of the items produced by the cabinetmaker?*

INTRODUCTION TO CHAPTER I

Woodworking is an old craft dating back thousands of years, as indicated by stone woodworking tools uncovered in various parts of the world. Metal woodworking tools dating to about 5,000 B.C. showed a vast improvement over the earlier stone tools. With the introduction of metal tools came an expansion in the building of articles made from wood and a trend toward specialization. Cabinetmaking is one of the specialized fields of woodworking. To understand cabinetmaking fully, it is necessary to review briefly the history of cabinetmaking. This chapter will acquaint you with some of the specialized fields of woodworking as they exist at present.

HISTORY OF CABINETMAKING

The early woodworkers performed all types of work, including the framing and erection of structures and ships, the cutting and assembling of interior woodwork, and the designing and making of furniture, which included woodcarving. History reveals that woodworkers began to specialize to some extent prior to the rise of the Roman Empire. Some woodworkers specialized in boatbuilding, some in structural work, and others in woodcarving. Early cabinets were little more than rectangular boxes used for storing valuables. Gradually a group of workers began to specialize in this field, taking over some of the duties of the interior woodworker and the furniture worker. This group of workers was called cabinetmakers. Cabinetmaking reached a status of fine art in the Eighteenth and Nineteenth centuries and produced such masters as Chippendale, the Brothers Adam, Sheraton,

1

and Hepplewhite in England, and Duncan Phyfe in the United States. Beautiful interiors in old cathedrals (Fig. 1) and castles attest to the skill and artisanship of these workers, who enjoyed a high place in society.

Fig. 1. Interior of Westminster Abbey
By Burton Holmes from Ewing Galloway

Modern Development. Early American woodworkers, called carpenters, cut trees, hewed the trees into timbers, made shingles, fashioned pegs for fastening the timbers, and erected structures. Door and window frames were sometimes made by ripping logs into boards with handsaws. With the advance of building methods requiring more trim (finish work of a building, including ornamental parts), some carpenters specialized in trim work and were known as finish carpenters.

Other carpenters specialized in the making of furniture and cabinets and were called cabinetmakers. With the introduction of power woodworking equipment, a new class of woodworkers, called millmen, was originated. These workers were primarily concerned with the grinding and shaping of cutter knives and with the setting up and operation of the woodworking machines. This trend reduced the work of the cabinetmaker and finish carpenters to fitting, assembling, or installing. It must be remembered that at present there are some cabinetmakers who still do all the work in the making of custom-made furniture and other articles. No sharp line can be drawn over the whole of the United States to divide the work of the cabinetmaker and the millman. In some areas where the woodworking industry has been highly specialized, the millworkers are strictly machine operators, while the cabinetmakers are primarily assemblymen, performing the hand operations necessary to fit and assemble parts of cabinets and other items of wood as prepared by the machine operators or millmen.

Regardless of specialization, the cabinetmaker is essentially a worker in wood, performing such jobs as cutting, shaping, and assembling high-grade articles of furniture, including store fixtures, office equipment, and home furnishings. The skilled cabinetmaker must be able to use both hand and machine woodworking tools. He must have a thorough knowledge of the materials used in the trade; he must be able to lay out and dimension cabinets and other items of wood; he must be able to read blueprints and make various kinds of joints; he must be able to select and install hardware such as hinges, catches, and drawer pulls; and he must be able to perform all these tasks with skill and precision.

The material in the following chapters will be concerned with the work of the cabinetmaker and millman, since the two occupations will be found in most woodworking areas. In highly specialized shops the work of the millman may even be divided into several specialist classifications. The present trend in cabinetmaking is toward specialization; but, regardless of this trend, there will always be a demand for the person who is skilled in all phases of cabinetmaking. Such persons will always be held in high esteem.

BRANCHES OF THE CABINETMAKING INDUSTRY

Millwork Plants. Cabinet shops, planing mills, and sash and door factories all produce what, in general terms, is called millwork. Millwork includes such items as sash (frames holding panes of glass), doors, interior and exterior trim, door and window frames, cabinets, paneling, staircases (Fig. 2), wardrobes, mantels (Fig. 3), and all other items of woodwork needed for the finishing of a house, office, or store building.

Some large plants are devoted to the wholesale manufacture of doors, windows, and frames. Other plants manufacture a complete line of special and stock millwork. Smaller shops may specialize in only a few items which they can produce economically.

Fig. 2. Walnut Staircase
Courtesy of American Walnut Mfg. Association, Chicago, Ill.

Fixture Plants. The manufacture of store, office, and market fixtures has become a highly specialized branch of the woodworking industry. Large factories are equipped to furnish completely the fixtures for a department store. Others may be devoted to fixtures of only one type, such as for restaurants, drug stores, ladies' apparel stores, men's wear stores, markets of all types, including stores that require extensive refrigeration.

The products of fixture plants consist of all kinds of display and storage cases, show windows, paneling, partitions, and, to some extent, custom built furniture (Figs. 4, 5, and 6).

Furniture Plants. The manufacture of furniture is a diversified branch of the woodworking industry. Large factories may manufacture a complete line of household furniture, while others may specialize in such items as furniture for the dining room, living room, bedroom, or office. Some factories may specialize in single items, such as chairs, cedar chests, breakfast sets, and outdoor furniture.

Specialty Plants. This branch of the industry covers a multitude of products, such as musical instruments, scientific and photographic instruments, medical equipment, and novelties, such as toys and kitchenware. Pattern making, aircraft woodworking, church furniture, and casket making are all important segments of the specialty branch of woodworking.

OTHER CLASSIFICATIONS IN CABINETMAKING

Cabinetmaking, like many of our industries, has in most areas been placed on a mass-production basis which makes it necessary to classify the jobs performed by each worker. Such classifications are not necessarily found in all areas, but they are used in a large number of highly specialized plants. The following classifications are of this type:

Benchman. The accomplished cabinetmaker is often referred to as a *benchman*. He can fashion joints, fit, glue, and assemble machined parts, read working drawings, and plan assembly and construction of intricate designs in wood. He can execute the work in a first-class manner and prepare the surface for finishing. He fits and installs metal molds and parts. He often operates the basic

Fig. 3. An Architecturally Designed, Custom-Made Mantel Assembly
Courtesy of Los Angeles Trade-Tech Junior College

woodworking machines, such as the cutoff saw, rip saw, jointer, planer, trim saw, and boring machine. In highly specialized plants, the work of the benchman has been reduced to the assembling of prepared parts.

Millman Classifications. The *millman* or *machine woodworker* who is skilled in the maintenance, setup, and operation of all woodworking machinery is often referred to as an "all-round man." In some shops, jobs requiring only certain specific skills are classified according to the following employment levels: *stock cutter, trim sawyer,*

Fig. 4. A Jewelry Store Unit. The Manufacture of Such Display Fixtures
Has Become a Highly Specialized Branch of the Woodworking Industry
Courtesy of Grand Rapids Store Equipment Co., Los Angeles Factory

Fig. 5. Low-Rail, Wood and Glass Partition
Courtesy of Weber Showcase and Fixture Co., Los Angeles, Calif.

shaperman, stickerman, sash and doorman, sanderman, band sawyer, and *turner.*

The Detailer. *The detailer* has become, of necessity, a product of modern industry. This individual, coming up through the ranks, has an over-all view of the whole job. He takes measurements at the job; makes working drawings; designs construction details, and makes out stock bills, hardware and glass lists. Fig. 7 is a typical example of the work done by a detailer.

Fig. 6. Modern Banking Fixtures
Courtesy of Weber Showcase and Fixture Co., Los Angeles, Calif.

Layout Man. The *layout man* is responsible for marking the stock to guide the machine operators in shaping the wood. The work of the detailer and layout man is sometimes performed by the same person. The layout man in many instances is in a supervisory job and may be responsible for detailing, layout, and stock billing as will be explained in a later chapter.

GENERAL REQUIREMENTS FOR CABINETMAKERS

The cabinetmaker and millman must be able to multiply, divide, subtract, and add whole numbers, fractions, and decimals. They must be able to make cost and material estimates and must have a good understanding of the various products used in the industry.

The person entering this field should possess keenness of vision and a high degree of eye-hand co-ordination. An understanding of mechanical devices is also very helpful.

The minimum age requirements are, of course, subject to state and federal requirements. In most cases there are no maximum age limitations, and men over 70 years of age are often employed in various types of cabinet and millwork.

WORKING CONDITIONS

Modern mills and shops are equipped with dust and waste collectors and are well lighted. Older shops are sometimes lacking in these respects. There is, of course, the possibility of accidents due to the various kinds of high-speed cutter heads.

Fig. 7. Typical Example of Detailer's Layout Work
Courtesy of Grand Rapids Store Equipment Co., Los Angeles Factory

The number of working hours in a week varies with the various branches of the industry. The pay is usually on an hourly basis. Some workers are given paid vacations, and many employers recognize the legal holidays.

Highly skilled workers are generally assured of year-round employment. Less skilled workers may experience unemployment for short periods during each year because of seasonal demands.

REVIEW QUESTIONS

1. Name three branches of the woodworking industry.
2. At what period of time did cabinetmaking reach the status of a fine art?

3. What has changed the status of the cabinetmaker today?
4. Name four items which are usually identified by the term "millwork."
5. Name four items of woodwork which can be termed a specialty.
6. Explain the work of a benchman.
7. Explain the work of a detailer.
8. Name five employment levels in the field of "millman."
9. What physical requirements have to be met by the cabinetmaker?
10. Describe the general working conditions of a cabinetmaker.

Safety Practices in Cabinetmaking

QUESTIONS CHAPTER II WILL ANSWER FOR YOU

1. *What is the most important step in safety education?*
2. *Why is industry concerned with safety education?*
3. *Why is loose clothing a safety hazard?*
4. *When should guards and other safety devices be used?*
5. *When should accidents be reported?*

INTRODUCTION TO CHAPTER II

Safety education today has become an important phase of every training program. The safety rules that are important to the cabinetmaker are briefly outlined in this chapter. For your own safety and the safety of others, you should study and know these safety rules.

"Safety First" is a slogan adopted on a national scale by all branches of industry. Laws and regulations governing manufacturing, construction, and transportation are enforced by departments of safety in each state. However, instruction in safety regulations, by industry itself, pays dividends by reducing injuries and loss of time.

Of first importance in a "Safety First" campaign is the education of the worker. This education must become a part of his daily training as he learns the technical and manipulative skills of his job. Generally, a person becomes injured because of his own carelessness or the carelessness of some other person. To prevent accidents and injuries, observe all safety regulations, use all safety devices and guards when working with machines, and learn to control your work and actions so as to avoid danger. Training for safety is every bit as important as learning to be a skillful craftsman and should be a part of the worker's education.

In the performance of his work, the woodworker handles materials, manipulates hand tools, and operates machines which if improperly handled or used may result in serious injury. Seek first aid no matter how slight the injury. Blood poisoning may result from an insignificant sliver. Take a first aid course at the first opportunity. The following safety rules should always be observed by the person who works with wood.

GENERAL SAFETY

1. Always practice "Safety First." It pays in the long run. Pay strict attention to all safety rules and instructions. Be alert.

2. Wrestling, throwing objects, and other forms of horseplay should be avoided. Serious injuries may be the result.

3. Provide a place for everything and keep everything in its place.

4. Keep the arms and body as nearly straight as possible when lifting heavy objects. Lift with the legs—not with the back.

5. Never place articles on window sills, stepladders, or other high places where they may fall and cause injuries.

6. Oil or water left on the floor may cause a serious accident.

7. Keep all work spaces clear of scraps of lumber, tools, and material. Remove or bend down all protruding nails.

8. Piles of waste or debris left scattered on the floor may cause stumbling and result in serious injury from a fall. Pick them up.

9. Notify your immediate superior of any known violations of safety rules or condition you think may be dangerous.

10. When loading factory trucks with lumber, cross-stick the load at intervals. When the truck stakes are removed, the lumber will not fall off.

11. Inspect ladders carefully before mounting. Weak rungs or steps may cause a fall.

12. When using a ladder, be sure that the bottom rests on solid footing so that it cannot slip. Do not slant it at such an acute angle that the weight of the body would pull the top of the ladder out from the wall.

13. Remove slivers immediately which have pierced the skin, and go to a doctor for treatment.

14. Immediately report all accidents, no matter how slight, to your superior, and report for first aid treatment.

CLOTHING

1. Do not wear ragged sleeves, long neckties, or loose clothing of any sort, as it may get caught in rotating machinery.

2. Roll up your shirt sleeves.

3. Wear thick-soled shoes for protection against sharp objects such as nails.

HAND TOOLS

1. Cut away from the body when using sharp-edged tools. A slip of the tool may result in a serious cut.

2. Keep sharp-edged tools away from the edge of the bench.

Brushing against the tool may cause it to fall and injure a leg or foot.

3. Keep tools sharp and clean. The extra force exerted in using dull tools often results in losing control of the tool.

4. Always use a handle on a file. Otherwise, the tang may cut into your hand.

5. Do not strike hardened metal or tools with a hard-faced hammer. Chips of metal may break loose and cause injury.

6. Batter-heads of metal tools must be kept ground smooth and square to avoid mushrooming. When the head of a tool that has been allowed to mushroom is struck, bits of metal often break loose, causing serious injuries.

GENERAL SAFETY RULES FOR OPERATING MACHINES

1. Never speak to, or try to attract the attention of, any person operating a machine. Distraction for a single second may be the cause of a serious injury.

2. Keep away from machines that are being operated by another person.

3. Never attempt to operate machines or equipment in another department unless you have been instructed to do so.

4. Never attempt to operate a machine until you thoroughly understand how the machine operates.

5. Never oil or clean machines while the machine is running.

6. Check all adjustable parts on a machine before starting it. Adjustable parts that are loose may cause a serious mishap.

7. Remove tools or other articles from a machine before starting it.

8. Use safety guards whenever possible; they are made for your protection.

9. Replace safety devices which have been removed from the machine, provided that they do not interfere with the operation of the machine.

10. When repairing or adjusting a machine, remove the fuses to avoid accidental starting of the machine.

SPECIFIC SAFETY RULES FOR MACHINES

Cut-Off Saw

1. Stock must always be held solidly against the fence.

2. Do not force the saw. Crowding the saw is dangerous and may result in breaking the saw.

3. Keep hands away from the direction of travel of the saw.

4. Never attempt to cut more than one piece at a time.

RIP AND TRIM SAW

1. The saw should project only one-fourth inch above the stock when cutting.

2. The saw should fit the arbor properly. Never use a saw that is too large for the arbor.

3. Use the splitter attachment whenever possible.

4. No stock should be lifted over a saw when it is running.

5. Do not brush off the bed or remove small pieces from the saw table with the hand while the saw is running.

6. When feeding stock through the saw, arch the hand. Never lay the hand flat on the stock.

7. Use a pusher stick for small pieces or whenever possible.

8. No stock should be *stop-cut* unless a stop is used.

9. No free-hand cutting should be done under any circumstances. Always use a guide.

JOINTER

1. Use pusher stick when facing short stock.

2. Take a light cut when facing stock.

3. Do not let the fingers project over stock or pass near the knives.

4. Operations involving stop-cuts must be held in place by a stop.

5. Examine the stock for knots and splits before running it over jointer.

PLANER

1. Stock of varying thickness should not be planed at the same time.

2. Do not look into the planer.

3. Keep hands away from feed rolls.

MORTISER

1. Keep hands away from the chisel when the machine is in operation.

2. Make sure the stock is securely held by the clamps before starting the machine.

3. Turn the machine over at least one complete revolution by hand to make certain everything is properly adjusted before turning on the power.

Tenoner

1. Set the hold-down lever so that the work is under pressure while the cut is being made.

2. All cuttings should be done while the sliding bed is being pushed away from the operator.

Band Saw

1. Do not have more of the saw exposed than is necessary.

2. Do not remove the throat while the saw is running.

3. Always keep the hands at a safe distance from the saw blade.

4. Stop the machine whenever the upper guide wheels have to be raised or lowered.

5. The height of the saw guide should be adjusted before power is turned on.

6. Do not permit the hands to cross the saw line when the saw is operating.

7. Cylindrical stock should never be cut on a band saw except by an experienced operator.

Drum Sander

1. Set up the sander to take as small a cut as possible.

2. Keep the hands off the bed of machine while it is running.

3. If a piece of stock gets caught on the edge of the bed of the machine, do not try to save the stock. Stop the machine.

Belt Sander

1. Make certain that the stock being sanded is resting firmly against stop on the bed of the machine.

2. Keep the hands away from the belt.

Shaper

1. Knives should be correctly balanced before being used. This is very important. An unbalanced set of knives will throw out when the spindle is rotating at high speed.

2. Examine the knives carefully and see that they are correctly seated before tightening them in position.

3. Remove all loose articles and tools from the bed of the shaper before starting operations.

4. Whenever possible, use a fence.

5. Feed all work on the shaper in a direction against the rotating cutters.

6. Never back up work. If this becomes necessary, take the material out of the machine and start again.

7. Use the pressure bar whenever possible.

LATHE

1. Examine the stock for flaws, and test glued joints.

2. See that the centers are properly entered into the stock before starting the lathe.

3. Keep the tool rest as close to the work as possible.

4. Govern the speed of lathe according to diameter of work.

GRINDER

1. Never operate the grinder without the glass guards being in place. Get in the habit of wearing safety goggles for all grinding operations.

2. Hold the work firmly on the tool rest.

3. See that the rest is set close to wheel and that it is properly secured.

4. Do not use a rag to hold anything that is being ground.

5. Small pieces should not be ground on the emery wheel without a proper holder.

STICKER

1. Use the correct wrench and hold the handle at a right angle to the shaft when tightening knife bolts.

2. Make sure that all knives are secure before turning on the power.

3. Stand back of the chip breaker when the machine is in operation.

4. Let the machine come to a full stop before making any adjustments.

REVIEW QUESTIONS

1. Why should heavy objects be lifted with the back as nearly straight as possible?

2. What safety measures should be taken in using a ladder?

3. Why is it important to remove slivers immediately?

4. Why should all work spaces be kept clear of lumber, tools, and other material?

5. Why is crowding a cut-off saw dangerous?

6. Name eight general safety rules for operating machines.

7. What is the reason for removing the fuses before adjusting or repairing a machine?

8. Why is free-hand cutting dangerous when using a cut-off saw?

9. When should a pusher stick be used in jointing stock?

10. Name four precautions to take in using the grinder.

Woodworking Tools

QUESTIONS CHAPTER III WILL ANSWER FOR YOU

1. *Why are quality tools important?*
2. *What hand tools are commonly used by the cabinetmaker?*
3. *When is a block plane used?*
4. *What power tools are commonly used by the cabinetmaker?*
5. *How is the size of an auger bit determined?*

INTRODUCTION TO CHAPTER III

A craftsman is judged by the way he selects, uses, and cares for the tools of his trade. Since the work of the cabinetmaker is varied, no attempt has been made to establish a list of recommended tools or even a minimum list of tools. The material in this chapter is devoted primarily to associating tools with the type of work most frequently done with that tool. In this manner it will be easy for you to select the proper tools for the type of work in which you are employed and the particular job to be done. It is common practice to buy additional tools as more complicated jobs are encountered. Remember that in buying tools *it is good economy to buy quality tools from name companies.*

The tools have been divided into five broad classifications for easy reference: layout tools, sharpening tools, forming and cutting tools, assembling tools, and power tools.

LAYOUT TOOLS

Layout tools are used for measuring distances and laying out circles, angles, plumb lines, and level lines. Fine workmanship requires precision in the use of these tools. Accurate results cannot be obtained with forming tools unless the layout is accurate.

Rules. The rules used for measuring distances in woodwork are based on the standard English *yard* measure and are divided into feet, inches, and fractions of an inch—usually to 16ths. The rules shown in Fig. 1 are those most commonly used in cabinetmaking.

Straightedge. The straightedge is used for marking and checking straight lines when doing layout work and in checking the straightness of surfaces such as counter tops or paneled frames (Fig. 2).

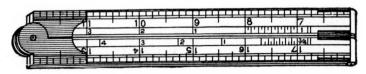

FOLDING RULE

SIX-FOOT ZIG-ZAG RULE

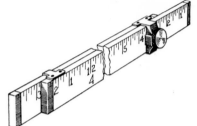

EXTENSION RULE

FLEXIBLE PUSH-PULL RULE

STEEL TAPE

Fig. 1. Measuring Tools Frequently Used in Cabinetmaking

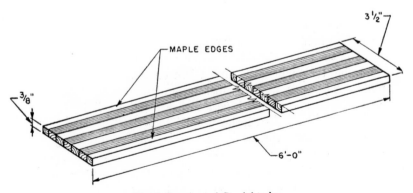

MAPLE EDGES

3 1/2"

3/8"

6'-0"

Fig. 2. Laminated Straightedge

Steel Square. The steel square (Fig. 3) is used for measuring and laying out angles. A full description and application of principles of the steel square are found in the chapter, "Steel Square Layout."

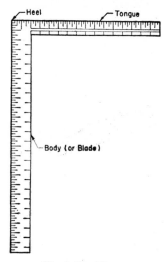

The steel square gages or *clips* are used in layout work involving the steel square (Fig. 4).[1]

Combination Square. The combination square is used to measure, mark, and check right angles, 45° angles, or by use of the protractor feature, any degree angle desired (Fig. 5).

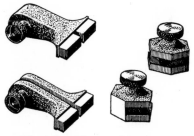

Fig. 3. Steel Square

Fig. 4. Steel Square Gages or Clips

Try Square. The try square is used mainly for checking the squareness of surfaces, for laying out lines square with an edge, and for testing 90° angles. The blade is marked in eighths of an inch along the top edge (Fig. 6).

Fig. 5. Combination Set with Center Square, and Protractor Heads
Courtesy of The L. S. Starrett Company, Athol, Mass.

[1] Square gages are technically called *stair gages.*

T Bevel. The T bevel (Fig. 7), often called a *bevel square,* is used for laying out any desired angle.

Compasses and Dividers. Compasses and dividers are used for striking circles or segments of circles and for stepping off equal spaces (Fig. 8).

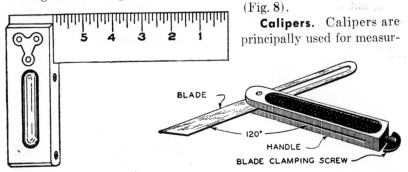

Calipers. Calipers are principally used for measur-

Fig. 6. Try Square with Fixed Blade   Fig. 7. T Bevel Adjustable to Any Angle

ing outside and inside diameters of turnings, or in places where a measurement cannot be established with an ordinary rule (Fig. 9).

Trammel. Trammel points attached to a straight rod are used to strike circles with diameters too large for the ordinary compass (Fig. 10).

Spirit Level. A level is used when work is installed permanently on the job, such as in setting a cabinet or fixture in a true horizontal or vertical position. See Fig. 11.

Fig. 8. Dividers

Plumb Bob. The plumb bob, Fig. 12, is used to establish a true vertical position between two points when a straightedge of sufficient length is not readily obtainable. A stair builder may use a plumb bob to establish a vertical position when measuring a building for a flight of steps.

Marking Gage. The marking gage (Fig. 13) is used principally in laying out lines parallel to the side of stock, locating the center for dowels, laying out mortise and tenon joints, or for *gaining* in hinges.

Mortise Gage. The mortise gage is provided with two pins for marking the width of a mortise or tenon with one stroke and for keeping the shoulder offset parallel.

Butt Gage. The butt gage is used for laying out the width and depth of a hinge seat such as the butt hinge (Fig. 14).

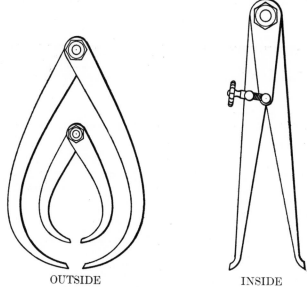

OUTSIDE   INSIDE
Fig. 9. Outside and Inside Calipers

SHARPENING TOOLS

Files. Files (for metal) are used primarily by the woodworker for sharpening tools. While there are a number of files, the most commonly used are the mill file, auger bit file, and various kinds of saw files (Fig. 15).

Mill File. An eight- or ten-inch smooth mill file is used for sharpening scraper blades and for smooth filing in fitting hardware.

Bit File. The auger bit file is used in sharpening the cutting edges and spurs of auger bits. One end of the file is provided with safe edges while the other end has safe sides.

Fig. 10. Trammel Points

Saw Files. The saw file, primarily used for sharpening handsaws, is single cut, and comes in various lengths from four to ten inches. The saw file is three-cornered and tapered. There are four sizes available, called regular taper, slim taper, extra slim taper, and double-extra slim taper. The number of points per inch

of the saw to be filed determines the length and degree of slimness of
the file.

Fig. 11. Aluminum Level

Table I shows the kind and size of file that will give the best results, depending on the number of points per inch of the saw.

TABLE I. SAW FILES*

NUMBER OF POINTS	FILES RECOMMENDED
5	7-inch regular taper
6	7-inch or 8-inch slim
7	6-inch or 7-inch slim
8	7-inch extra slim
	6-inch slim
	8-inch double extra slim
9	6-inch extra slim
	7-inch double extra slim
10	5-inch or 6-inch extra slim
11	5-inch extra slim
	6-inch double extra slim
12	4½- or 5-inch extra slim
13, 14	4½-inch extra slim
	5-inch double extra slim
15, 16	4-inch double extra slim

*Triangular saw files are made for filing all types of hand saws
with 60° angle teeth. The edges are set and cut for filing the gullet
between saw teeth.

In filing handsaws it is important to select the right file. In
general, the above suggestions as to kind and size will give the
best results. The choice depends on the filer's preference.

Half-round cabinet files and half-round cabinet rasps (Fig. 16)
are used for smoothing and shaping wood. The rasps are used where
a large amount of stock is to be re-
moved. Flat wood files are used for
finer work. *All files should be equipped
with handles.*

Fig. 12. Plumb Bob

Saw Set. The teeth of a handsaw
are *set* with a saw set, when the saw is
sharpened, to provide clearance for
the blade (Fig. 17). A saw set is adjustable as to the degree of set required for fine and coarse saws.

Saw Clamp. A saw clamp is used to hold a handsaw while being filed (Fig. 18).

Oil Stones. Oil stones are used for whetting sharp-edged tools (Fig. 19). The stones may be purchased in coarse, medium, or fine grits, depending upon the results desired. Some stones are combination

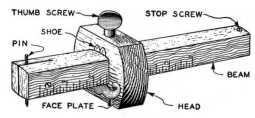

Fig. 13. Marking Gage

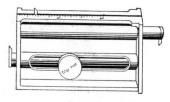

Fig. 14. Butt Gage

stones having a coarse grit on one side and a fine grit on the other.

Slip Stone. A slip stone (Fig. 20) is used to whet gouges, carving tools, and molding cutters. Various shapes, sizes, and fineness of grit are available.

Burnisher. A burnisher (Fig. 21) is used to turn the edge of scraper blades after sharpening the edges.

MILL FILE

Courtesy of Henry Disston & Sons, Philadelphia, Pa.

AUGER BIT FILE

Courtesy of Henry Disston & Sons, Philadelphia, Pa.

EXTRA-SLIM TAPER SAW FILE

Fig. 15. Commonly Used Files

FORMING AND CUTTING TOOLS

Saws. Saws are used primarily for cutting stock into various widths and lengths. There are several types of saws, each designed for a particular job. The hand crosscut saw is used for cutting across the grain of wood and the ripsaw for cutting with the grain. The shape of the teeth for both saws is shown in Fig. 22. The number of points per inch of a saw (there is always one more point to the inch than there are teeth) determines to some extent the use of the saw. Finer work can

Fig. 16. Half-Round Cabinet Rasp
Courtesy of Henry Disston & Sons, Philadelphia, Pa.

Fig. 17. Saw Set

Fig. 18. Saw Clamp
Courtesy of Henry Disston & Sons, Philadelphia, Pa.

Fig. 19. Oil Stone

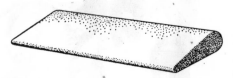

Fig. 20. Round Edge Slip Stone

Fig. 21. Burnisher

be done with a saw having finer teeth (more points to the inch), while coarser saws are better for green lumber and faster work. For average work a crosscut should have eight points per inch, a ripsaw five and one-half or six. For fine joinery work a ten- or eleven-point saw is used.

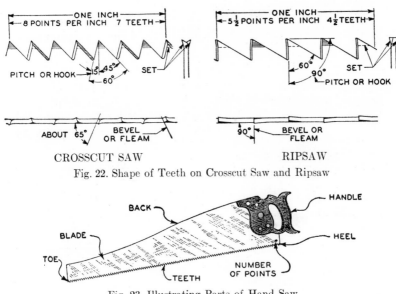

Fig. 22. Shape of Teeth on Crosscut Saw and Ripsaw

Fig. 23. Illustrating Parts of Hand Saw

Fig. 25. Dovetail Saw
Courtesy of Henry Disston & Sons, Philadelphia, Pa.

Fig. 24. Back Saw

The length of a handsaw is measured from the heel to the toe. The standard length is 26″. The number of points per inch is stamped on the blade near the heel (Fig. 23). Handsaws are available with either a curved (skew) back or a straight back. The straight-back saw can be used as a straightedge in drawing lines. Skew-back saws are preferred by some workers because of balance and design.

Panel Saw. The panel saw is made for use in lighter work, such as fine panels. It is available in 20″, 22″, and 24″ lengths and carries much the same specifications as the 26″ handsaw.

Backsaw. The backsaw (Fig. 24), so-called because of the back stiffener, is used for cutting finish miters. It is available in 10″, 12″, 14″, and 16″ lengths with 12 or 14 points to the inch.

Fig. 26. Miter Box Saw
Courtesy of Stanley Tools, New Britain, Conn.

Dovetail Saw. The dovetail saw (Fig. 25), so-called because of its use in making dovetailed joints by hand, is also used in other finish work. The blade may be 8″, 10″, or 12″ long with 15 or 17 points to the inch.

Miter Box Saw. The miter box saw (Fig. 26), used in a metal miter box as illustrated, is made to fit a given capacity miter box and varies in width from 4″, 5″, and 6″. The length variations are 24″, 26″, 28″, and 30″. The number of points may be 11 or 12 to the inch.

Fig. 27. Coping Saw

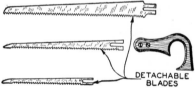

Fig. 28. Keyhole Saws

Coping Saw. The coping saw (Fig. 27) is used for light scroll work or for coping the ends of moldings to fit in inside corners rather than to make an inside miter, which may be more difficult to fit.

Compass and Keyhole Saws. The compass saw and keyhole saw (Fig. 28) are used for cutting inside circles, keyholes, and other rough scroll work.

Fig. 29. Cabinet Saw
Courtesy of Henry Disston & Sons, Philadelphia, Pa.

Cabinet Saw. The cabinet saw (Fig. 29) has one edge for ripping and one edge for crosscutting, and makes a convenient saw for light cabinet work. A saw of this type can be used as a panel saw, ripsaw, backsaw, or miter saw.

Planes. Planes are used for surfacing, smoothing, jointing, and fitting cabinet work. There are a great many different types of planes, each designed for a specific job. The smooth plane (Fig. 30) is used

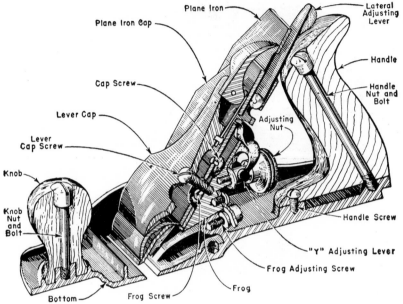

Fig. 30. The Stanley Smooth Plane

for surfacing and planing of all kinds. A smooth plane 9″ long with a 2″ cutter is ideal for average work. Planes have smooth or corrugated bottoms; the smooth bottom plane is better suited for the work in cabinetmaking.

Other types of commonly used planes are shown in Fig. 31.

Scrub Plane. The scrub plane, sometimes called a roughing plane, has a 1¼″ narrow rounded blade, which makes it an ideal tool for quickly roughing boards down to size and for backing out casings.

Jointer Plane. A jointer plane is longer than other planes to provide more bearing surface, which makes a straighter joint or surface. The plane is made in two sizes: 22″ long with a 2⅜″ cutter, and 24″ long with a 2⅝″ cutter.

Fore Plane. The fore plane, so-called because of its use in straightening the surface of boards *before* the use of a jack plane, is often used in place of a jointer, since it is lighter. The fore plane is 18″ long and has a 2⅜″ cutter.

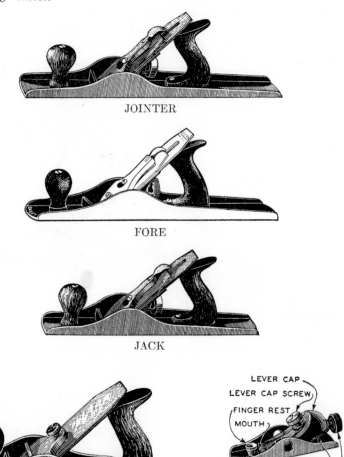

Fig. 31. Various Planes Used in Cabinetmaking

Jack Plane. The jack plane is an all-round plane that has many uses. The most popular sizes are 14″ long, with a 2″ cutter, and 15″ long, with a 2⅜″ cutter.

Block Plane. The block plane is made in a variety of sizes and styles. The cutter is placed at a low angle to obtain smooth cuts on the end grain of wood. Its chief purpose is in fitting short surfaces, such as miters, and in planing end grain.

Rabbet Planes. Rabbet planes are made in a variety of styles for special purposes. Cabinetmakers prefer the low-angle plane for all-round work in smoothing rabbets.

Router Plane. The router plane is indispensable for use in leveling the bottom of dadoes, gains, or rabbets if a uniform depth is desired.

Circle Plane. A circle plane operates on the same principle as

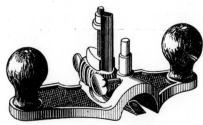

ROUTER

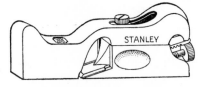

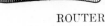

CABINETMAKER'S RABBET

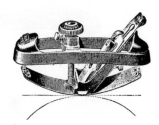

CIRCLE

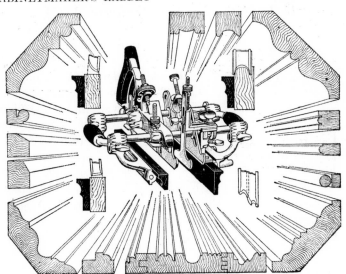

STANLEY "FIFTY-FIVE" MOLDING PLANE

Fig. 31. Various Planes Used in Cabinetmaking—*Continued*

the ordinary plane and is used for planing convex and concave surfaces. It has a flexible steel bottom which can be adjusted to fit any size curve within a minimum radius.

Molding Plane. Molding planes are useful in a small shop where a shaper or sticker is not available, as many moldings can be shaped with this tool.

Spokeshave. The spokeshave (Fig. 32) is used by the cabinet-maker to shape irregularly curved surfaces. Some spokeshaves have a straight bottom; others a convex or concave bottom.

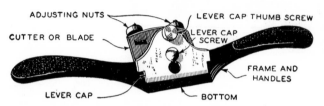

Fig. 32. Spokeshave

Scrapers. Scrapers are used to smooth a surface after it has been planed. There are several types of scrapers used by the cabinetmaker.

Cabinet Scraper. The cabinet scraper is fitted with a beveled-edge scraper blade, which, when properly sharpened, will smooth any ridges or torn grain left by the smoothing plane. It is primarily used on large surfaces.

Fig. 33. Hand Scraper

Courtesy of Henry Disston & Sons, Philadelphia, Pa.

Hand Scraper. The hand scraper (Fig. 33) is a piece of steel about .035″ thick, 2″ or 3″ wide, and 4″ to 6″ long. It has a square edge, which, when properly sharpened, is turned to form a fine cutting surface. A properly sharpened scraper will actually remove a very fine shaving, not just fine dust. It is preferred by some cabinetmakers for all uses and is especially adaptable in close quarters where the grain meets at right angles, as in the joining of a stile and rail.

Chisels. Chisels are used for cutting mortises, fitting hardware, and other irregular shaping that cannot be done with a plane or saw. There are two types of chisels—the socket or firmer chisel and the tang chisel (Fig. 34). In the socket type, the handle fits into a socket which is actually a part of the blade. In the tang type, the tang of the chisel runs into the handle. The socket type chisels withstand pounding better than the tang type.

The blade of a chisel may vary in width by eighths of an inch up to one inch and by quarters of an inch from one to two inches. The

SOCKET CHISEL   TANG-TYPE CHISEL
Fig. 34. Chisels Classified According to Construction

length and sturdiness of the blade determines its purpose. Several different styles of chisels are shown in Fig. 35.

Paring Chisel. The paring chisel is a light tool used for paring and carving. The chisel is short, with a blade about 2½″ long.

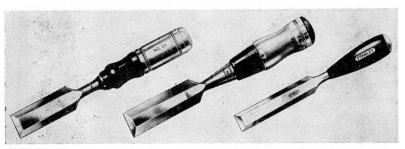

Fig. 35. Illustrating Paring Chisel (*left*), Butt Chisel (*center*),
and Pocket Chisel (*right*)
Courtesy of Stanley Tools, New Britain, Conn.

Butt Chisel. The butt chisel, so-called because it is used in fitting hinges and other hardware, has a short blade about 3″ long, making the chisel well balanced.

Pocket Chisel. Pocket chisels have a blade about 4½″ long and are used to mortise hardwoods or for other rugged work.

Mortise Chisel. The mortise chisel has a very thick blade and is used for making mortises by hand.

Gouges and Carving Tools. Gouges (Fig. 36) come in various diameters and may be sharpened with an inside or outside bevel, depending on the use. The two most commonly used types are the straight-shank and the bent-shank gouge, the latter of which is used when working or gouging out short, deep curves. Carving tools are made in numerous shapes for carving various shapes and designs in wood.

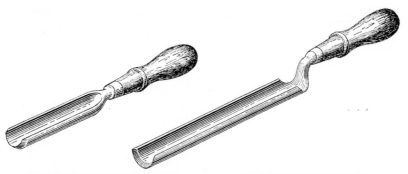

STRAIGHT-SHANK GOUGE   BENT-SHANK GOUGE

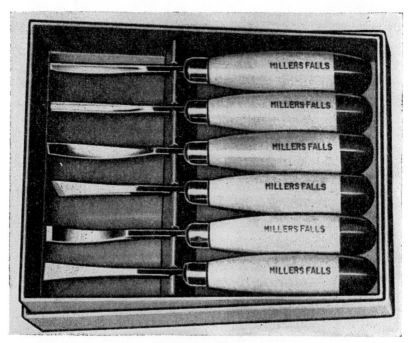

CARVING TOOLS
Fig. 36. Types of Gouges and Carving Tools
Courtesy of Miller Falls Company, Greenfield, Mass.

Boring Tools. The most commonly used boring tools are the auger bit, the twist drill, and various patented bits for special uses. See Fig. 37.

Auger Bits. Auger bits for woodworking are available from $\frac{3}{16}''$ to $1\frac{1}{8}''$ by 16ths, and up to $2''$ by 8ths. A number stamped on the shank indicates the size in 16ths. To illustrate, a No. 12 bit is $\frac{3}{4}''$. Bits may be purchased with slow, medium, and fast feed screws. Double-thread screws are made to provide slower feed and cleaner boring.

Expansive Bits. Large size holes are bored with an expansive bit. Most types are equipped with cutters to provide for cutting holes up to $3''$ in diameter.

Forstner Bit. The Forstner bit has no feed screw and relies on the sharp circular rim for centering. It may be used in place of the auger bit and is particularly adapted to boring holes part way in thin wood where the feed screw from the auger bit would go entirely through the board. It produces a flat-bottomed hole suited for such jobs as housing a stair stringer.

Bit Stock Drill. The bit stock drill is used for wood *or* metal and is available in sizes from $\frac{1}{16}''$ to $\frac{3}{4}''$ by 32nds. The sizes are stamped on the shank.

Bit Extension. The brace bit extension (Fig. 37) is used to extend the reach of an auger bit. The bit extensions are $15''$, $18''$, or $24''$ long.

Straight-Shank Twist Drill. This drill is used primarily for boring screw and nail holes and is used in the hand drill. The angle of the point is adaptable to either wood or metal. Most hand drills have a $\frac{1}{4}''$ capacity. Drills graduated in 32nds from $\frac{1}{16}''$ to $\frac{1}{4}''$ are ideal for this type of hand drill.

Numbered drills are primarily the tool of a metal worker. However, the cabinetmaker sometimes finds it necessary, when fitting hardware, to bore holes of a size not found in the fractional-sized drills. Numbered drills are made in sizes from No. 80 to No. 1 to correspond with standard wire gage numbers. The largest is No. 1, which has a diameter of 0.2280″, while the smallest is No. 80, with a diameter of 0.0135″.

Gimlet Bit. Gimlet bits are used for boring holes of small diameter in wood. The size varies by 32nds from $\frac{1}{16}''$ to $\frac{3}{8}''$.

Countersink Bit. The countersink is used to recess the head of the flat head and oval head wood screws flush with the wood.

Brace. The ratchet bit brace (Fig. 38) is used for holding boring tools with rectangularly shaped bit tang. The jaws of the chuck are

EXPANSIVE BIT

BIT STOCK DRILL

FORSTNER

STRAIGHT SHANK TWIST DRILL

BIT EXTENSION

COUNTERSINK BIT

TANG

FEED SCREW

SPUR

TWIST

SHANK

CUTTING EDGE

AUGER BIT

GIMLET BIT

Fig. 37. Bits and Drills

made to center the bit, and the tapered square part of the bit tang keeps the bit from turning in the chuck. A brace with a 10″ sweep is best suited for ordinary work. Most braces have a ratchet arrangement to permit boring holes in corners and other tight places.

Automatic Hand Drill.
The automatic hand drill shown in Fig. 39, also called a push drill, is used for drilling small holes to receive nails or screws. The drills are fluted and without twist. The sizes vary from $\frac{1}{16}$″ to $\frac{11}{64}$″ by 64ths.

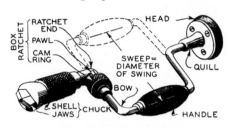

Fig. 38. Ratchet Brace

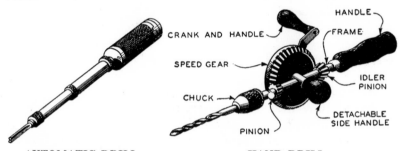

AUTOMATIC DRILL   HAND DRILL

Fig. 39. Automatic and Hand Drills

Hand Drill. The hand drill in Fig. 39 has a chuck which grips the straight round shank of the twist drill. It is used in boring holes larger than is possible with the automatic hand drill.

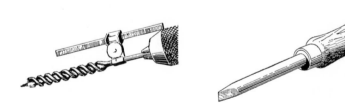

Fig. 40. Bit Gage   Fig. 41. Brad Awl

Bit Gage. The bit gage (Fig. 40) serves as a stop when boring holes to a definite depth.

Brad Awl. The brad awl (Fig. 41), while not a boring tool, is used to start a hole for brads or screws.

Fig. 42. Star Drill

Star Drill. The star drill (Fig. 42) is used to drill holes in masonry when fastening woodwork to the masonry wall by means of an expansion sleeve and lag bolt or by any other types of fasteners.

ASSEMBLING TOOLS

Assembling tools are essentially those tools which are used to assemble the parts of furniture, cabinets, and similar articles. Hammers are used primarily as driving or pounding tools (Fig. 43).

Claw Hammer. The claw hammer or nail hammer should be selected on the basis of balance and quality of steel. The face should not mushroom, and the claw slot should stay sharp. The claw slot should be sharp to enable it to grip the smallest brad or nail, even if the head of the nail is missing.

The weight of the head, expressed in ounces, determines the size of a hammer. Sizes available are from seven to twenty ounces. Some cabinetmakers prefer two sizes, one about nine ounces for use on brads, and another thirteen or sixteen ounces for heavier nails. For all-round work, a thirteen-ounce hammer is a good selection for cabinet making.

Ripping Hammer. The ripping hammer, so-called because of its claw, is used in ripping work apart or in splitting boards.

Ball Peen Hammer. The ball peen hammer is used primarily by the cabinetmaker in clinching rivets or riveting bolt ends to prevent the nut from being unscrewed.

Wooden Mallet. The wooden mallet (Fig. 44) comes in many shapes and sizes. Mallets are used primarily to provide a more resilient impact on the chisel handle and to prevent the head of the tool handle from mushrooming. When used for assembling work, the surface of the material should be protected by a scrap piece of wood.

Screw Drivers. Screw drivers (Fig. 45) are available in various lengths, diameters of shank, and styles to fit the various sizes of slotted screws. A type especially made for driving screws which are to be deeply countersunk is made with the sides of the tip parallel to the shank. This prevents marring the work.

Phillips Screw Driver. The screw driver made for Phillips screws must be selected to fit the cross-slot in the screw head. Four sizes, 1, 2,

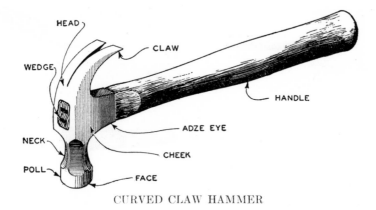

CURVED CLAW HAMMER

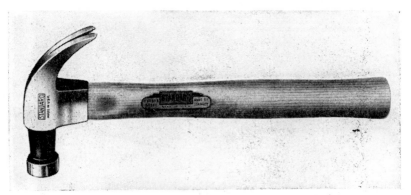

CURVED CLAW SEMI-RIPPING HAMMER
Courtesy of Stanley Tools, New Britain, Conn.

BALL PEEN HAMMER
Courtesy of Henry Cheney Hammer Corp., Little Falls, N.Y.

Fig. 43. Types of Hammers

3, and 4, will fit the entire range of Phillips screws. Size 1 is for screws up to and including No. 4, size 2 for screws No. 5 to 9 inclusive, size 3 for screws No. 10 to 16 inclusive, and size 4 for screws No. 18 and over.

Fig. 44. Wooden Mallet

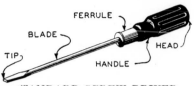

STANDARD SCREW DRIVER

PARALLEL-SIDED TIP SCREW DRIVER
Courtesy of Stanley Tools, New Britain, Conn.

PHILLIPS SCREW DRIVER
Courtesy of Stanley Tools, New Britain, Conn.

OFFSET SCREW DRIVER
Courtesy of Goodell Pratt Co., Greenfield, Mass.

SCREW DRIVER BIT

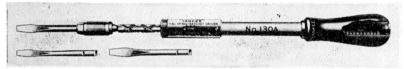

RATCHET SCREW DRIVER
Courtesy of Stanley Tools, New Britain, Conn.

Fig. 45. Types of Screw Drivers

Offset Screw Driver.   The offset screw driver is made for use in close quarters.

Screw Driver Bits.   A screw driver bit has a brace bit shank to fit the ratchet brace and is used for heavy screws where a large amount of force is required.

Ratchet Screw Driver.   The ratchet screw driver is designed for production work. It is available in various styles and sizes with interchangeable screw driver points.

Screw Holder. The screw holder is convenient for use in holding screws when the screw cannot be reached or held by hand while starting it into the wood.

Clamps. Clamps (Fig. 46) in general use by the cabinetmaker, are of four types as follows: the handscrew is used for gluing stock

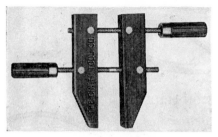

HAND SCREW

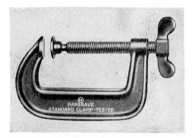

CARRIAGE OR C CLAMP

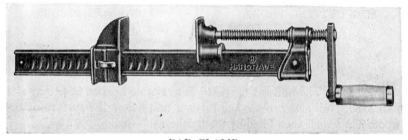

BAR CLAMP

Fig. 46. Types of Clamps

Courtesy of Cincinnati Tool Company, Cincinnati, Ohio

face to face or for clamping small pieces; the bar clamp is used for edge-clamping larger pieces; the C clamp for light work when neither handscrew nor bar clamp can be used, and the column clamp, indispensable for gluing stave columns.

Wrenches. Wrenches (Fig. 47) are often used by cabinetmakers when parts are assembled with bolts. The adjustable wrench is a convenient tool. The length of the wrench is available in sizes from 4″ to 20″.

Monkey Wrench. The monkey wrench is a sturdy tool that makes a good, all-round wrench.

Pliers. Various types of pliers (Fig. 48) are a must in any complete tool list.

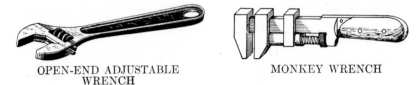

OPEN-END ADJUSTABLE   MONKEY WRENCH
        WRENCH

Fig. 47. Types of Wrenches

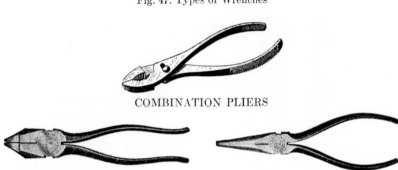

COMBINATION PLIERS

SIDE CUTTING PLIERS   LONG NOSE PLIERS

Fig. 48. Types of Pliers

Courtesy of Crescent Tool Co., Jamestown, N.Y.

MISCELLANEOUS

Nail Set.   The nail set (Fig. 49) is available in sizes to fit any size nail head. Nail sets are used to drive a nail below the surface of the wood. The hole is then filled by the finisher.

Fig. 49. Nail Set   Fig. 50. Scriber

Self-Centering Punch.   The self-centering punch is used to start holes for wood screws, as it will center the punch mark for a screw hole, such as on a hinge.

Brad Pusher.   The brad pusher is used to drive brads in difficult corners.

Scribers.   Scribers (Fig. 50) are used to mark the edges of cabinets to make them fit an irregular surface, such as a plastered wall. They are also useful when coping one molding to another.

Equipment such as work benches, sawhorses, bench hooks, shooting boards, etc., are all items that the cabinetmaker may use. These items are usually made by the shop to suit the requirements of the work to be done.

POWER TOOLS

The power tools described in this chapter embrace the basic woodworking machines designed for the production of a variety of work in custom woodworking plants. Such machines are found in many of the small woodworking shops operating in many cities throughout the nation. Typical machines, which will do the same type of work but are much smaller and lighter, are also found in hundreds of home workshops.

Fig. 51. Cut-Off Saw
Courtesy of Skilsaw, Inc., Chicago, Ill.

Cut-Off Saw. The purpose of the cut-off saw (Fig. 51) is to cut rough stock to approximate length with an allowance for trimming after it is milled. Two basically different types are in use: the stationary type where the material moves into the saw, and the movable type where the saw moves into the material.

Ripsaw. The purpose of the ripsaw is to rip rough stock to approximate width with an allowance made for jointing and sizing. The ripsaw is ordinarily not designed for fine accuracy. This machine is of simple but sturdy construction.

The standard ripsaw machine is fed by hand. The power-feed ripsaw is designed for production work and may be fitted with a gang of saws to cut a board into several pieces at one time. The straight-line ripsaw (Fig. 52) is a machine designed with an endless bed which automatically feeds the material in a straight line.

Jointer. The jointer (Fig. 53) is designed for straightening wood by planing the surfaces. The operation of straightening the face of a board is called *facing*. The operation of straightening the edge is called

Fig. 52. Straight-Line Precision Ripsaw
Courtesy of Yates-American, Beloit, Wis.

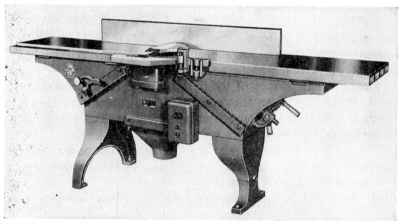

Fig. 53. Hand Jointer
Courtesy of Northfield Foundry & Machine Co., Northfield, Minn.

jointing or *edging*. Jointing usually implies that the edge is to be jointed at right angles to the face side. Other operations that may be performed on the jointer include beveling, chamfering, tapering, and rabbeting. Hollow glue joints can also be made. The standard jointer is fed by hand.

Jointers are made in a variety of sizes and mechanical designs, though the operating principles involved are basically the same in all makes. Power-feed jointers are built for facing only. The glue jointer is built only for jointing edges for gluing.

Fig. 54. Single-Surface Cabinet Planer
Courtesy of Baxter D. Whitney & Sons, Inc., Winchendon, Mass.

Fig. 55. Trim or Combination Saw
Courtesy of The Tannewitz Works, Grand Rapids, Mich.

Planer. The planer (Fig. 54), often called a surfacer, is designed to surface lumber to a specific thickness. The cabinetmaker is concerned primarily with the cabinet or thickness planer, which is provided with only one cutterhead. The cabinet planer is designed for precision work and should be used only for stock that has been faced on the jointer. If the lower feed rolls are raised to enable feeding of rough stock, it can no longer be relied on to do exact work.

The double-planer surfacer has a top and bottom cutterhead and will, in one operation, surface rough stock on two sides to finished thickness.

Matchers are heavy-duty surfacers with four cutterheads, designed to surface in one operation dimension stock and timbers on all four sides to net thickness and width. Matchers were primarily designed for production of matched (tongued and grooved) flooring or ceiling, hence the name.

Trim Saw. The trim saw (Fig. 55) has several trade names, such as bench saw, table saw, combination saw, tilting arbor saw, and variety saw. The term "trim saw" is comprehensive, as it accurately designates the type of work done on it. If properly adjusted, the trim saw will do accurate work in sizing jointed stock to width, in trimming sized stock to length, and will perform many other milling operations, such as beveling, chamfering, mitering, grooving, dadoing, rabbeting, slotting, and tenoning.

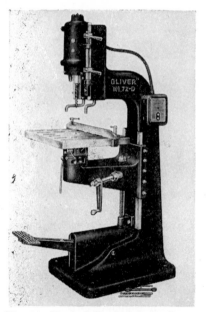 

Fig. 56. Vertical Single-Spindle Borer   Fig. 57. Horizontal Two-Spindle Borer
Courtesy of Oliver Machinery Co., Grand Rapids, Mich.

The trim saw, although used for certain types of production work, is designed primarily for detail work; that is, work which is not repetitive in nature. Modern trim saws embrace such features as sliding table, tilting arbor, graduated markings for the miter fence, and screw adjustment for the ripping fence.

Boring Machine. Boring machines are of two general types: horizontal and vertical. The vertical boring machine (drill press) shown in Fig. 56 is designed to do a variety of work on flat surfaces. The horizontal boring machine (Fig. 57) is primarily designed to bore holes for dowels in the edge and ends of face work, such as stiles and rails.

The vertical boring machine usually has only one spindle. The horizontal boring machine with one spindle is designed for detail work, while the multiple-spindle horizontal borer is designed for quantity production. Specially-designed, multiple-spindle borers are made for the mass production of doors and furniture.

Mortiser. Except in the manufacture of sash, the mortiser, to a large extent, has been replaced by the horizontal boring machine for mass-production work. However, the mortiser continues in favor for certain types of detail work.

The hollow chisel mortiser is made in a variety of horizontal and vertical designs and with either or both power feed and foot feed.

Tenoner. The tenoning machine was designed primarily to make tenons. However, with the addition of coping heads and trim saw, together with the development of the double-end tenoner, it is now a highly versatile and important production machine used for tenoning, coping, shaping, trimming, and the milling of joints such as used in some types of drawer construction.

The single-end tenoner, although used in production work, is more adaptable for custom work than the double-end tenoner, which represents a large investment.

Band Saw. The band saw (Fig. 58) designed to saw curved surfaces, is useful for a variety of purposes, such as relishing, trimming circles, cutting notches, vertical stop cuts, light resawing, and ripping.

Band saws are manufactured in a great variety of sizes and styles with various limits of adjustments. Band saws designed for specific purposes include the band ripsaw (power feed), the band resaw, and the band-saw mill for cutting lumber from logs.

Shaper. The spindle shaper is designed for shaping moldings on curved stock. It is a versatile machine which may be adapted to numerous operations, including the shaping of joints, fluting, reeding, grooving, rabbeting, slotting, and tenoning. The shaper is more economical for short runs of straight molding than a sticker setup.

Spindle shapers are designed with single or double spindle. When designed with two spindles, they rotate in opposite directions so that cuts can be made in the direction of the grain.

Various designs of automatic shapers are made for mass production purposes. Overhead spindle shapers are adapted for shaping and routing to a template which is guided by a pin in the table.

Molder. The molder (sticker) is designed to shape moldings with irregular faces. Molders are built to meet the requirements of various types of work. Examples are high-speed molders for production, molders specially adapted for quick change to produce short runs of custom work, and molders designed to handle short stock, such as furniture parts.

The sash sticker is specially designed for the production of milled sash stock and has attachments for boring and slotting for sash cord.

Matchers, built on the same principle as molders, are designed for mass production of flooring and other production items.

Fig. 58. Steel Disk Wheel Band Saw

Courtesy of The Tannewitz Works,
Grand Rapids, Mich.

Fig. 59. Jig or Scroll Saw

Courtesy of Oliver Machinery Co.,
Grand Rapids, Mich.

Jig Saw. The jig saw (scroll saw), shown in Fig. 59, is designed for sawing irregular curves in scroll or fretwork. The saw blade has a vertical, reciprocal action. It is removable so that it may be inserted through a hole bored for that purpose when doing inside sawing.

Various mechanical features reduce vibration caused by the reciprocal action.

Turning Lathe. The wood turning lathe (Fig. 60) is made with a powered spindle which revolves the wood at various r.p.m. while the cutting tools are manipulated by hand to shape the required design.

The lathe may be adapted for boring or to perform semiautomatic work.

The automatic back-knife lathe differs from the hand-operated wood lathe in that the cutters are mounted on a shaft at the rear of the machine. When the machine is in operation, the cutters revolve at a moderate speed while the work is moved slowly into the cutters and revolved a complete turn.

Overhead Router. Overhead routers are designed for dadoing and shaping recessed moldings into flat surfaces, such as housing a stair stringer or shaping a recessed panel in the end of a church pew.

Two types of machines are built. The arm router provides for the bit to move into the work, guided by the arm. The spindle router is provided with a stationary spindle and the work is guided into the cutter by means of a template.

Sander. Many types of sanders are built to accommodate different kinds of work. The drum sander is built on the principle of the planer in that it has a power feed and is set for the thickness of the mate-

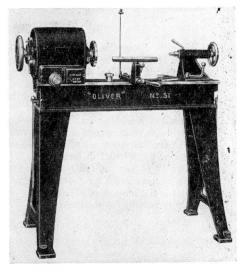

Fig. 60. Motor Head Wood Turning Lathe
Courtesy of Oliver Machinery Co., Grand Rapids, Mich.

rial to be sanded. Power-feed drum sanders are usually made with several drums. Each drum is covered with a different grade of abrasive so that the material, in being sanded, passes the coarser drums first. The final sanding is done by a drum covered with a fine abrasive.

Single-spindle drum sanders are made to sand flat-faced curves which are fed by hand. The belt sander is designed to smooth flat surfaces ready for finishing. In first-class work, the belt sander is used to remove the snake marks left by the drum sander. The belt sander is also used to smooth the faces of contoured moldings. This is done with flexible, cloth-backed abrasives, pressed to the work by shaped sanding blocks. With a specially built jig, the belt sander may also be used for edge sanding. Other types of sanders include vertical and horizontal edge sanders, vertical disk sanders, horizontal disk sanders, oscillating spindle sanders, and sanders designed for smoothing wood turnings, called shape sanders.

Specialty Machines. Specialty machines and equipment include machines such as the dovetailer, single spindle carver, multiple spindle carver, emery stand (grinding wheel), knife grinder, band saw filer, circle saw filer, gumming (gullet) grinder, veneer jointer, veneer taper, glue press, thermoelectric gluing machines, bending press, and clamping machines.

REVIEW QUESTIONS

1. Where is the combination square used?
2. When is a plumb bob used?
3. What is the principal use of the marking gage?
4. What file is used for sharpening scraper blades?
5. What is meant by the grit of an oilstone?
6. What is the purpose of a burnisher?
7. Name five kinds of saws and give the principal use of each one.
8. How is the coarseness of a saw determined?
9. What are the two types of chisels as to construction?
10. When are numbered drills used?
11. Name two types of boring machines.
12. Give another name for the tilting arbor saw.
13. What is the purpose of a jointer?
14. Give three uses for the band saw.

Cabinet and Millwork Joints

QUESTIONS CHAPTER IV WILL ANSWER FOR YOU

1. *What type joints are used when joining boards edge to edge?*
2. *Where are dovetail joints used?*
3. *What joints are commonly used when joining the end of a board to the face of a board?*
4. *Where are coped joints used?*
5. *What is a cleat joint?*

INTRODUCTION TO CHAPTER IV

Joints are used to fasten or secure two members together. These members may be butted against each other end to end. They may be joined edge to edge, or they may meet in various other ways. There are many different types of woodworking joints. Only those joints that are commonly used in cabinet-making are shown here. It is not the purpose of this chapter to explain how each joint is laid out, cut, fitted, and assembled, but rather to give an over-all view of the various methods of fastening, together with the trade terminology applied to each joint. This information will be useful in helping you to visualize the best methods of construction to use, as detail drawings seldom give this information. Each shop uses methods of construction which are convenient to handle with the equipment available to them. Only when unusual construction problems arise does the detail drawing show how the joints are to be made.

Remember that the holding power of any joint depends upon a good, snug fit. A joint that does not fit properly is always a weak joint and a sign of poor craftsmanship.

TYPES OF JOINTS

The basic types of joints used in cabinet construction are the butt, spline, tongue and groove, rabbet, dado, miter, scarfed, half lap, coped, dovetail, mortise and tenon, and doweled.

SELECTION OF JOINTS

The type of joint selected for a specific construction problem is determined by the following factors: (1) The material to be used; its working qualities and strength. (2) Serviceability: Is the job to be used on the interior or exterior, and is the project stationary or movable? (3) Ease of manufacture: Can the joint be made economically with the equipment available? (4) Method of fastening: Will the project be fastened with glue, nails, screws, metal fasteners, or by a combination of several methods? (5) Angle of grain: Will the parts be fastened with the grain running in parallel directions, at right angles, or at an oblique angle such as an end miter?

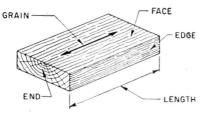

Fig. 1. Grain Direction in Boards

Grain direction, as used in this chapter, refers to the general direction of the wood fibers which run with the length of a board, as shown in Fig. 1. The face, edge, and end of the board are also shown in the illustration. These terms will be used in reference to the position of the members comprising the various joints.

PARALLEL GRAIN JOINTS

Joints made with the grain of the members parallel are classified as parallel grain joints.

Edge Joints. Parallel grain joints that are used for joining wood edgewise are shown in Fig. 2. These joints are used primarily to glue material to a required width. The strength of the butt joint is dependent upon carefully joined edges. Such joints, correctly made with a good grade of glue under proper conditions, are as strong as the wood itself. The other types of joints shown are shaped or milled edge joints and a dowel joint. Milling does not increase the strength of the joint in the majority of woods. Milled joints do, however, allow faster assembly time since the parts are easily aligned. Also, when gluing conditions are not well controlled, the milled joint will give better results. Wood dowels help to reinforce a joint.

Right-Angle Joints. Shown in Fig. 3 are a group of joints used to join material while keeping the grain parallel and the faces at right angles. The simplest joint of this type is the plain butt joint which is sometimes reinforced by the use of nails or screws. These same joints may be used to join members where the grain meets at right angles.

Oblique-Angle Joints. The plain miter, splined miter, tongue-and-groove miter, milled miter, and the plain rabbet are all types of joints which may be used to join material at an oblique angle with the grain parallel, such as in making an octagon-shaped post.

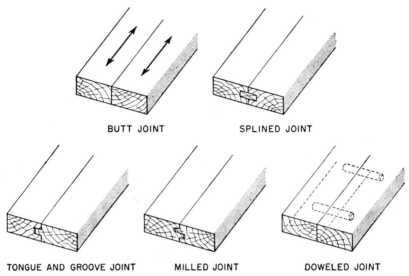

BUTT JOINT   SPLINED JOINT

TONGUE AND GROOVE JOINT   MILLED JOINT   DOWELED JOINT

Fig. 2. Types of Edge Joints

RIGHT-ANGLE GRAIN JOINTS

When wood is joined with the grain meeting at right angles, the joints are termed right-angle-grain joints (Fig. 4).

End To Side Joints. Joints in which the end of one member is fitted to the side of another member with the grain at right angles, are called end-to-side joints. The plain miter joint is frequently used in situations of this type, such as in making casings, and decorative edges for furniture, moldings, etc. The doweled miter and half-lapped miter are used where a joint stronger than the plain miter is required. The slotted mortise and tenon is used in light construction work such as in making double-hung windows (a window with an upper and lower sash). The haunched mortise and tenon is used in panel work.

Cleat Joints. Shown in Fig. 5 is a cleat joint made with a tongue and groove. Joints of this type are often used to reinforce a butt-edge joint such as in drawing boards and pull-out leaves. The grain of the cleat is at right angles to the grain of the other members of the joint.

End-To-Face Joints. In the construction of cabinets, it is often necessary to make joints at right angles where the end grain is to be

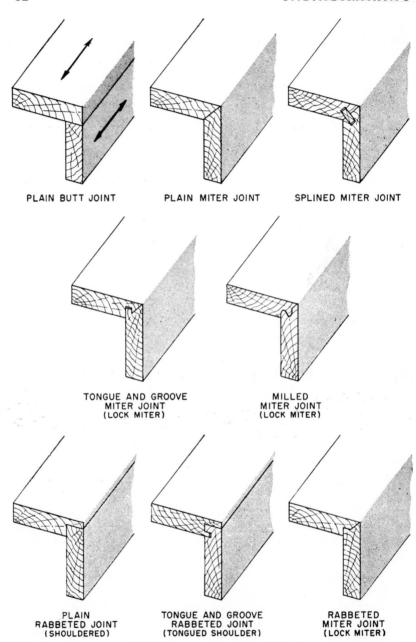

Fig. 3. Types of Right-Angle Joints

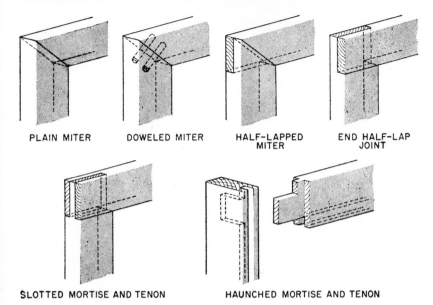

PLAIN MITER   DOWELED MITER   HALF-LAPPED MITER   END HALF-LAP JOINT

SLOTTED MORTISE AND TENON   HAUNCHED MORTISE AND TENON

Fig. 4. Types of Right-Angle Grain Joints

joined to the face or flat side of a board, such as in drawer construction (Fig. 6). Dovetail joints are used where great strength is required. Dovetail joints may be made by hand or by machine. Machine-made dovetails (see milled dovetail, Fig. 6) are used extensively in constructing drawers for furniture and fixture work.

Fig. 5. Cleat Joint

COPED JOINTS

Coped joints are used extensively in sash work and in molding work (Fig. 7) where only the face of the molding is visible.

SCARF JOINTS

Scarf joints (Fig. 8) are used in cabinetmaking to extend the length of a board. Doweling is the most common means of reinforcing a scarf joint since the dowels keep the joint from slipping as it is being glued.

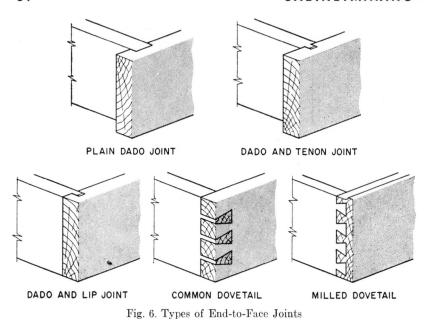

PLAIN DADO JOINT   DADO AND TENON JOINT

DADO AND LIP JOINT   COMMON DOVETAIL   MILLED DOVETAIL

Fig. 6. Types of End-to-Face Joints

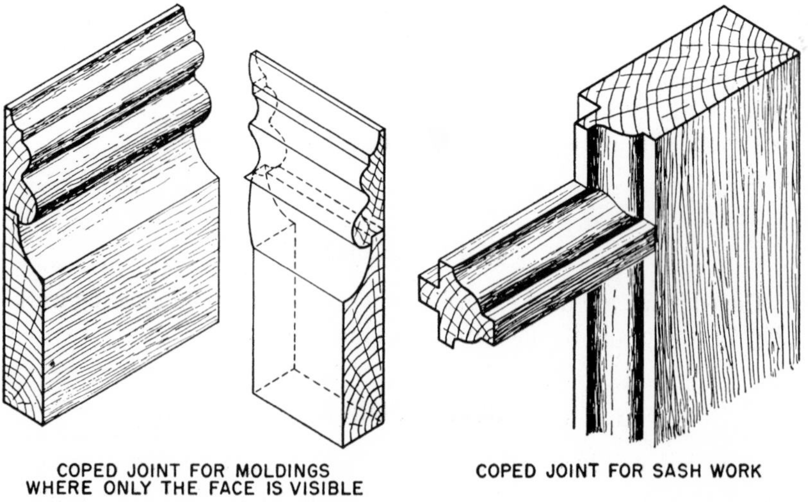

COPED JOINT FOR MOLDINGS
WHERE ONLY THE FACE IS VISIBLE   COPED JOINT FOR SASH WORK

Fig. 7. Coped Joints

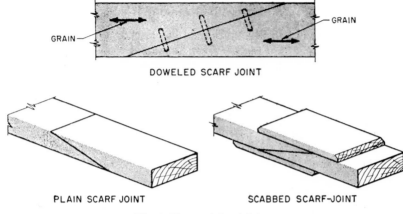

DOWELED SCARF JOINT

PLAIN SCARF JOINT   SCABBED SCARF-JOINT

Fig. 8. Types of Scarf Joints

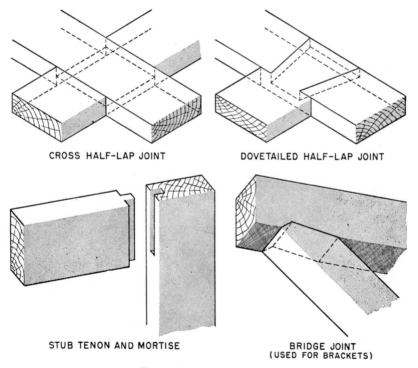

CROSS HALF-LAP JOINT   DOVETAILED HALF-LAP JOINT

STUB TENON AND MORTISE   BRIDGE JOINT
(USED FOR BRACKETS)

Fig. 9. Miscellaneous Joints

MISCELLANEOUS JOINTS

The joints shown in Fig. 9 are used in various woodworking situations. The cross-half lap joint is frequently used in making flush cross braces. The dovetail half-lap joint is used where there is a pull or a strain, since the joint cannot be pulled apart. The stub tenon and mortise is used only in cheap production work or where a frame aids in holding the parts together, since the holding power of a stub tenon and mortise is not great.

The bridge joint is used primarily for seating braces into the horizontal member of a bracket.

REVIEW QUESTIONS

1. Name ten basic types of joints.
2. How are joints generally secured?
3. Where are plain miter joints used?
4. Where are dovetail joints generally found?
5. Name three kinds of mortise and tenon joints.
6. Make a sketch of a haunched mortise and tenon.
7. What is a coped joint?
8. Where is the coped molding joint used?
9. When are scarf joints used?

Fundamentals of Blueprint Reading

QUESTIONS CHAPTER V WILL ANSWER FOR YOU

1. *What is blueprint reading?*
2. *Why is blueprint reading important?*
3. *What is a cabinet drawing?*
4. *What are plan views?*
5. *What is a schedule?*

INTRODUCTION TO CHAPTER V

Blueprints are reproductions of working drawings. A working drawing is a drawing which gives full directions and information for making a project. The term "blueprint" has come to have a general meaning and refers to any print regardless of the method of reproduction. Originally, blueprints were made by reproducing the drawing on a chemically treated paper which gave white lines on a blue background; hence the name.

Today, prints are made on any number of special papers which may produce white lines on a dark-brown background or black lines on a white background. Blueprints can be made from pencil or ink drawings, and any number of copies can be made quickly and cheaply. Regardless of the method used, the purpose is to reproduce the drawing so that the prints can be placed in the hands of the workmen. The original drawing is always kept in the office where it will be available for making additional copies.

Since blueprints are originally made by draftsmen, it is necessary to interpret the work of the draftsman in order to read blueprints. To interpret the work of the draftsman, it is necessary to know something about his language.

This chapter will be devoted to the work of the draftsman and the procedures for reading blueprints.

PURPOSE OF DRAWING

Drawing is a language which describes an object in sufficient detail so that a workman can make that object without actually seeing it. In order for the workman to make the object, he must be able to understand the language of drawing. Drawings are composed of lines and symbols that convey meaning to the observer trained in reading drawings and blueprints.

TYPES OF DRAWINGS

Objects are described by views which reveal the general appearance, size, and shape of the object as seen from different directions. These views must be in sufficient detail to enable the worker to make the project.

Pictorial Drawings. Pictorial drawings are used to show the general appearance of the object and to give the worker an idea of the relationship of the parts. A pictorial drawing shows the object as it appears to the eye or as a view taken with a camera. The three most commonly encountered types of pictorial drawings in cabinetmaking are the perspective, isometric, and cabinet drawing.

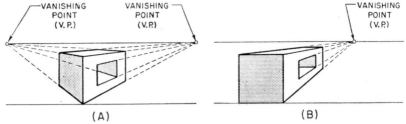

Fig. 1. Perspective Drawings

Perspective Drawings. Perspective drawings closely resemble photographs and are often used to show the finished appearance of a building, cabinet, or other item. The true size and shape of the various parts are not shown on the drawing since some of the horizontal lines representing the sides converge toward a point called the vanishing point (V.P.). The vanishing points lie on the horizontal level of the eye called the horizon. An object may be drawn as an angular or "two point perspective," as shown in (A) of Fig. 1, or as a "one point perspective," as shown in (B) of Fig. 1.

Isometric Drawings. Isometric drawings are drawn around three lines called axes, one vertical and two at thirty degrees with the horizontal, as shown in Fig. 2. All measurements on an isometric drawing are drawn in true proportion; usually only the dimensions of the main parts are shown in this manner. The parallel sides of the object are represented by parallel lines in the drawing.

Cabinet Drawings. In a cabinet drawing the front view is drawn with the horizontal lines of the object horizontal and the vertical lines vertical. The depth dimension is made at a 45° angle (Fig. 3) and all dimensions on this line are reduced one-third or one-half. This makes cabinet drawings appear more natural than isometric drawings.

While any of the preceding drawings are useful in showing how a finished project will look, the actual size and shape of each side or part is not shown. To show the true size and shape of each part, working drawings are used. The working drawing, with dimensions and notes, gives complete information for making the project.

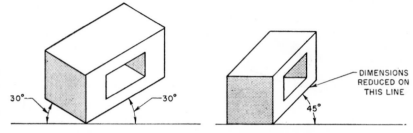

Fig. 2. Isometric Drawing   Fig. 3. Cabinet Drawing

Working Drawings. Working drawings are often referred to as shop working drawings, shop drawings, or detail drawings. In order for a worker to make a project, he must know something about the method of making a working drawing. A working drawing consists of a sufficient number of views to show the exact size and shape of the project. Each view must give the true size and shape of that particular surface or part. To make each view appear in true size and shape, the draftsman visualizes the surface from a position directly in front of the object, or at a right angle to the surface, and draws just what is before him.

For a simple object such as a tenon, three views, as shown in Fig. 4, would give the worker enough information to visualize the project. Notice carefully the position of the views. The top view is directly above the front view, and the right-side view is directly in line to the right of the front view. Each drawing represents a surface of the object as seen at right angles. The front is considered the main view, with the other views arranged around it. As a general rule, a drawing is made in each direction in which the shape is different. Generally, a minimum of two views is necessary to show the shape of an object. These may be any two adjacent views. However, some objects, such as a cylinder, can be drawn with one view which shows the length, since the width can be given as a diameter. In addition to showing the shape of an object, the draftsman must give the size and any other information that is necessary to make the project. The size is shown by dimension lines as will be explained later.

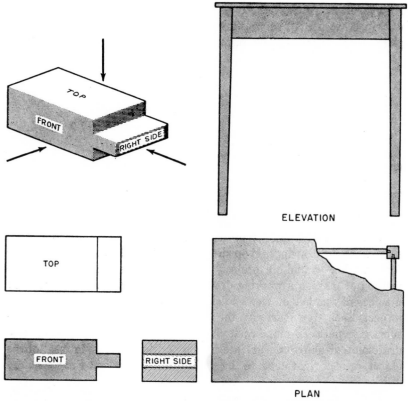

Fig. 4. Views for Working Drawing of Tenon

Fig. 5. Plan View and Elevation View of Table

Elevation. In cabinetmaking, the term "elevation" is applied to any drawing which shows the height of the project. This is usually the front view. The elevation shows the width and height, but not the depth.

Plan View. The term "plan view" is used for any view looking directly down on the object from above. In many cases, the plan view shows the object as being cut horizontally at a particular height to expose the interior details. In some cases a corner of the project is shown removed, exposing the details of construction (Fig. 5). The plan view shows the length and depth of an article, but not the height.

Section Views. Parts of an object that cannot be seen are represented by dotted lines. When the object is simple, this procedure is

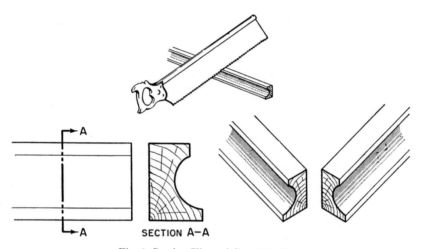

SECTION A–A

Fig. 6. Section View of Cove Molding

satisfactory, but when the interior contains a number of details, the dotted lines become confusing. Also, it is sometimes desirable to show the shape of an object at a particular point. To show these details, section views are used. This view is obtained by making an imaginary cut with a cutting plane line in the same manner as actually cutting the piece with a saw (Fig. 6). This procedure shows how the interior looks. The arrows indicate the direction in which the draftsman was looking

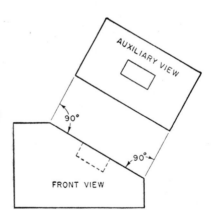

Fig. 7. Auxiliary View, Showing Exact Shape of Slanted Surface

when the drawing was made. Letters are sometimes used to identify the sections, especially when several sections are shown on the same page.

Auxiliary Views. As previously explained, a drawing is necessary in each direction in which the shape of an object is different. For objects that have surfaces at right angles, the true size and shape can be shown in the usual manner, but when the object has a slanting surface, another view must be drawn. A drawing made by looking directly at the slanted surface is called an auxiliary view. This is shown in Fig. 7. An auxiliary view, however, is not necessary for every slanted surface. Such a drawing is made only when the slanted surface has some details that would not show in true size and shape in the usual views.

ALPHABET OF LINES

The draftsman uses various kinds of lines (Fig. 8) in conveying information. This alphabet of lines must be fully understood before a drawing can be read properly.

Outline of Parts. Lines that show the outline of the parts of an object that can be seen are shown as solid black lines.

Section Lines. Section lines are used to give a shaded effect to a cut section. The design and arrangement of the section lines indicate the type of material.

Hidden Lines. A hidden line is a line composed of short dashes representing the edge of a flat surface or the outline of a part that is not visible to the eye.

Center Lines. Center lines are used to indicate the centers of circles and other symmetrical shapes.

Dimension Lines. Dimension lines show the size of an object. The arrowheads indicate the exact extent of each dimension.

Extension Lines. An extension line is drawn much lighter than the visible line, but is actually an extension of the outline, with a break between.

Cutting Plane Line. A cutting plane line indicates the exact location at which an imaginary cut is made.

Adjacent Parts and Alternate Position Lines. An alternate position line represents the limiting positions of a movable part, such as a hinged door in a closed and open position. Adjacent parts added on a drawing to show the use of the part represented are drawn with the same lines.

Ditto Lines. A ditto line indicates that the detail shown in a symmetrical object is to be repeated.

Break Lines. A break line indicates that the object is theoretically broken at that point, and usually means that the same condition continues indefinitely or until another condition appears on the drawing. The break line is often used when it is impossible to make the drawing large enough to show the complete part. A break line always indicates that part of the object shown is "bridged" by the dimension appearing in the dimension line.

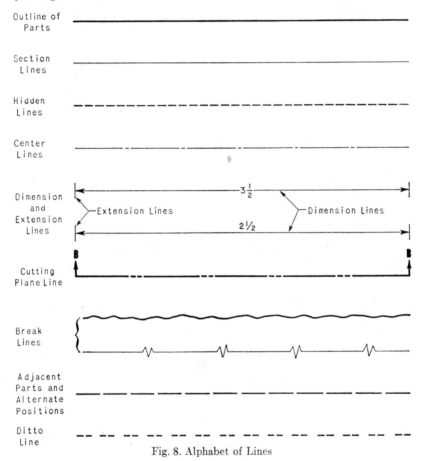

Fig. 8. Alphabet of Lines

SCALE DRAWINGS

The draftsman uses a scale (Fig. 9) in making a drawing, since each drawing must be made to an exact size. When the drawing is made the same size as the part or object, it is called a full-scale drawing. While this procedure works well with small objects, larger ones cannot be drawn to full size on ordinary paper. Large objects are drawn to scale, i.e., some smaller unit of measure is used. For example, a part that is 24' long may be drawn 6" long. This drawing then would be drawn on the $\frac{1}{4}'' = 1'0''$ scale, since each quarter inch on the drawing represents one foot of the object. The most commonly used scales for making reduced drawings are $\frac{1}{4}'' = 1'0''$, $\frac{3}{8}'' = 1'0''$, $\frac{1}{8}'' = 1'0''$, $\frac{1}{2}'' = 1'0''$, $\frac{3}{4}'' = 1'0''$ and $1'' = 1'0''$. The reductions may also be

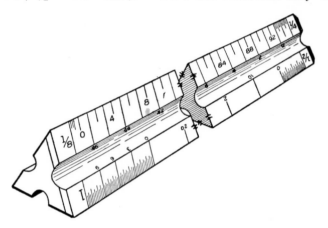

Fig. 9. Triangular Architect's Scale

made in inches. For example, a line 24" long may be represented by a line 6" long, or three inches equal one foot. The scale used to make the drawing should always be indicated, and the dimensions should be actual dimensions of the object, not the dimensions of the drawing.

DETAIL DRAWINGS

Drawings are sometimes made larger than the object if the object to be drawn is too small to show details clearly. Sometimes only sections of a drawing are enlarged to show the details of construction. In such cases, the area to be drawn enlarged and the enlarged section are identified by the use of a cutting plane line (Fig. 10). Detail numbers are often shown enclosed in a circle (Fig. 22). This procedure eliminates drawing the same details several times, since all subsequent parts requiring the same details can be indicated by using the same number (Fig. 11).

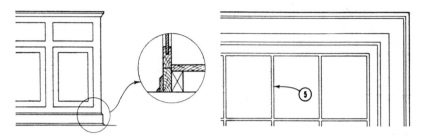

Fig. 10. Method of Showing Details of Construction for Cabinet Part

Fig. 11. A Number Is Used Where the Same Detail Occurs Several Times

ARCHITECTURAL WORKING DRAWINGS

The same general principles are used for architectural drawings as are used for other types of drawings. Often, the cabinetmaker has to obtain information from a set of architectural drawings. In such cases, it is important to know how to read the prints.

A number of symbols, conventions, and abbreviations are used in architectural drawings because of the small scales used in making the drawings.

Blueprint Symbols. Professional practice in the architectural field has developed a set of symbols which are now in common use.

A typical list of symbols can be classified into the following groups:

Materials. Brick, wood, steel, glass, tile, concrete, etc., are represented by symbols as shown in Fig. 12.

Doors. Symbols for single-acting and double-acting doors, and doors with sill, doors without sill, inside doors, and other types, are shown in Fig. 13.

Windows. Windows with sills, windows without sills, casement single, casement in pairs, double hung, stationary sash, and other types of windows are shown by the symbols in Fig. 14.

Electrical. Symbols for switches, buzzers, outlets, three-way switches, center lights, drop lights, wall lights, telephones, etc., are shown in Fig. 15.

Plumbing and Heating. Floor drains, sinks, wall lavatories, boilers, drinking fountains, radiators, registers, etc., are shown in Fig. 16.

Abbreviations. Due to lack of space, the draftsman often abbreviates words used on the drawings. A few of the abbreviations in common use which may concern the cabinetmaker in reading blueprints are as follows:

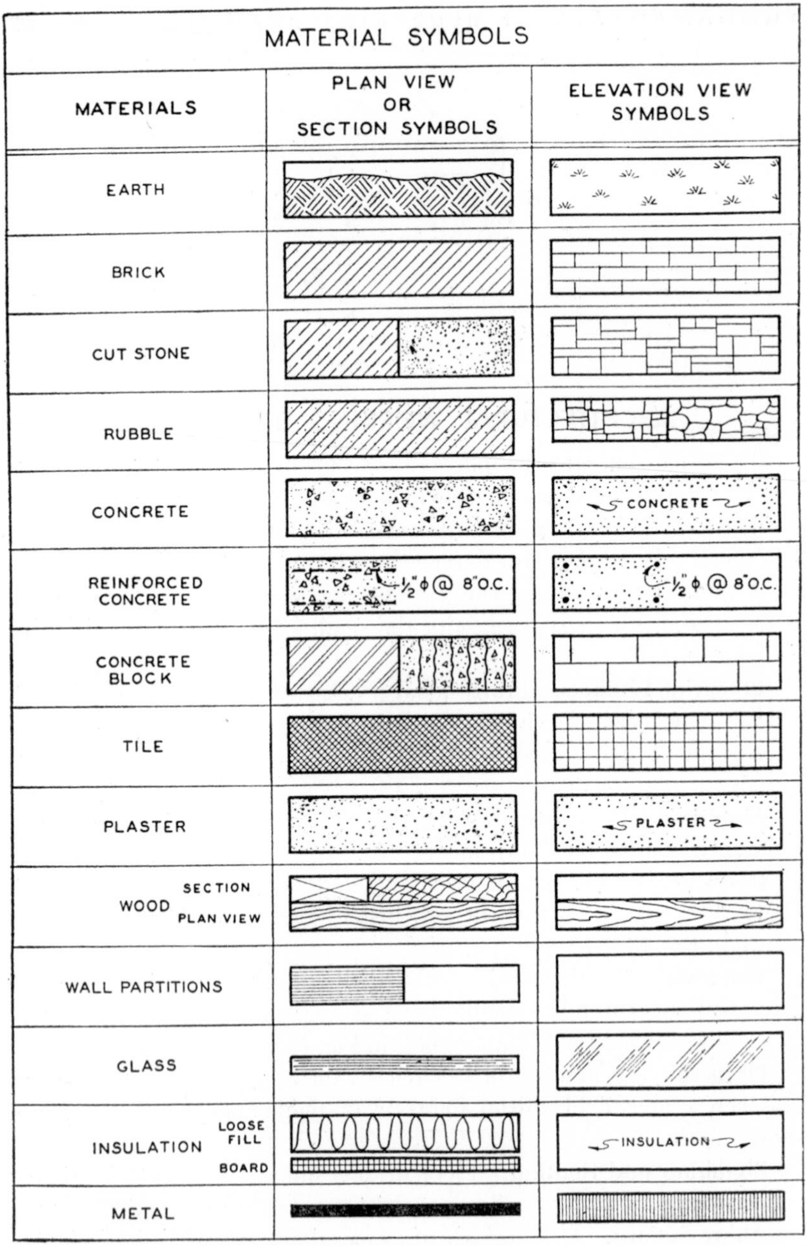

MATERIAL SYMBOLS		
MATERIALS	**PLAN VIEW OR SECTION SYMBOLS**	**ELEVATION VIEW SYMBOLS**
EARTH		
BRICK		
CUT STONE		
RUBBLE		
CONCRETE		CONCRETE
REINFORCED CONCRETE	$\frac{1}{2}"\phi$ @ 8"O.C.	$\frac{1}{2}"\phi$ @ 8"O.C.
CONCRETE BLOCK		
TILE		
PLASTER		PLASTER
WOOD SECTION PLAN VIEW		
WALL PARTITIONS		
GLASS		
INSULATION LOOSE FILL BOARD		INSULATION
METAL		

Fig. 12. Symbols Used for Indicating Materials

G.I.	Galvanized iron	P.	Plumbing
T&G	Tongue and groove	H.	Hot water
S1S	Surfaced one side	W.	Cold water
S1S1E	Surfaced one side, one edge	G.R.	Gas range
S2S	Surfaced two sides	K.C.	Kitchen cabinet
S4S	Surfaced four sides	R.F.	Refrigerator
Flg.	Flooring	W.P.	White pine
Clg.	Ceiling	Y.P.	Yellow pine
Rwd.	Redwood	O.C.	On center
D.F.	Douglas fir	₵	Center line
B.M.	Bench mark	B.R.	Bedroom
Bldg.	Building	Dn	Down
F.G.	Fuel gas	H.B.	Hose bib
L.T.	Laundry tray		

Schedules. A schedule is a method used by architects to simplify a drawing and make plans easier to read. A schedule is made in the form of a chart and includes information and specifications pertaining

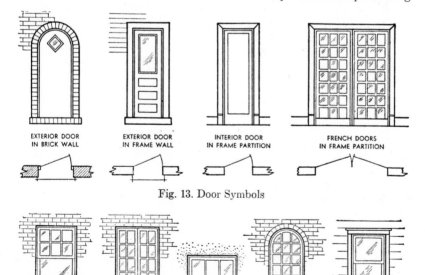

EXTERIOR DOOR
IN BRICK WALL

EXTERIOR DOOR
IN FRAME WALL

INTERIOR DOOR
IN FRAME PARTITION

FRENCH DOORS
IN FRAME PARTITION

Fig. 13. Door Symbols

DOUBLE-HUNG WINDOW
IN BRICK WALL

CASEMENT WINDOW
IN BRICK WALL

BASEMENT WINDOW
IN CONCRETE WALL

CASEMENT WINDOW
IN BRICK WALL

DOUBLE-HUNG WINDOW
IN FRAME WALL

Fig. 14. Window Symbols

ELECTRICAL SYMBOLS FOR ARCHITECTURAL PLANS

Ceiling Wall   GENERAL OUTLETS

O   —O   Outlet.

B   —B   Blanked Outlet.

D   Drop Cord.

E   —E   Electrical Outlet; for use only when circle used alone might be confused with columns, plumbing symbols, etc.

F   —F   Fan Outlet.

J   —J   Junction Box

L   —L   Lamp Holder.

L_{PS} —L_{PS} Lamp Holder with Pull Switch.

S   —S   Pull Switch.

V   —V   Outlet for Vapor Discharge Lamp.

X   —X   Exit Light Outlet.

C   —C   Clock Outlet. (Specify Voltage.)

CONVENIENCE OUTLETS

Duplex Convenience Outlet.

Convenience Outlet other than Duplex. 1=Single, 3=Triplex, etc.

Weatherproof Convenience Outlet.

Range Outlet.

Switch and Convenience Outlet.

Radio and Convenience Outlet.

Special Purpose Outlet. (Des. in Spec.)

Floor Outlet.

SWITCH OUTLETS

S   Single Pole Switch.

S_2   Double Pole Switch.

S_3   Three-Way Switch.

S_4   Four-Way Switch.

S_D   Automatic Door Switch.

S_E   Electrolier Switch.

S_K   Key Operated Switch.

S_P   Switch and Pilot Lamp.

S_{CB}   Circuit Breaker.

S_{WCB} Weatherproof Circuit Breaker.

S_{MC}   Momentary Contact Switch.

S_{RC}   Remote Control Switch.

S_{WP}   Weatherproof Switch.

S_F   Fused Switch.

S_{WF}   Weatherproof Fused Switch.

SPECIAL OUTLETS

O_{a,b,c,etc}
⊖_{a,b,c,etc}
S_{a,b,c,etc}

Any Standard Symbol as given above with the addition of a lower case subscript letter may be used to designate some special variation of Standard Equipment of particular interest in a specific set of Architectural Plans. When used, they must be listed in the Key of Symbols on each drawing and if necessary further described in the specifications.

PANELS, CIRCUITS, AND MISCELLANEOUS

Lighting Panel.

Power Panel.

——— Branch Circuit; Concealed in Ceiling or Wall.

– – – Branch Circuit; Concealed in Floor.

----- Branch Circuit; Exposed.

Home Run to Panel Board. Indicate number of Circuits by number of arrows.

Note: Any circuit without further designation indicates a two-wire circuit. For a greater number of wires indicate as follows —⫫— (3 wires) ⫫⫫ (4 wires), etc.

——— Feeders. Note: Use heavy lines and designate by number corresponding to listing in Feeder Schedule.

Underfloor Duct and Junction Box Triple System. For double or single systems, eliminate 1 or 2 lines. This symbol equally adaptable to auxiliary system layouts.

G   Generator.

M   Motor.

I   Instrument.

T   Power Transformer (Or draw to scale)

Controller

Isolating Switch.

AUXILIARY SYSTEMS

Push Button.

Buzzer.

Bell.

Annunciator.

Outside Telephone.

Interconnecting Telephone.

Telephone Switchboard.

Bell Ringing Transformer.

D   Electric Door Opener.

FP   Fire Alarm Bell.

F   Fire Alarm Station.

X   City Fire Alarm Station.

FA   Fire Alarm Central Station.

FS   Automatic Fire Alarm Device.

W   Watchman's Station.

W   Watchman's Central Station.

H   Horn.

N   Nurse's Signal Plug.

M   Maid's Signal Plug.

R   Radio Outlet.

SC   Signal Central Station.

Interconnection Box.

Battery.

----- Auxiliary System Circuits.

Note: Any line without further designation indicates a 2-Wire System. For a greater number of wires designate with numerals in manner similar to ---12-No. 18W-¾" C., or designate by number corresponding to listing in Schedule.

_{a,b,c} Special Auxiliary Outlets. Subscript letters refer to notes on plans or detailed description in specs.

Fig. 15

Courtesy of American Standards Association, New York, N.Y.

to different units or parts of the building. Each unit is numbered on the chart, and all corresponding units on the drawing are given the same number. The specifications for any unit shown on the drawing can easily be found by referring to the corresponding number on the chart. This procedure saves repeating the specifications for each unit.

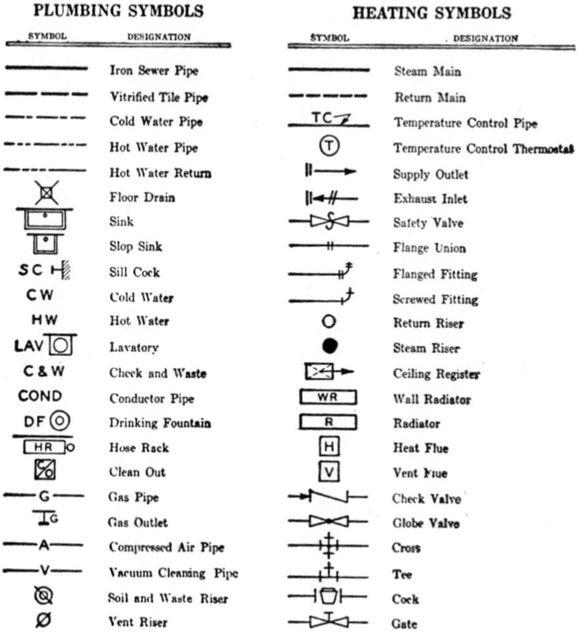

Fig. 16. Plumbing and Heating Symbols

Symbols Used in Architectural, Plumbing, and Heating Trades.
Courtesy of H. A. Rogers & Company, Minneapolis, Minn.

Door and window schedules are of importance to the woodworker, since reference to the schedules must be made for such construction information, as size, thickness, kind of glass, and shape of the item.

Room schedules show the kind of wood and finish for each room. Typical door, window, and room schedules are shown in Fig. 17. Other schedules refer to structural information with which the building contractor is primarily concerned.

Specifications. The term "specifications" refers to written descriptions and instructions accompanying a set of plans. They are a very important part of the drawings. Items written in the specifications or shown on the plans must be furnished or adhered to throughout the making of the project.

A set of specifications usually contains information of the following character: the kind of materials to be used; the grade of these materials; the sizes of the materials; the standard of workmanship acceptable; the responsibilities of the contractor, subcontractor, and owner in practically all matters; and the time limits of the contract.

ROOM SCHEDULE

No.	FLOOR	TRIM	FINISH	OTHER
1	¾"x2¼" Oak	Oak	Varnish	See Specifications
2	"	W. Cedar	Paint	"
3	Tile	Fir	Enamel	"
4	¾"x2¼" Oak	Fir	Paint	Wall Paper

WINDOW SCHEDULE

	SIZE	DESCRIPTION
A	3'0"x4'6"x1⅜"	Double Hung, 12 Lt. 3 Wide
B	3'0"x4'6"x1⅜"	Pr. Casement, 2 Lt. Wide
C	2'0"x3'0"x1⅜"	Sgl. Casement, 1 Lt.

DOOR SCHEDULE

	SIZE	DESCRIPTION
D₁	3'0"x7'0"x1¾"	6 Panel — See Detail
D₂	2'8"x7'0"x1⅜"	1 Pan. 1 Lt. Sash Door
D₃	2'0"x7'0"x1⅜"	Slab

Fig. 17. Typical Schedules

Kinds of Architectural Working Drawings. A set of architectural working drawings may consist of plans, elevations, and details. Other drawings, which sometimes accompany the architectural working drawings, become necessary when the project is a large one. These are separate sets of plans and may include any of the following: structural plans, electrical plans, heating and ventilating plans, plumbing and piping plans, and landscaping plans.

On small jobs, this information is generally included in the architectural plans.

The Key to Blueprint Reading. *The ability to know in what direction to look, or to discover in what direction the draftsman was "mentally" looking when he drew the plans, is the key to all blueprint reading.* The draftsman employs many different methods to make drawings easy to read.

Floor plan. A plan view is a view of each floor of a building showing room arrangements; sizes of rooms; building dimensions; location and size of window and door openings; location of electrical fixtures, switches, and outlets; location of plumbing fixtures; and location of cabinets and built-in features. A typical floor plan is shown in Fig. 18.

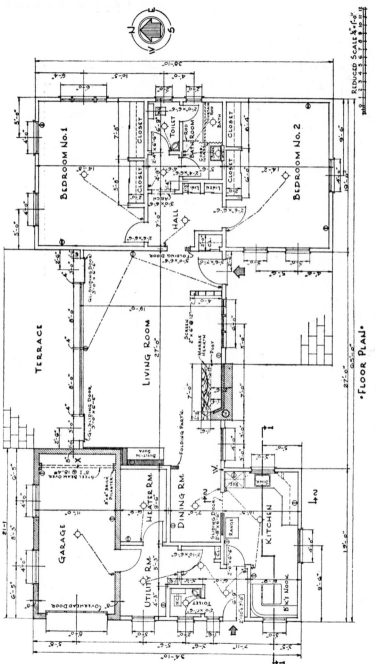

Fig. 18. Typical Floor Plan of a House

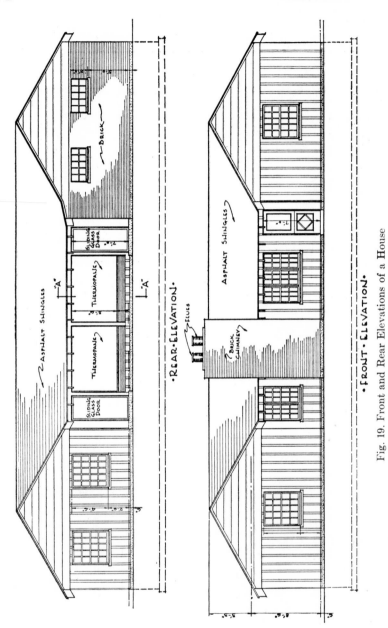

Fig. 19. Front and Rear Elevations of a House

Elevations. When "mentally" looking in a horizontal direction at the exterior of the building, the view is known as an elevation. A set of drawings sometimes requires four elevations.

Front Elevation. A representation of a building as viewed from a point directly in front of the building is called a front elevation (Fig. 19).

Rear Elevation. A view of a building as viewed from a point directly in back of the building is called a rear elevation (Fig. 19).

Right-Side Elevation. The right-side elevation is the view which is to the right as the building is viewed from a point directly in front.

Left-Side Elevation. The left-side elevation is that part of the building which is to the left when looking at the front. Elevations occasionally are called north, south, east, or west, depending on which way the respective sides of the building face.

Details. The conventions and symbols used in small scale drawings make it necessary to draw the details of construction to a larger scale. If no details are shown, the type of construction may be selected by the cabinetmaker. Objects such as doors, windows, stairs, cornices, and cabinetwork are often detailed.

The required dimensions for the length, width, height, and thickness of the detailed part to be drawn are taken from the plan views, elevations, and sections.

Fig. 20 is a detailed drawing of a double-hung window which should be studied carefully. It shows enlarged sectional details of the various parts and the cutting planes represented in those sections.

Sometimes an architect simply refers in the specifications to stock numbers or standard methods of construction. This method serves to indicate what construction is required and what dimensions to follow.

HOW TO READ A SET OF WORKING DRAWINGS

The first and most important factor in reading a drawing is actual shop experience. From shop experience comes a knowledge of materials, an understanding of methods of construction, work procedures, and standard practices in general. Experience can be gained only through work, but the process can be speeded up by study and practice in reading drawings.

Another important factor is obtaining the necessary information from a set of plans and being able to fit together the information given in the various drawings and specifications. A study of the information given in the preceding parts of this chapter will help you to understand how the draftsman goes about presenting what he wants to convey. A set of drawings may consist of plans, elevations, sections, details, and specifications. Each and every one of these sheets may

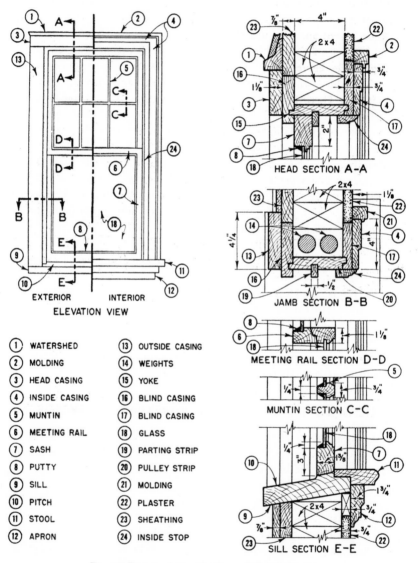

① WATERSHED	⑬ OUTSIDE CASING
② MOLDING	⑭ WEIGHTS
③ HEAD CASING	⑮ YOKE
④ INSIDE CASING	⑯ BLIND CASING
⑤ MUNTIN	⑰ BLIND CASING
⑥ MEETING RAIL	⑱ GLASS
⑦ SASH	⑲ PARTING STRIP
⑧ PUTTY	⑳ PULLEY STRIP
⑨ SILL	㉑ MOLDING
⑩ PITCH	㉒ PLASTER
⑪ STOOL	㉓ SHEATHING
⑫ APRON	㉔ INSIDE STOP

Fig. 20. Detail of Double-Hung Window Frame

have to be referred to in order to determine the requirements of a given item.

For example, consider the problems of blueprint reading involved in an ordinary window opening with frame and sash.

1. The size may be given on the floor plan or in a schedule.

2. The size may be given in inches of glass measure or in feet and inches of opening measure.

3. The thickness of the sash may be given on the plan, in the schedule, or in the specifications.

4. The number of lights may be given in the plan, in the elevation, in the schedule, on the detail, or in the specifications.

5. The type of window may be check rail, plain rail, hinged in, hinged out, or stationary. The information may be found in the plan, elevation, detail schedule, or specifications.

6. The kind of wood required may be found in the schedule or specifications, or, if a stock item is used, the kind of wood is already determined.

7. The kind and weight of glass required may be found in the plan, elevation, schedule, or specifications.

8. The frame may be a stock or standard item such as a double-hung window or casement with sash swinging in or out. Also, the type of wall construction used (such as standard 2 x 4 wall) must be determined, as well as the thickness of inside plaster, the thickness of outside plaster, whether or not it is sheathed, and the type of siding used.

9. The frame may require spring sash balance, pulleys and weights, or some other type of balance. This information is usually given in the specifications.

10. The frame may be box construction, plank for a brick wall, or standard construction for a 2 x 4 or 2 x 6 wall. Standard construction may be taken for granted on a plan which shows no other method of construction.

11. Thickness of jambs, types of blindstop, types of casing, brick mold, or plaster mold may be standard practice or they may be detailed.

12. Special construction of frames is always detailed. However, the measurements, kind of wood, type of glass, etc., must be found in other parts of the plans or specifications.

Specific information must be found for every phase of the work. If certain information is lacking, it must be obtained from the architect, if he supervises the job, or from the owner, if the architect is released from that responsibility.

Procedure to Follow. The procedure to follow in reading a set of plans will vary with the specific information sought. The following procedure will be found effective.

1. Read the specifications and notes thoroughly for general information. Note any specific information which deviates from standard practice.

2. Get a general idea of the structure by reading the drawings of plans and elevations.

3. Read the sections for general information about the construction and materials used.

4. When concentrating on a given item, refer to the plan views, elevations, sections, details, and specifications for whatever information they may contain about that item.

5. Seek information that may be lacking in the plans and specifications from those who have authority to determine what is required.

6. Check any discrepancy or contradiction which may be found in the drawings or specifications, and refer the matter for settlement to those in authority.

PRACTICE IN READING DRAWINGS

The following questions and answers are based on Fig. 21. The cabinet is shown cut by the cutting plane line *A-A* to expose the interior. Check your blueprint reading ability by studying the illustration and locating the answers to the questions.

SELF-CHECK PROBLEMS

1. How deep is the recessed section for the cabinet?
ANSWER. *The recess in the wall is 11″ deep.*
2. What are the over-all dimensions of the recessed section?
ANSWER. *The recessed section is 6′8½″ x 1′8″ x 11″.*
3. What is the thickness of the counter?
ANSWER. *The counter is 1″ in thickness.*
4. What is the distance from the top of the counter to the floor level?
ANSWER. *The distance is 3′5½″.*
5. Where is plywood used in the construction of the cabinet?
ANSWER. *Plywood is used for the back of the open section of the cabinet; also the back of the bell box section and the closed section.*
6. What scale was used in making the drawing?
ANSWER. *A scale of ¾″ equals 1′ was used in making the drawing.*

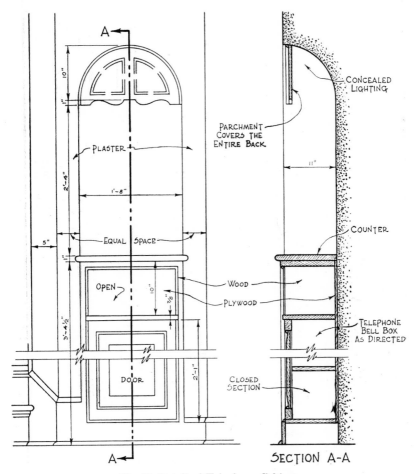

Fig. 21. Detail of Telephone Cabinet

7. What is the thickness of the bottom piece for the open section?

ANSWER. *The thickness of this piece is ⅞″.*

8. What is the distance from the top of the counter to the bottom of the curved portion?

ANSWER. *The distance is 2′4″.*

9. What is the radius for the curved portion of the cabinet?

ANSWER. *The radius for the curved portion is 10″.*

10. How many shelves are required in the closed section?

ANSWER. *One shelf is shown in the closed section.*

11. What other material, other than wood and plaster, is shown on Section *A-A?*

ANSWER. *Parchment is shown on the back of the curved portion.*

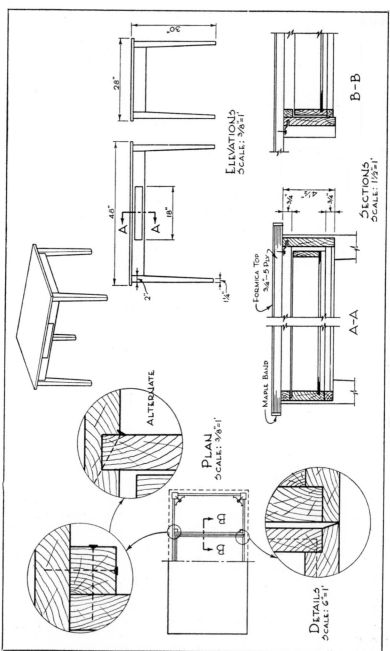

Fig. 22. Working Drawing of a Table

12. What is the distance between the counter top and the cabinet top? ANSWER. *The distance is 3′ 3″.*

QUESTIONS

Study Fig. 22 carefully and answer the following questions:

1. What scale is used for the section views?
2. What scale is used for the elevation views?
3. How long is the table?
4. What is the width of the table? Height?
5. From what view did you obtain the width and the height?
6. What are the dimensions of the table legs?
7. What is the size of the opening for the drawer?
8. How is the top to be constructed?
9. How is the top to be fastened?
10. Where is a maple band shown?
11. What construction is shown for fastening the bottom of the drawer?
12. Describe the construction for the drawer guides.

Study Fig. 23 carefully, and answer the following questions:

1. What is the over-all height of the cabinet?
2. What type of drawers is indicated? How many?
3. What are the dimensions of the flush panel doors?
4. What is the width of the trim around the flush panel doors?

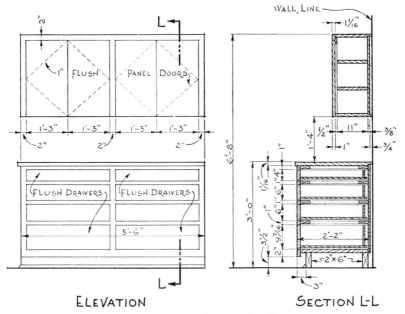

ELEVATION   SECTION L-L

Fig. 23. Utility Cabinet Detail

5. How many shelves are shown in the cabinet?
6. What is the depth of the shelves?
7. How much space is between the drawer section and the cabinet section?
8. Where are 2 x 6 shown?
9. How much space is between the front of the cabinet and the 2 x 6?
10. How far is the front of the cabinet above the floor?

REVIEW QUESTIONS

1. Draw the following lines:
   a) Section
   b) Hidden outline
   c) Center
   d) Dimension
   e) Extension
   f) Cutting plane
   g) Break
2. Indicate the plan symbols for the following:
   a) Brick in section
   b) Plaster
   c) Concrete
   d) Glass
3. Indicate the plan symbols for the following:
   a) Double-acting door
   b) Door with sill
   c) Casement window in brick wall
   d) Double-hung window in frame wall
4. Give the terms for the following abbreviations: S4S, Flg, K.C., W.P., O.C., D.F., F.G., Bldg.
5. Name four items usually shown in a door or window schedule.
6. Name two items usually shown in a room schedule.
7. Name five types of basic information usually given in a set of specifications.
8. What is a cabinet drawing?
9. What is the purpose of an auxiliary view?
10. What is the "key" to all blueprint reading?
11. Name three divisions or parts to a set of architectural drawings.
12. Name five items usually found in a floor plan.
13. What is a front elevation?
14. What is the purpose of a detail drawing?
15. List in logical order six steps to follow when reading a set of plans.

Board Measure

1. *What is a board foot?*
2. *What is meant by* nominal size?
3. *How are plywoods and veneers bought and sold?*
4. *What is the basis for pricing lumber?*
5. *What basic rule is used in figuring board feet?*

INTRODUCTION TO CHAPTER VI

An appreciation of the value of material is as essential as knowing how to perform the operations involved in processing that material into a useful article. The nature of lumber is such that some waste is unavoidable. However, the selection of the proper size will often result in a considerable saving in material and time.

The cabinetmaker should have a thorough knowledge of the standards by which lumber is bought and sold. He should know how lumber is measured and the rules that are followed in measuring different kinds of lumber.

This chapter will acquaint the cabinetmaker with the basic rules for figuring lumber sizes and the methods used for pricing the various types and grades of lumber.

NOMINAL SIZES OF LUMBER

Nominal, meaning "not real or actual," is the term used in the lumber trade to designate the size of lumber. A board is cut to a certain size at the sawmill, but this does not mean that the same board will be that size when it is dried and surfaced by planing. A board cut to a $1''$ thickness at the mill will perhaps be only $2\frac{5}{32}''$ in thickness as a finished board. The same conditions hold true for the width of lumber. A board cut $8''$ wide at the mill may be only $7\frac{5}{8}''$ wide as a finished board. Since lumber shrinks very little in length, rough boards are always cut close to the length specified. Boards are cut to odd and even lengths in foot measurements, depending upon the grade and species of lumber.

Nominal, then, refers to the size of the rough board and does not actually indicate the size of the finished board. The lumber industry, however, has standardized the finished sizes so that there is a uniformity in finished lumber. A 2 x 4, for example, will measure approximately 1⅝″ x 3⅝″ after it is dried and surfaced.

The remainder of this chapter will be devoted to a discussion of the various standards and rules used in the lumber industry.

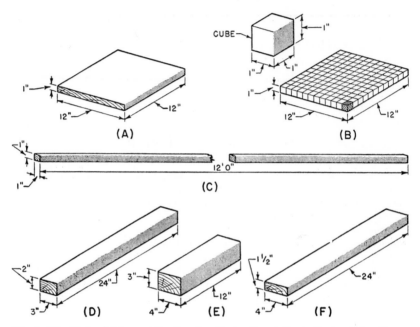

Fig. 1. The Unit of Measure for Lumber Is the Board Foot. Each of the Above Pieces Is One Board Foot

BOARD FOOT

A board foot (bd. ft.) is the unit of measure by which lumber is bought and sold. A board 1″ thick, 12″ wide, and 12″ long contains one board foot as shown in (A) of Fig. 1. A board foot contains 144 cubic inches as shown in (B) of Fig. 1. A cube is a solid, having squares as faces. Hence, one cubic inch is a square with dimensions of 1″ as shown in the illustration. Any piece of lumber that contains 144 cubic inches is equivalent to one board foot. The pieces of lumber shown in (C), (D), (E), and (F) each contain one board foot.

The measurements for figuring board feet are based on nominal sizes rather than the actual dimensions of the stock.

The number of board feet in any piece of lumber is found by multiplying the thickness by the width by the length. Since this procedure often involves the use of fractions, the cabinetmaker should review fractions. A fraction is a part of a whole number, 1, and consists of a numerator and denominator as shown by the following example:

$$\frac{1}{4} \quad \text{(numerator)} \atop \text{(denominator)}$$

A proper fraction, such as ⅜, has a denominator larger than the numerator. An improper fraction, such as 6/4, has a numerator larger than the denominator. Mixed numbers are made up of a whole number and a fraction, such as 2½.

A basic rule for figuring board feet can be stated in very simple form as follows:

$$\frac{\text{Thickness in inches} \times \text{width in inches} \times \text{length in feet}}{12} = \text{board feet}$$

Applying this rule, a board 1″ x 6″ x 12′ would contain

$$\frac{1 \times 6 \times \overset{1}{\cancel{12}}}{\underset{1}{\cancel{12}}} = 6 \text{ or } 6 \text{ bd. ft.}$$

Notice that cancellation was used. That is, the denominator 12 and the numerator 12 were divided by 12, leaving 1 and 6, which, when multiplied together, gave the answer 6.

When the size of a board is entirely in inches, such as 1″ x 6″ x 8″, 144 is used as the denominator of the fraction, thus:

$$\frac{1 \times \overset{1}{\cancel{6}} \times \overset{}{\cancel{8}}}{\underset{\underset{3}{\cancel{18}}}{\cancel{144}}} = \frac{1}{3} \text{ bd. ft.}$$

Notice in this problem that 144 was divided by 8, leaving 18, and that the 6 and 18 were divided by 6.

TRADE APPLICATIONS OF BOARD MEASURE

There are a number of trade applications that are used in figuring board feet. However, all are a variation of the basic rule previously explained.

When figuring lumber thicker than 1″, the thickness in inches is substituted in place of the 1″ thickness such as 1¼″, 1½″, 2″, 3″, 4″, 6″, etc. Certain species and grades of lumber are listed as 4/4, 5/4, 6/4, 8/4, 10/4, etc., in thickness. For example, the number of board feet in a board 1¼″ x 8″ x 16′0″ would be figured by counting the thickness as 1¼″, thus

$$\frac{5 \times \overset{2}{\cancel{8}} \times \overset{4}{\cancel{16}}}{\cancel{4} \quad \underset{3}{\cancel{12}}} = \frac{40}{3} = 13\tfrac{1}{3} \text{ bd. ft.}$$

Notice that in this problem the mixed number, 1¼, was changed to an improper fraction, 5/4. When figuring lumber less than 1″ in thickness, disregard the stated thickness and figure as 1″. For example, a board 5/8″ x 12″ x 4′ would contain

$$\frac{1 \times \overset{1}{\cancel{12}} \times 4}{\underset{1}{\cancel{12}}} = 4 \text{ bd. ft.}$$

When figuring the board feet in a number of pieces, multiply by the number of pieces. For example, the number of board feet of lumber in 5 pieces 1½″ x 8″ x 14′ would be

$$\frac{5 \times \overset{1}{\cancel{3}} \times \overset{\overset{1}{\cancel{4}}}{\cancel{8}} \times 14}{\underset{1}{\cancel{2}} \quad \underset{\underset{1}{\cancel{4}}}{\cancel{12}}} = 70 \text{ bd. ft.}$$

When figuring narrow stock using lineal feet (lineal pertains to straight measurements), multiply thickness by width by the number of lineal feet and divide by 12. For example, the number of board feet in 270 lineal feet of 2 x 4 would be

$$\frac{\overset{1}{\cancel{2}} \times \cancel{4} \times \overset{90}{\cancel{270}}}{\underset{\underset{1}{\cancel{3}}}{\cancel{12}}} = 180 \text{ bd. ft.}$$

Furniture stock is calculated in fractional foot lengths (nominal size). The length in feet is changed to an improper fraction and the usual procedure followed. For example, the number of board feet in 200 pieces $1\frac{1}{4}'' \times 4'' \times 5'6''$ would be

$$\frac{\overset{25}{\overset{\cancel{50}}{\cancel{200}}} \times 5 \times \overset{1}{\underset{\cancel{12}}{\cancel{4}}} \times \overset{}{\underset{\cancel{2}}{11}}}{\underset{1}{\cancel{4}} \quad \underset{3}{\cancel{12}} \quad \underset{1}{\cancel{2}}} = \frac{1375}{3} = 458\frac{1}{3} \text{ bd. ft.}$$

Notice in this problem the 5'6'' was changed to $5\frac{1}{2}$ and then to the improper fraction, $\frac{11}{2}$.

Furniture squares which have fractional-inch widths are reduced to improper fractions. The same procedure is then followed. For example, the number of board feet in 408 pieces $2\frac{1}{2}'' \times 2\frac{1}{2}'' \times 3'6''$ would be

$$\frac{\overset{17}{\overset{\cancel{34}}{\cancel{408}}} \times 5 \times 5 \times 7}{\underset{1}{\cancel{12}} \quad 2 \quad 2 \quad 2} = 743\frac{3}{4} \text{ bd. ft.}$$

In all calculations, fractional parts of a board foot (final count) $\frac{1}{2}$ or over, are counted as whole board feet.

Board feet can readily be figured by using tables which show the number of board feet for each lineal foot in standard stock sizes. In Table I, for example, a 1 x 6 is shown to contain $\frac{1}{2}$ board foot for each lineal foot of length. A ten-foot length of such a piece would contain 5 board feet ($10 \times \frac{1}{2} = \frac{10}{2} = 5$).

STANDARD LUMBER SIZES	NUMBER OF BOARD FEET IN EACH LINEAR FOOT
1 x 2	$\frac{1}{6}$
1 x 3	$\frac{1}{4}$
1 x 4 or 2 x 2	$\frac{1}{3}$
1 x 5	$\frac{5}{12}$
1 x 6 or 2 x 3	$\frac{1}{2}$
1 x 8 or 2 x 4	$\frac{2}{3}$
1 x 10	$\frac{5}{6}$
1 x 12	1
2 x 8 or 4 x 4	$\frac{4}{3}$
2 x 10	$\frac{5}{3}$

Table I. Table for Figuring Board Feet

LUMBER TALLY

Methods of Tally.   Tally (meaning to count) is the term used by the lumber industry to indicate the actual count of a definite number of pieces and their board foot content.

Two methods of tallying lumber are in common use: (1) by calculating the board foot content when listing (tallying) lumber by number of pieces and their sizes; and (2) by calculating board foot content by using the *board rule* (also called tally stick), and listing the number of pieces containing a like number of board feet, regardless of size, on a tally sheet.

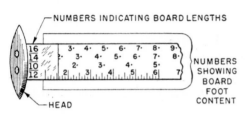

Fig. 2. Board Rule or Tally Stick

Use of Board Rule. The numbers on the board rule next to the head (the numbers are also next to the handle), as shown in Fig. 2, indicate the lengths of the boards that can be measured. This particular rule can be used to determine the number of board feet in boards ten, twelve, fourteen, and sixteen feet long by using the tables shown. On the other side of this rule (not shown in illustration) are tables for figuring the board feet in lengths of nine, eleven, thirteen, and fifteen feet. Rules may be purchased for various lengths of boards. For example, an $\frac{8}{22}$ rule is marked for boards from eight to twenty-two feet long. The scales are all based on boards having a nominal thickness of 1″.

To use the board rule, the length of the board to be measured must be known or determined by measurement. To determine the number of board feet in a board known to be 12′ long, simply hook the head of the rule on the edge of the board as shown in Fig. 3. Now take the reading where the edge of

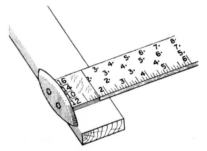

Fig. 3. Using a Board Rule

the board lines up with the 12′ scale. In this case, it is 2, which would be the number of board feet contained in this board. If the board is ten feet long, the numbers in the second horizontal line opposite the 10 are used (2, 3, 4, 5, etc.). If the board is fourteen feet long, the scale opposite the 14 is used, and for a sixteen-foot board, the scale opposite the 16 is used.

Rules for Tally. When tallying lumber with a tally stick, the general practice followed is to drop fractions less than one-half board foot to the next lower number. Fractions over one-half board foot are raised to the next higher number. One-half board foot measures are counted alternately to the next higher number. The others are dropped. For example, in a group of readings such as 4½, 1½, 2½, 6½, 8½, and 3½, the first 4½ would be raised to 5, the 2½ to 3, and the 8½ to 9. The ½ would be dropped from 1½, 6½, and 3½, making a simple addition of 5, 1, 3, 6, 9, and 3, as shown by the following example:

4½	raise to	5
1½	lower to	1
2½	raise to	3
6½	lower to	6
8½	raise to	9
3½	lower to	3
		27

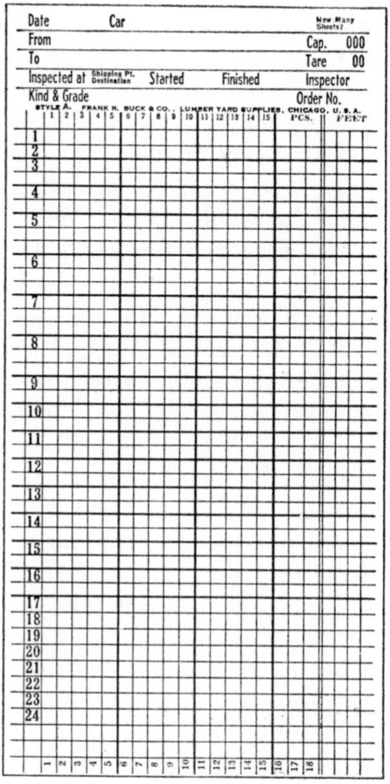

This manner of counting will average very close to the actual board foot count of a load of lumber and will eliminate the listing of fractions.

Use of Tally Sheet. A tally sheet is a standardized printed form used in the lumber industry to simplify the process of counting board feet (Fig. 4). Each number in the vertical column of figures on the left edge of the form represents the board foot content of a single piece of lumber, 1″ nominal thickness.

The squares under the horizontal line (1 to 15 inclusive) may be used to designate a tally of five pieces by making slant lines in

Fig. 4. Tally Sheet Form

each square; hence 75 pieces can be listed horizontally (15 × 5 = 75).

The total board feet is determined by multiplying the total number of pieces by board feet per piece (vertical column). This procedure will be more fully explained under the heading, "Totaling a Tally Sheet."

This tally sheet is used *only* in connection with the board rule. When a board is measured with the board rule, a check is placed on the tally sheet on the horizontal line next to the number. For example, if a board were found to contain five board feet, a check would be placed next to the five.

Factory and shop grades, as well as some hardwoods, are manufactured in random widths and lengths. This practice permits the greatest yield from a log and also allows a greater selection for cuttings by the processing plant, be it a sash and door factory, store fixture plant, or furniture factory. It is obvious that the great variety of sizes possible would make an endless piece list, while listing by board foot content limits the list to board foot content only.

Totaling a Tally Sheet. To figure the total board foot content in a load of lumber that has been recorded on a tally sheet (Fig. 5), the following steps are used:

1. Total the tally on each horizontal line and place the number under the heading, *PCS*. Notice that there are two marks made opposite the figure 5. Therefore, a 2 is placed under the heading, *PCS*. Note also that there are twenty marks opposite the figure 10. A **20**, therefore, is placed under *PCS*.

2. Total the number of board feet in each horizontal column by multiplying the number of pieces by the board foot content shown in the vertical column. Again notice the 5 column. The total number of pieces indicated here is 2. Therefore, $5 \times 2 = 10$, the number of board feet. The ten is placed under the heading, *Feet*. The remaining pieces are tallied in the same manner.

3. Total the number of board feet in the load by adding the figures in the *Feet* column (vertical). Total the number of pieces in the load by adding the figures in the *PCS* column. This number can be used as a check against the number of pieces listed in the order.

When the boards measured with the board rule are over 1″ in thickness (Fig. 6), the same procedure is followed with one exception. The total under *Feet* must be multiplied by the thickness of the lumber to obtain the correct number of board feet, since the scales are based on lumber of 1″ nominal thickness. In this case, the total, **824**, must be multiplied by $1\frac{1}{4}$, or, as shown on the tally sheet, $\frac{5}{4}$. Hence,

$$\overset{206}{\underset{\underset{1}{1}}{\frac{\cancel{824} \times 5}{4}}} = 1,030$$

which is the total number of board feet in the load. Shown on the tally sheet is another method of figuring the total in board feet. Since the

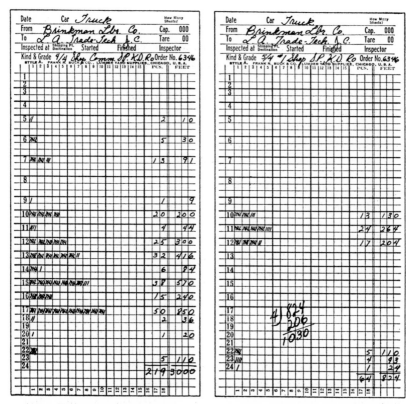

Fig. 5. Tally Sheet Filled Out To Check an Order of Lumber

Fig. 6. How To Use Tally Sheet for 5/4 Nominal Thickness Lumber

thickness of 1¼ makes each board foot short one full quarter, in this case 824/4 in all, the 824 is divided by 4, making 206, which, when added to the 824, gives the total of 1,030 board feet. Lumber listed as 6/4 would be short one half board foot for each board foot figured with the board rule, and one half would have to be added to the total. Lumber listed as 8/4 would, of course, contain double the board count taken with the tally stick.

RULES FOR FIGURING LUMBER

Rough Nominal Sizes. Lumber less than 1″ in thickness is counted as 1″. Lumber above 1″ in thickness is sold in 1¼″, 1½″, 2″, 3″, 4″, 6″, etc., as previously explained. Standard widths are 3″, 4″, 5″, 6″, 8″, 10″, 12″, etc.

Lumber lengths are generally on an even foot basis, such as 8′, 10′, 12′, 14′, 16′, and up to 24′. Lengths above 24′ can be obtained on special order. Lengths such as 5′, 7′, and 9′ can be cut from boards twice these lengths; for example, two 7′ boards can be cut from one 14′ board.

Hardwoods are usually sold in random widths and lengths because of their scarcity.

Finish Lumber and Yard Stock. Standard sizes of stock are dressed at sawmills or at large planing mills to specific net sizes established by the lumber association. Such surfaced stock is sold on the basis of rough nominal sizes before surfacing, and the board foot content is calculated on that basis.

In figuring board feet, any board less than an even number of inches in width is counted as the next even width (except 1″ x 3″, 1″ x 5″ and the hardwoods). For example, a board ¾″ x 6½″ must be counted as 1″ x 8″, and a board 4⅞″ wide is figured as 6″.

Milled and Cut Sizes. Lumber that is milled to detail or odd measure is figured to the next larger rough nominal size.

Cut lengths up to and including 8′ are figured in odd and even foot lengths.

Cut lengths over 8′ are figured in even foot lengths only.

Cut lengths (shorts) are figured in terms of multiples obtainable from standard lengths, with allowance for split ends and trimming.

Glued Squares and Flats. Glued squares are figured in terms of the number of pieces of standard nominal size required, plus milling allowances after they are glued.

Glued flats are figured in terms of standard nominal sizes, plus allowance for milling.

Plywood and Veneers. Plywood and veneers are bought and sold by the square foot, regardless of the thickness. The difference in thickness is adjusted in the price. For example, a panel 24″ x 60″ x ⅜″ or 2′ x 5′ would contain 10 square feet, and a panel 24″ x 4′0″ x 1½″ = 8 square feet.

CALCULATING LUMBER COSTS

Basis of Pricing Lumber. Lumber prices are based on the price of one thousand board feet, usually written as MBF (MB.F.) or simply as M. The M stands for thousand and the B.F., of course, for board feet. When the price of lumber is quoted, it is always understood that the price is quoted per thousand. Lumber prices can be easily figured by the use of decimal fractions. Decimal fractions are fractions, the denominators of which are in multiples of 10, such as $\frac{2}{10}$, $\frac{11}{100}$, and $\frac{153}{1000}$. In writing decimal fractions, the denominator is not used, but a decimal point indicates what the denominator would be if written as a common fraction. For example, the common fraction $\frac{2}{10}$ would be written as .2, the common fraction $\frac{11}{100}$ as .11, and the common fraction $\frac{153}{1000}$ as .153. Note that there is always one less figure to the right of the decimal than there are figures in the denominator of the common fraction. A zero is considered as a figure, and a decimal fraction such as .06 would be read as six hundredths. The numbers to the left of the decimal point are read as whole numbers.

Since the price of lumber is based on the figure one thousand, one of the multiples used in decimal fractions, lumber prices can easily be figured by applying some of the rules governing the use of decimals. The first rule that can be applied states:

To divide a decimal by 1,000, move the decimal point three places to the left.

This rule can be applied to figure the cost per board foot when the cost per thousand is known. For example, lumber quoted at $120.00 per M will cost $.12 per board foot. Lumber quoted at $48.00 per M will cost $.048 per board foot.

Notice that in moving the decimal point in this problem, a zero had to be added to make the three places. The $.048 is read as four and eight-tenths cents. If the quoted price were $27.00 per thousand, the price per board foot would be $.027, read as two and seven-tenths cents. Also, lumber quoted at $115.00 per thousand would cost $.115 per board foot, read as eleven and one-half cents.

The second decimal rule that can be applied to figuring lumber costs states:

To multiply a decimal by 1,000, move the decimal point three places to the right.

This rule is applied in figuring the cost of lumber per thousand when the cost per board foot is known. For example, lumber costing $.14 per board foot will cost $140.00 per M. Note that the decimal point was moved three places to the right. A zero had to be added to make the three places. If the price per board foot is $.07, the cost per thousand is $70.00. At $.175 per board foot, the cost will be $175 per M.

Plywood and veneers are priced by the square foot and may be $.04, $.06, $.30, $.40, etc.

In figuring the cost of lumber, there are a number of situations that may arise. The following rules will aid in meeting these situations.

Rule 1. When the price quoted is in even cents per board foot, multiply the footage by the price and point off two decimal places. Examples:

1. Find the cost of 180 bd. ft. of lumber at $.18 per bd. ft. Solution:

$$
\begin{array}{r}
180 \\
.18 \\
\hline
1440 \\
180 \\
\hline
32.40 \text{ or } \$32.40 \quad Ans.
\end{array}
$$

Decimals are multiplied in the same manner as whole numbers. After multiplying the numbers, the number of decimal places to the right of the decimal are counted in both the multiplicand and multiplier. This same count is used to count off the number of places in the product starting at the right as shown by the following example.

(multiplicand)	.225	(3 places)
(multiplier)	.16	(2 places)
	1350	
	225	
(product)	.03600	(5 places)

Notice that a zero had to be added to make the five places.

2. Find the cost of 348 sq. ft. of veneer at $.26 per sq. ft. Solution:

$$
\begin{array}{r}
348 \\
.26 \\
\hline
2088 \\
696 \\
\hline
90.48 \text{ or } \$90.48 \quad Ans.
\end{array}
$$

Rule 2. When the price quoted is in cents and a fraction of a cent per foot, convert the fraction to its decimal equivalent, multiply by the footage, and point off the required decimal places.

Examples:

1. Find the cost of 420 bd. ft. at 22½¢ per foot. The 22½¢ is changed to the decimal .225.

Solution:

$$
\begin{array}{r}
.225 \\
420 \\
\hline
4500 \\
900 \\
\hline
94.500 \text{ or } \$94.50 \quad Ans.
\end{array}
$$

2. Find the cost of 89 bd. ft. at 17¾¢ per bd. ft. The 17¾¢ is changed to the decimal .1775.

Solution:

$$
\begin{array}{r}
.1775 \\
89 \\
\hline
15975 \\
14200 \\
\hline
15.7975 \text{ or } \$15.80 \text{ total cost.} \quad Ans.
\end{array}
$$

Notice that the decimal .7975 was rounded to .80. In rounding decimals, if the numbers dropped are 5 or over, the number is raised. For example, .365 is rounded to .37. Numbers below 5 are dropped without change. For example, .663 is rounded to .66, and .8742 is rounded to .874.

Rule 3. When the price quoted is in dollars per M, multiply the price in dollars by the footage, and point off three decimal places.

Example:

1. Find the cost of 1,500 bd. ft. at $88.00 per M.

Solution:

$$
\begin{array}{r}
1500 \\
88 \\
\hline
12000 \\
12000 \\
\hline
132000 \text{ or } \$132.00 \text{ total cost}
\end{array}
$$

Rule 4. When the price quoted is in dollars and cents per M, multiply the price in dollars and cents by the footage, and point off five decimal places.

Example:

1. Find the cost of 3,684 bd. ft. @ $56.75 per M.

Solution:

$$
\begin{array}{r}
3684 \\
5675 \\
\hline
18420 \\
25788 \\
22104 \\
18420 \\
\hline
\end{array}
$$

20906700 or $209.07 total cost. (Note that the .067 is rounded off to .07.)

Summary of Rules for Calculating Lumber Costs. While four different rules are given for figuring lumber, plywood, and veneer costs, these may be stated in two simple rules as follows:

Lumber: Board measure × price = cost.

Plywood and Veneers: Square feet × price = cost.

PROBLEMS

The preceding information should be carefully studied before attempting to solve the following problems.

Solve the following problems for board foot content.

1. 3 pcs. 2½″ x 8″ x 10′0″.
2. 5 pcs. 1¼″ x 6″ x 16′0″.
3. A yard man delivered the following pieces of lumber to the stock cutter as per instructions on the stock bill:

6 pcs. 1″ x 6″ x 14′0″
21 pcs. 2″ x 10″ x 10′0″
3 pcs. 1″ x 4″ x 18′0″

How many board feet of lumber are contained in the foregoing list?

4. A job order calls for 38 table tops each 3′6″ wide and 5′6″ long. The lumber bill indicates that 114 pieces 1″ x 8″ x 12′0″ were required to do the job.

How many bd. ft. of lumber were used?

5. Figure the total bd. ft. in each of the following items listed on a lumber bill:

4 pcs. 2″ x 4″ x 8′0″ Douglas Fir
8 pcs. 1″ x 10″ x 14′0″ White Pine
3 pcs. 1″ x 5″ x 12′0″ Redwood
16 pcs. 1″ x 6″ x 20′0″ Douglas Fir

6. How many board feet of lumber are there in 13 pieces $1\frac{1}{4}''$ x 10" x 16'0"?

7. A stock cutter receives the following shop pine material to make a number of stock size windows:

22 pcs. $1\frac{1}{2}''$ x 16" x 16'0"
38 pcs. $1\frac{1}{2}''$ x 22" x 14'0"
10 pcs. $1\frac{1}{2}''$ x 18" x 12'0"

How many bd. ft. of lumber are there in the order?

8. How many bd. ft. of lumber are there in the following lumber bill?

18 pcs. 1" x 4" x 6'0"
44 pcs. 1" x 3" x 8'0"
76 pcs. 1" x 5" x 12'0"
82 pcs. 2" x 3" x 14'0"
4 pcs. 1" x 10" x 20'0"

Dressed Finished Lumber and Yard Stock. The lumber sizes in the following problems are listed net surfaced sizes. Convert to nominal sizes and then figure the bd. ft. content.

9. 2 pcs. $\frac{3}{4}''$ x $10\frac{1}{2}''$ x 11'6"
10. 4 pcs. $1\frac{3}{4}''$ x $7\frac{1}{2}''$ x 15'0"
    3 pcs. $1\frac{5}{16}''$ x $9\frac{1}{4}''$ x 10'6"
    10 pcs. $\frac{5}{8}''$ x 8" x 7'0"
11. 7 pcs. $1\frac{1}{16}''$ x $4\frac{7}{8}''$ x 8'6"
    1 pc. $2\frac{1}{4}''$ x $6\frac{1}{2}''$ x 10'0"
    16 pcs. $1\frac{5}{8}''$ x $9\frac{1}{4}''$ x 13'6"
12. 12 pcs. 1" x 8" x 5'10"

Lineal Foot Content. Lumber sizes in the following problems are both nominal and net surfaced sizes. Compute the bd. ft. for each problem.

13. How many bd. ft. are contained in 980 linear feet of 2 x 4 nominal size?

14. Convert into bd. ft. 682 linear feet of 2 x 10 nominal size and 496 linear feet of $1\frac{1}{4}''$ x $5\frac{1}{2}''$ net sizes vertically grained Douglas Fir.

Summarizing Tally Sheet. Nominal sizes only are considered in the following problems.

Billing lumber that has been calculated on a tally sheet is listed on an invoice in the following form.

	FEET	PRICE	TOTAL
¼ F.A.S., ¼ W.O., K.D., Rough	185	$250	$46.25

$\frac{2}{6}, \frac{5}{7}, \frac{1}{8}, \frac{10}{9}, \frac{4}{10}$

This is read as follows:

Four quarter (1″) firsts and seconds, quarter sawed, white oak, kiln dried, rough, 2 pcs. with a content of 6 bd. ft. each, 5 pcs. 7 bd. ft. each, 1 pc. 8 bd. ft., 10 pcs. 9 bd. ft. each, and 4 pcs. 10 bd. ft. each. When combined, the total bd. ft. content is 185 bd. ft. At $250.00 per mbf, the cost is $46.25.

15. Figure the bd. ft. content of the following:

¼ Shop Common Sugar Pine K.D. Rough.

$\frac{12}{4}, \frac{6}{5}, \frac{3}{6}, \frac{10}{7}, \frac{15}{9}, \frac{40}{12}, \frac{21}{13}$

Factory Sizes of Furniture Squares. The sizes listed in these problems are nominal sizes.

16. How many bd. ft. of lumber are there in 296 table legs each 3′0″ long and made from 3″ x 3″ rough nominal size stock?

Cut and Milled Net Sizes. 17. How many bd. ft. of lumber are there in 17 stair treads each of which is 1″ net x 11½″ net x 3′10″ long?

18. How many bd. ft. of lumber in 284 pcs. 1¼″ net x 7¼″ net x 6′9″?

Glued Squares and Flats, Net Sizes. Solve the following problems for bd. ft. content.

19. 48 pcs. 2¼″ x 2¼″ x 2′6″

20. 32 pcs. 4½″ x 10″ x 0′10″

Plywood and Veneer. Solve the following problems to find number of square feet.

21. 6 pcs. ⅜″ x 30″ x 60″

22. 4 pcs. ¾″ x 24″ x 72″

Lumber Costs. 23. Compute the cost of

6 pcs. 1½″ x 14″ x 12′0″

12 pcs. 1½″ x 16″ x 14′0″

28 pcs. 1½″ x 20″ x 16′0″

108 pcs. 1½″ x 3″ net x 5′8″

All White Pine @ $55.00 per *M*

Plywood and Veneer Costs. 24. If Birch veneer is worth $.08 per square foot, how much will 148 pcs. $\frac{3}{16}''$ x 8" x 12'0" cost?

25. A store window is constructed with $\frac{1}{2}''$ plywood paneling which is worth $.15 per square foot. What is the cost of the window back if two pieces each 48" wide and 84" long are required to do the job?

REVIEW QUESTIONS

1. Define "nominal size."
2. What is the standard size of a board foot?
3. Give three rules for figuring the board foot content of a piece of lumber.
4. What is a tally stick?
5. How is surfaced lumber figured when determining board foot content?
6. How are veneers and plywood bought or sold?
7. What is the price unit for lumber?
8. What is a proper fraction? What is an improper fraction?
9. Change the following mixed numbers to improper fractions: $3\frac{1}{2}$, $4\frac{1}{2}$, $8\frac{1}{3}$, $2\frac{1}{4}$.
10. Reduce the following fractions to lowest terms: $18\frac{2}{3}$, $21\frac{1}{2}$, $14\frac{1}{4}$, $20\frac{2}{5}$.

Fundamentals of Stock Billing

QUESTIONS CHAPTER VII WILL ANSWER FOR YOU

1. *What is a quantity survey?*
2. *What is a stock bill?*
3. *What are the responsibilities of the detailer?*
4. *How are stock bills routed?*
5. *What is the order of "take off" in making a stock bill?*

INTRODUCTION TO CHAPTER VII

The woodworking industry has expanded in recent years due to newly developed materials and additional uses for many wood products. This expansion has required changes in methods of procedure necessitating more systematic methods of planning, laying out the work, and in record keeping.

Variations in record forms and layout procedures will vary somewhat according to the types of products turned out by the factory or shop. Since the fundamentals are essentially the same in every system, these fundamentals will be described in this chapter.

In order to understand fully the importance of stock billing, which is basic to any cabinet shop layout method, an over-all view of the processes involved before and after a stock bill is made out will also be discussed. This information will broaden the knowledge of the cabinetmaker and give him the necessary background for stock billing. It will also give him a better understanding of the work of a stock biller and stock cutter.

The terminology used in this chapter is the common terminology used in the United States. The material is divided into two main divisions: (1) general procedures, (2) detailing and stock billing practices and procedures.

GENERAL ORDERING PROCEDURES

There are several phases which pertain to general ordering procedures which can be roughly classified as follows: quantity surveying, or listing from plans and specifications, factory orders, and segregation of factory orders.

Quantity Survey. Quantity surveying is the process of listing as a complete unit such items as doors, windows, sash, frames, built-in fixtures, etc. This procedure is done *before* a stock bill is made.

Stock billing is the process of billing *every* piece required for a mill item, giving exact dimensions and milling required for each *piece* of material. For example, in a quantity survey, cupboard doors may be listed as follows: 90 cupboard doors, 1'6" x 2'0" x 1" net, 1 panel square sticking, mortise and tenon construction.

In a stock bill, each piece that makes up the door is listed as follows:

180 pcs. Pine 1" x 2¼" x 2'0" stiles
  90 "   "   1" x 2¼" x 1'3½" rails—1'1½" between shoulders
  90 "   "   1" x 3¼" x 1'3½" rails—1'1½" between shoulders
  90 "   3-ply Pine, ¼" x 14⅛" x 1'7⅛" panel

Cabinet shops receive fixture and millwork contracts on the basis of quantity survey estimates. Too much time would be lost and unprofitable labor would result if a detailed estimate had to be made covering each part in a piece of cabinet work. The making of full size details and supporting stock bills is done after the shop has received the contract order. The cabinet shop must, therefore, "sell" a job on the basis of a quantity survey, made from either the architect's drawings or from drawings made by the factory staff of draftsmen.

To prepare a quantity survey, a list of all the fixture or mill work items contained in the plans and specifications is made, but only those items which are to be furnished by the shop are priced. The bid, when finally completed, shows the priced items, and also lists other cabinet items which are called for in the plans, but which are not to be furnished by the shop. This eliminates any later misunderstanding of what the contract is to actually include.

Pricing a quantity survey is based on records of previous jobs constructed in the plant. To illustrate, the cost of producing a drawer or a standard size cabinet door, once established, can be used when pricing a new job. This procedure is followed for any cabinet which can be divided, for cost purposes, into several main divisions or parts. Accuracy is very important when making a quantity survey estimate, even though many details need not be considered.

The estimator who makes the quantity survey and the estimator who does the pricing may be different persons. Usually one person is responsible for the job.

A list of millwork may include all finish woodwork, such as sash, doors, windows, cabinets, paneling, or trim. Such a list, when prepared for presentation to the contractor, is known as a "full mill bid." The list, however, may contain only doors or such items as the contractor chooses to buy from that mill.

In store fixture work, the fixture and showcase requirements for a complete store may be handled by one fixture firm, or sometimes the various cabinets and cases are contracted to different firms that specialize in the manufacture of certain types of store equipment.

Factory Orders. Factory orders, sometimes known as shop orders or production orders, are issued only on the authority of the "front office." When a job contract is signed, a blanket order is issued to the detailing and billing department which receives a copy of the bid estimate with plans and specifications covering the entire job. Some detailing departments receive orders only for those items that are to be detailed. All stock items (standard items carried in stock) are billed directly into the factory or warehouse.

After an order is received by the detailing department, the complete job may be assigned to one man or it may be departmentalized and assigned to specialists in their respective fields of work. This procedure depends on the size of the plant.

Segregation of Factory Orders. The actual production part of a cabinet shop or plant is usually departmentalized for the efficient manufacture of various types and kinds of work. Each department specializing in its field has the equipment and "know-how" to efficiently produce certain products. Therefore, each department receives factory orders for only the items it is equipped to handle.

DETAILING AND STOCK BILLING PRACTICES

Detailing and stock billing are described under several headings as follows: the detailer's responsibilities, the stock biller's responsibilities, the stock cutter's responsibilities, stock billing procedures, typical stock bill forms, routing a stock bill, milling allowances, and estimating board feet of lumber in a stock bill.

The Detailer's Responsibilities. The detailer has three distinct duties or functions to perform: (1) make detail drawings, (2) issue factory orders, and (3) make stock bills.

The detailer must thoroughly study the plans, specifications, and quantity survey to acquaint himself with every phase of the work. As he works, he makes notes of any deficiencies which may be found, either on the plans or in quantity survey. He also looks for any peculiarities such as special construction requirements.

The detailer must check measurements at the building in which the cabinet work is to be installed and check the openings to see that the cabinet job, when completely assembled, is not too large to get into the building. He decides the type of construction to be followed. He determines the items for which detail drawings must be made, segregating the items for billing and the factory orders into the various shop departments.

The detailer who makes the drawing usually makes the stock bill for the item detailed. However, this is not always the case. For instance, a factory order may include 1,000 doors of various sizes and designs to be placed in "stock." The door department then makes its own stock bills.

A second type of factory order may call for a single item, such as a showcase, which is a standard item and for which the shop department already has stock plans and standard stock bills. These bills need only duplicating and then are ready for use.

A third type of factory order is for the specially designed and constructed item for which shop drawings and accompanying stock bills must always be made by the detailer.

The Stock Biller's Responsibilities. The stock biller may be the detailer. He may be a layout man in a given shop department, or he may be a department foreman. Stock billing duties are assigned according to the factory organization. The stock biller in a millwork plant or fixture factory is the man who reads plans and specifications or, more often, the full-sized details which have been drawn on the basis of these plans. He then lists on a stock bill each part of the article to be constructed.

Stock billing must be done accurately, as all dimensions given in a stock bill, plus all descriptive notes pertaining to the machining work to be done, are followed minutely by the mill.

The work of the stock biller involves considerable mathematical knowledge and ability; also a knowledge of construction is very essential. The methods of construction to be used for a given article are determined largely by the detailer. However, the stock biller must know the actual machining possibilities of the shop in which he is working. The kind and amount of equipment is a basic determining factor; limited machine equipment will allow fewer methods of fastening or shaping of the parts to be machined.

The stock biller's experience should also include a thorough knowledge of lumber, including kinds and types, grades, defects, standard nominal sizes, standard finish sizes, moisture content, cost, and purpose or suitability for the job to be billed.

The Stock Cutter's Responsibilities. The stock cutter is the mill-man who is charged with the responsibility of reading the stock bill, and selecting and cutting the stock according to the instructions given. In large mills and factories, the stock cutter is a specialist; he rarely handles finish hand tools and operates only the cut-off saw, rip saw, jointer, and planer.

The information given on a stock bill should be very clear and specific so that there can be no doubt in the mind of the stock cutter as to what is wanted.

STOCK BILLING PROCEDURES

Stock billing procedures are described under five headings: fundamental practices, order of take-off, lumber dimensions, moldings, and measurement rules.

Fundamental Practices. A careful stock biller observes the following practices:

1) Lists parts for doors, drawers, paneled ends, etc. Groups items for each subassembly separately.

2) Groups various parts of a similar size or design.

3) Where more than one ticket is required for a job, or where the routing is specialized in a department for different items on a job, the stock bill may and should be used to segregate kinds and types of work such as cabinet parts, glue work, and sticker work.

4) When billing a paneled frame, face frame, drawer, or door, it is good practice to group and bracket the stock for this type item; also show a sketch, if needed, with the dimensions of the complete part.

5) The listing should be grouped so as to avoid duplication of set-ups or processes: (a) List the same kind of wood in the same group to facilitate savings in lumber. (b) List the stock requiring the same machine operations in a group or give cross reference to these items if listed on a separate bill. (c) Note the ticket number on a stock bill on which other parts for the same job are ordered.

6) On a job requiring only one stock bill, the various parts should be segregated in a similar manner even though the department may not be specialized.

7) A check and "double-check" of every bit of information given in the stock bill should be made. The cost of the material is very important but if an expensive machine setup has to be duplicated because of an error in stock billing, the subsequent delay and effort will prove even more costly.

Order of "Take-Off." The order in which to take off and list the material for cutting varies with individuals and with factories. No system can be strictly adhered to under the various conditions encountered. However, the following guide should be observed as closely as possible:

1) List the "face" pieces first—those exposed pieces such as counter tops and drawer fronts requiring first selection of lumber for quality of grain or texture.

2) List the longer sizes. Length is more important than width if the item can be glued to make the required width.

3) List the outside vertical members, such as stiles; with few exceptions they are more important than the horizontal members. Follow with inside verticals such as mullions, then the muntins or bars.

4) List plywood in a group unless it is bracketed on the bill for a complete part.

5) Group the listings for size: first for thickness, second for width. Where this is possible, it will facilitate the stock cutter's work.

6) List every piece, no matter how small. If such items as glue blocks, ratchet strips, drawer guides, and stops are carried in stock, so note in the "remarks column" for that item.

Lumber Dimensions. The term *net* is a most important term which must be properly understood. It means the stock to be cut must be made to the *exact dimensions* as listed. The stock cutter, or whoever reads the stock bill, knows immediately that a piece of lumber larger than the listed size must be selected, so that the millman will have sufficient stock for machining purposes.

The practice followed in a given shop determines the method used by the stock biller when listing lumber to net sizes. Some factories and millwork plants may list net thickness and width while the length is given as rough, that is $\frac{1}{2}''$ to $1\frac{1}{2}''$ longer than the required net length. Modern practice requires that *all* three dimensions be given in net sizes on the stock bill.

Moldings. Moldings that are to be cut into short pieces are usually listed by lineal feet. That is, the sum total of all of the various lengths are computed, plus allowance for waste in fitting. Lineal footage of any item is understood to be rough length.

Measurement Rules. The following summary gives in concise form the rules to follow when writing or stating a measurement or dimension:

1) List all soft woods, hardwoods, and plywoods in the order of thickness, width, and length.

2) If necessary to list otherwise, always indicate which is the thickness, width, or length measurement.

3) When getting measurements from a layman (one not of the trade) be sure to ask which measurement is thickness, which is width, and which is length.

4) Always write the thickness and width measurements in inches and fractions of an inch *only,* even if the width is more than one foot. In the width column, write measurement of less than one inch thus: $0^{13}/_{16}''$.

5) Always express the length measurement in feet and inches regardless of whether the measurement is less than one foot, thus: $0'8''$, $2'0\frac{3}{4}''$, $1'10''$, etc.

NOTE: Furniture factories, as a rule, express length measurements in inches only.

6) Always list thickness, width, and length measurements in terms of "net finished sizes." The stock cutter makes allowances for milling as required.

7) Always write fractions with a horizontal line, thus: $\frac{1}{2}''$.

8) Write the foot mark with a horizontal line below it to avoid mistaking it for a 1, thus: $2\underline{}0''$.

9) Make the inch mark distinct and short. It may be mistaken for two ones.

10) Never take a figure for granted unless it is clear and distinct. Always check with available information or go to the source for verification.

11) Always use the same type of measuring rule that you are accustomed to use. Costly errors are committed by misinterpretation of different sizes and kinds of rules.

12) Always read the rule from the end starting with "one." Don't be too sure of the "backward" count. Take time to turn the rule end for end if need be.

Typical Stock Bill Forms. Many factories have stock bill forms designed to fit their particular needs. The stock bills shown in Fig. 1 are typical and give all necessary information for general use.

The stock biller and stock cutter should fully realize the importance of the information provided on the stock bill as explained under the following heads. These items are typical of most stock bills.

Name. This is the customer's name and is required to identify the order. Also, customers often have certain whims that the shop caters to in order to retain their trade.

STOCK BILL

DATE_____   JOB No._____

NAME_____   DESCRIPTION_____

DETAILED BY_____

	NO.	PCS.	WOOD	THICK	WIDE	LONG	EXT.	REMARKS	✓

Name_____   Date_____

Article_____   Job No._____

No. on Detail	Pieces	Wood	Thickness	Width	Length	Shoulder Length	Description
1							
2							

DETAIL No._____ STOCK BILL No._____ JOB No._____

For_____   Date_____ 19____

Article_____   12-46   5M   AP2492

NO.	CK.	PCS.	DESCRIPTION	WOOD	THICK	WIDTH	LENGTH	EXP.	REMARKS

Order No._____ Name_____ Bill No._____

Detailed by_____ Address_____ Date_____

Checked by_____ Article_____

Cut by_____ Trimmed by_____ Finish_____

ITEM	✓	PIECES	DESCRIPTION	PART NO.	WOOD	THICK	WIDTH	LENGTH	SHOULDER	EXPOSEC		OFFICE USE ONLY

Fig. 1. Typical Stock Bill Forms

Article. This is the name of the finished article which is necessary in order to select the right kind of material.

Date. This determines the start of the job and serves as a check on causes for delay in production.

Job Number. Job numbers are valuable as reference for a number of reasons. The same number is used for charging materials to the job, identifying detail drawings, marking the materials for identification during progress of the job through the shop, and recording the job on time cards.

Finish. Some stock bills state the finish of the completed article, whether paint, lacquer, stain, natural, color, etc. This allows the stock cutter to use his judgment as to the suitability of the material selected.

Name of the Detailer, Cutter, Trimmer, and Checker. This procedure allows direct reference in case of any errors. The name of the stock biller is also required by most shops.

Number on Detail. The detail numbers, as found on the working drawing, are often shown on the bill. This permits ready reference by the machine man and assembler in sorting the material and identifying the purpose of each piece.

Pieces. This column is sometimes marked "quantity," but on a stock bill it usually means "number of pieces."

NOTE: On orders of stock items which may call for several identical items, it is customary to make the stock bill for *one* item only, but the bill is marked "Cut 100 times" or "Cut 48 times," etc. The stock cutter reads the stock bill as usual, but cuts the required number of pieces for each listed item.

Kind of Wood. The kind of wood wanted is usually designated by standard abbreviations. Special kinds of wood are written out in full to avoid mistakes.

The "grade" of lumber is determined by the nature and use of the finished article, what purpose it serves in the article, to what extent it is exposed, the strength required of that particular item, and the average sizes required for the job.

Size of Stock. The dimensions of lumber are always given in order of sequence as follows: thickness by width by length. Thickness and width are given as net sizes in inches and fractions; the length is given in feet and inches and fractions.

Several methods of listing plywood are practiced, and the resulting confusion has been the cause of expensive mistakes through cutting plywood with the length of the grain in the wrong dimension. It is considered safest *to use the same rules for listing plywood as are used for listing solid lumber.* In the wood column on the stock bill is given the number of plies together with the wood. In the "remarks" column is given "good 1 side" or "good 2 sides" and the quality or grade of plywood. List the width in inches and fractions and the length in feet and inches.

NOTE: The plywood industry lists width, length, and thickness, and stock sizes are ordered in that manner. It does not necessarily follow that plywood should be listed on a cutting bill in the same way. In any case, it is advisable to follow the system prevalent in a shop unless a change is officially approved.

Shoulder Lengths. When an offset occurs on the "face" of the material, as when a rail is tenoned, the measurement between these offsets is called the "shoulder measure" or "shoulder length." The "net" or "over-all" length is the shoulder length plus the length of the tenons, and is given in the preceding column on the stock bill.

Provision for "shoulder length" is made on stock bills in factories where the cuttings are tenoned, such as doors, sash, and panel work. This allows the stock cutter to include minor defects in the cuttings not extending farther than the shoulder on either end, so long as these defects do not detract from the strength of the tenon. The shoulder length also informs the tenoner operator of the measurements which are required for his work.

Exposed Sides. Some stock bills will indicate what part of the material will be exposed in the finished article—whether two sides, one side and one edge, etc.

Description. This part of the stock bill is often designated as "remarks" or "information," and is used to give any information that will aid the stock cutter and others working on the job. The following information may be included:

1) NAME OF PARTS: The name of parts is important information to the stock cutter. Included with the name of the parts may be such information as shown by the following examples:

a) Rail (R. or Rl.) In addition to the information under "shoulder length" the description of the item showing that it is a rail, automatically informs the stock cutter that the item should be made of straight grained wood.

b) Stile (St.). The fact that the item is designated as a Stile informs the stock cutter that the wood should be of straight grained stock in order to minimize danger of twist, warp, or bend in the finished article.

c) Tops. Pieces to be used for tops should be so indicated, since tops are usually seen on one side only. This permits the stock cutter to select suitably grained material, good on one side with minor defects allowable for the side not seen.

2) FREEHAND SKETCHES: Freehand sketches, or exact details, may be included under this heading.

3) MOLDINGS (MLDG.): The stock cutter prepares the material for moldings, but he must know whether the stock is for shaper or sticker work. The stock bill should contain this information with a diagram or detail showing its shape and its use.

ROUTING A STOCK BILL

The stock bill is usually sent to the stock cutter, who either selects the lumber stock or requisitions the lumber from the yardman, who selects and delivers the rough lumber to the mill. The stock cutter and other woodworkers mill the stock to sizes as indicated on the stock bill. The material is then routed to the assembler, glue man, trim sawyer, or whatever department is indicated, for further machining or processing, and finally to the bench man, who assembles the article and prepares it for finishing.

MILLING ALLOWANCES

Milling allowance is the term used for the additional amount of stock added to each dimension of a piece of lumber to give sufficient material to allow for machining to the finished dimensions or net sizes given on the stock bill.

Milling allowance is primarily the concern of the stock cutter or millman. However, the stock biller should have some knowledge of this technical problem, as it will enable him to do a more intelligent job of stock billing. The millman who operates woodworking machinery and actually performs the machine operations must understand fully what milling allowance is and the necessity for it.

The amount of allowance usually given to certain milling operations is dependent on the kind of lumber being cut and what milling operations are to follow. There are several different methods used.

1) For cutting stock surfaced four sides (S4S) and trimmed to net length, the lumber is selected in a rough thickness sufficient to obtain the desired net thickness.

2) Rough lumber is cut to approximate sizes before facing, jointing, surfacing, sizing, and trimming, thus permitting the straightening of crooked lumber after it is cut to short lengths and narrow widths. From $\frac{1}{8}''$ to $\frac{3}{16}''$ is needed to surface a board on two sides. Usually,

¼" should be allowed on the width to joint a short board, size it, and joint it again.

NOTE: Rough width is sometimes referred to as *ripping size*.

3) Stock to be glued into wide tops must have extra allowances on the rough lengths to insure full net length. This allowance may be as much as two inches.

CONVERSION OF STOCK BILL ITEMS INTO STANDARD SIZES OF LUMBER

After a stock bill is completed, it must be converted into pieces of rough nominal size lumber or into board feet. This step is done in order to make it possible to select the proper sizes of lumber from which the various items on the stock bill are to be cut. This lumber bill shows the number of pieces required (or the board footage), the thickness, width, and length of each piece.

The conversion process in all cases is the same: selecting lumber that will cut with the least waste. Small cuttings are not difficult to convert to lumber sizes, as almost any width or length board can be selected. Large cuttings require that the lumber be carefully estimated so that the most economical sizes are selected.

The selection of rough nominal sizes of lumber must also take into account the machine milling to be performed so that the net finished sizes can be obtained from the rough nominal size lumber with a minimum of waste.

No set rule can be given on how to determine what lumber sizes are best to use. Two stock cutters could work from the same stock bill and list a different lumber bill. The stock of lumber on hand is the basic determining factor. Other jobs in the shop would also affect the selection of sizes and lengths of lumber, as overage from one job can often be utilized on another job.

ESTIMATING BOARD FEET OF LUMBER IN A STOCK BILL

An experienced stock cutter can approximate very closely the board foot requirements of a stock bill because of his knowledge of lumber standards, grades, defects, and sizes. His trade judgment, which has been gained from experience, indicates the multiples obtainable from standard sizes of lumber which are normally available from stock on hand.

In Example 1, which follows, the net sizes listed on the stock bill are converted to rough nominal sizes from which the board foot content is figured. The various items are combined "mentally" into nominal sizes from which the several items can be cut without waste. In the example given, each item was reduced to board feet to show the estimated board foot content as compared to the actual number of board feet in the lumber selected for the bill.

Example 1. A stock biller prepares a stock bill for a panel as follows:

| | | Stock Bill | | | | Estimated Requirement | | | |
| | | Net Sizes | | | | Rough Nominal Sizes | | | |
Item	No. Pcs.	Thick-ness	Width	Length	Thick-ness	Width	Length	Sq. Ft.	Bd. Ft.
1	1	$\frac{3}{4}''$	$3''$	$2'10^{15}\!/_{16}''$	$1''$	$4''$	$3'0''$	....	1
2	1	$\frac{3}{4}''$	$2\frac{9}{16}''$	$2'10^{15}\!/_{16}''$	$1''$	$4''$	$3'0''$	....	1
3	1	$\frac{3}{4}''$	$3\frac{1}{8}''$	$9'11''$	$1''$	$4''$	$12'0''$	....	4
4	1	$\frac{1}{2}''$	$5\frac{1}{2}''$	$9'11''$	$1''$	$6''$	$12'0''$	....	6
5	4	$\frac{3}{4}''$	$2\frac{1}{4}''$	$2'5^{5}\!/_{16}''$	$1''$	$3''$	$3'0''$	....	3
6	5	$\frac{1}{4}''$ 3 ply	$22''$	$2'2^{15}\!/_{16}''$	....	$24''$	$2'6''$	25	....

Estimated Totals 25 15

In converting the stock bill to nominal lumber sizes, a careful study shows that a piece of 1″ x 10″ x 16′0″ will yield items 2, 3, 4, and 5, as shown in Fig. 2, while a piece of 1″ x 4″ x 4′0″ gives ample allowance for item 1.

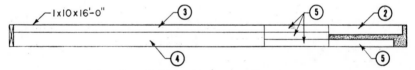

Fig. 2. How To Nest Cuttings for Maximum Yield

The board foot content of the lumber selected will total as follows:

$$1 \text{ pc. } 1'' \times 10'' \times 16'0'' = 13\frac{1}{3} \text{ bd. ft.}$$
$$1 \text{ pc. } 1'' \times 4'' \times 4'0'' = 1\frac{1}{3} \text{ bd. ft.}$$
$$\text{Total } 14\frac{2}{3} \text{ bd. ft.}$$

Note that this compares favorably with the estimate of 15 board feet. However, unless care is exercised in selecting the stock from which to cut a bill of material, the waste can easily exceed the allowance made when converting net sizes to rough nominal sizes.

An alternate choice of standard sizes can be made according to the stock on hand. In the preceding example, there is but one other choice unless the stock cutter accumulates "left-over pieces."

The net sizes in the stock bill may be obtained out of standard sizes as follows:

Items 3 and 4 from 1 pc. 1″ x 10″ x 12′, or 10 bd. ft.
Items 1, 2, and 5 from 1 pc. 1″ x 6″ x 10′, or   5 bd. ft.
                                        Total 15 bd. ft.

Good mill practices require that, as far as possible, each job carries its own waste so that a pile of shorts will not accumulate. Actually, the efficiency of a stock cutter can be quickly determined by merely inspecting the stock pile. Under normal conditions, with a wide selection of different sizes of lumber possible, and a continuing flow of job orders, only a few short ends should accumulate.

PROBLEMS

The information on stock billing can be applied in following chapters where stock bills are necessary.

REVIEW QUESTIONS

1. Define the term "stock bill."
2. Define the term "quantity survey."
3. Give two other names for "factory orders."
4. Give three functions of a detailer.
5. Why is it necessary to take measurements on the job prior to constructing a cabinet?
6. What are the functions of a stock biller?
7. What basic knowledge should a stock biller possess?
8. Describe the stock cutter's responsibilities.
9. Name six stock billing procedures.
10. What items on a stock bill should be listed when billing a cabinet job?
11. What is the meaning of the term "net" when applied to lumber?
12. How are moldings, which are to be cut into short pieces, billed?
13. What is the usual order to follow when listing soft woods, hardwoods, and plywoods?
14. How should a fraction be written on a stock bill?
15. How should the foot mark (′) be written on a stock bill?
16. How should a rule be read in taking measurements?
17. Name eight items which appear on a stock bill.
18. What is meant by the term "routing a stock bill"?
19. Define the term "milling allowance."
20. Why must a stock bill be converted into pieces of lumber of rough nominal size or into board feet?

Rod Layout

QUESTIONS CHAPTER VIII WILL ANSWER FOR YOU

1. *What is a rod layout?*
2. *When is the method of rod layout used?*
3. *What are the advantages of using a rod layout?*
4. *What order of procedure is generally followed in making a rod layout?*
5. *How does the stock cutter use the information on a rod layout?*

INTRODUCTION TO CHAPTER VIII

A working drawing of some type is usually used as a guide in cabinet-making. Normally, the drawing is made as described in previous chapters. Many shops, however, resort to the rod layout method. This method is commonly used in sash and door factories and in the layout of straight design cabinets where the details are simple. The information for making the rod layout may be obtained from elevations, sections, or from the experience of the person making the layout. A rod is simply a long piece of stock such as a "one by one" or a "one by two" on which the layout is made. A hole is bored in one end of the rod for convenience in storing. Each of the faces of the rod can be used in making the layout. In this manner, a full-size layout for a cabinet can be made on a single "one by two" rod several feet long. Detailed drawings of the same job would require a piece of paper 8' or 10' square. Some shops combine detail drawings with the rod layout where the work requires details that could not be shown on a rod.

In sash and door factories, the wall over the layout bench is often covered with rods all properly identified and ready for use when an order for that particular type of work is received. When layouts are made on rods for which repeat orders are not likely, the rod is planed clean and used for another job.

Cabinets laid out on a rod can be easily checked for all measurements, since all measurements are in line between the limits of the over-all dimension. The rod can be taken to the bench, where the material can readily be checked.

ROD LAYOUT PROCEDURE

The piece of lumber selected for the rod should be straight grained to prevent breakage, and surfaced on two sides and two edges to permit pencil marks to be made easily and clearly. The rod should be squared on the ends for accurate work and ease in handling. A strip

1″ x 1″ or larger, long enough for the longest dimension of the job, makes a good rod for average work.

Each face of the rod is used for the layout of one dimension of the job. If it is a cabinet, three dimensions must be laid out, namely, width, height, and depth. See Fig. 1. If a door is to be laid out, only the width and height dimensions are used, since the thickness of the door can be obtained from the order. The fourth face of a rod is sometimes used for laying out a part of a cabinet which has both drawers and doors.

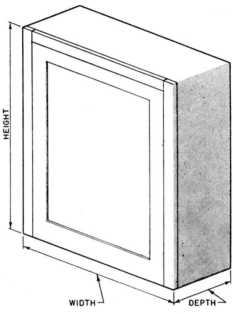

Layout work is usually started at the right end of the rod as it is laid down on the bench in front of the person doing the layout. Generally, no definite order of layout is followed. The height or the width, whichever is longer, usually is done first. In complicated layout work, it is sometimes necessary to alternate the layout of the width and height to secure the measurements needed to complete the one layout.

Fig. 1. Basic Measurements of Case or Cabinet

The over-all dimension is usually laid off first and all subdivisions must fit in between the over-all dimension.

The pencil or knife must be sharp, and all measurements accurately made, as the rod, when completed, should represent exact *full size* measurements of the project.

When the layout work on the rod is completed, the information and measurements established on it are used when listing the number of pieces, thickness, width, and length of each item on a stock bill. This information will be used by the stock cutter in milling the stock.

After the material is milled, it is delivered to the layout man, who places the rod on the material and marks the location of dadoes, mortises, tenons, or dowels which require additional milling before assembling the cabinet, door, or sash.

HOW TO MAKE A LAYOUT ON A ROD

Illustrative Problem. Make a rod layout for a cabinet door that is 24″ wide, 32″ high, and 1″ net thick. Stiles and top rail are 2½″, bottom rail is 3½″. The stiles and rails are grooved ⅜″ deep and ⅜″ wide, with square sticking (Fig. 2). The layout is actual size. Dimensions are not written on the rod but measured as needed when cutting the stock. The indicated measurements on the rod are shown to aid you in understanding the procedure. The sketch has been added to show the relationship between the layout on the rod and the parts of the door.

Procedure:

1. Select a suitable piece of rod stock of the required length. In this case it should be about 1″ x 2″ x 36″.

2. Square a line on all four faces, about ½″ from the right end of the rod. This is the starting point for the layout.

3. The height dimension of the door is 32″; lay off the 32″ from the starting point and square a line across the edge of the rod. This represents the height of the door.

4. From the starting point, lay off 3½″, the width of the bottom rail.

5. From the top of the door lay off 2½″, the width of the top rail.

6. Mark the depth of the panel groove.

7. Using a face of the rod, repeat the process for the width of the door, which is 24″. The stiles are 2½″ each.

8. The length of the mortise, or the location of the dowels may also be laid out on the rod.

9. Carefully label the rod on one of the faces, giving the job number or other description so that the rod can be quickly identified.

10. Bore a hole in the opposite end from which the layout work was started. The rod is now ready to hang up. If you take it off the wall with the right hand, it will lie on the bench in the same position as when originally laid out.

This rod can be used when making the stock bill. The size of the panel can be determined very accurately for width and length. The thickness of the panel is determined in the specifications for the job.

Typical Layouts. Shown in Fig. 3 is the same cabinet door laid out on a plywood panel. In this layout, section views are used; also the thickness is shown. The choice of which method to use is made by the layout man. In both methods, the layout is made full size.

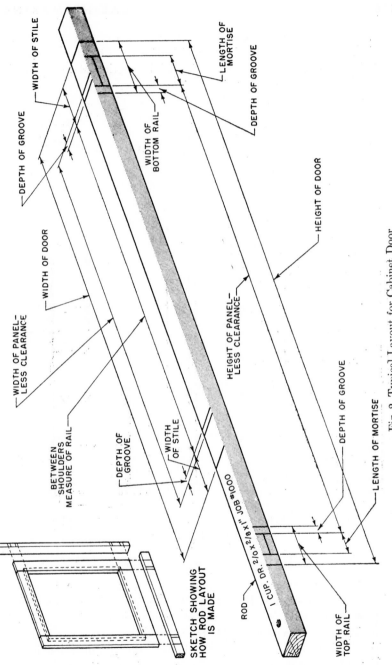

Fig. 2. Typical Layout for Cabinet Door

The cupboard detail (Fig. 4) which shows a front elevation and a vertical section, illustrates a typical problem for a rod layout. Notice that the cabinet has two depths as shown by section M-M. Shown in

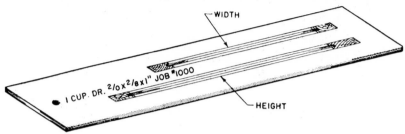

Fig. 3. Plywood Layout Rod of Cabinet Door

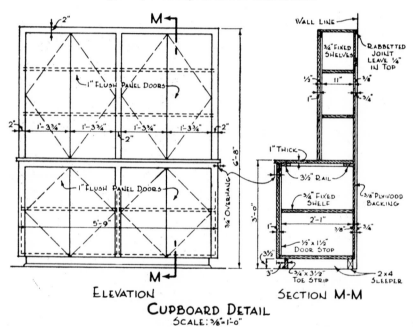

ELEVATION

CUPBOARD DETAIL

SECTION M-M

SCALE: 3/8"=1'-0"

Fig. 4. Typical Drawing from Which a Rod Layout Is Made

Fig. 5 is the rod layout for the cupboard detail. Remember, a rod layout consists of lines only. However, in this layout the dimensions of the cupboard parts have been added to show exactly how the layout was made. The sketch has been added to aid in following the procedure for making the layout. In making the layout, the *A* dimension of the cupboard is laid out on the face of the rod marked *A*. The *B* dimension

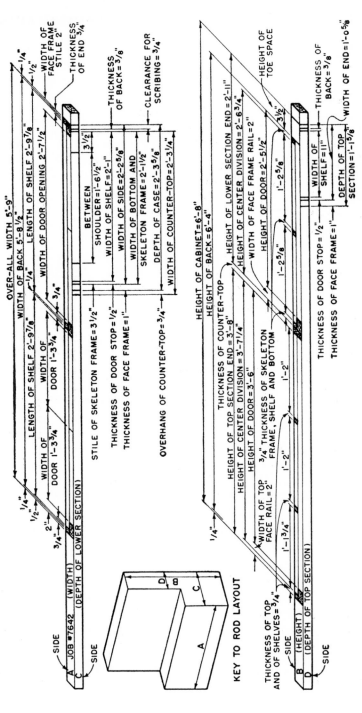

Fig. 5. Rod Layout for Cupboard Detail Consists of Lines Located in Exact Position

(height) is laid out on the face of the rod marked *B*. The two depth dimensions, *C* and *D*, are laid out on the edges of the rod marked *C* and *D*.

Starting with the face of the rod marked *A*, the dimension 5′9″ is obtained directly from the elevation view (Fig. 4). The width of the back is shown as 5′8½″ (¼″ less on each end as indicated). The marks indicating these dimensions are not shown on the rod, since this procedure is standard. The same is true for the depth of the dado. The length of each shelf is shown as 2′9⅞″. This length is obtained by taking the total of 5′9″, subtracting 1¼″, and dividing by 2. A depth of ¼″ is allowed for dadoing the ends and divisions to receive the shelves. Since the thickness of the ends and center piece is ¾″, this leaves ½″ on each end and ¼″ in the center division, or 1¼″ to be subtracted from 5′9″, leaving 5′7¾″. Dividing 5′7¾″ by 2 (two shelves) gives 2′9⅞″ as the length of each shelf. The width of each door is taken directly from the elevation view.

The face of the rod, *B*, shows the layout for the height of the cabinet. The 6′8″ measurement is obtained directly from the drawing. The height of the back is shown as 6′4″, since section *M-M* indicates a 3½″ sleeper on the bottom and a ½″ rabbeted joint, ¼″ of top thickness, making a total of 4″. The height of the top section end, 3′8″, is obtained by subtracting 3′0″ from 6′8″. The two latter dimensions are shown on the drawing. The height of the center division, 3′7¼″, is obtained by subtracting ¾″ from 3′8″ (¾″ is the thickness of the top). The door height of 3′6″ was determined by subtracting the width of the face rail 2″, from 3′8″. The distance between the shelves is figured directly from Section *M-M*. The height of the lower section end, 2′11″, is figured from the floor line to the underside of the counter top (3′0″ minus 1″). The height of the center division, 2′6¾″, is the measurement from the face of the bottom piece to the underside of the counter top (3′0″ minus 5¼″). (The 5¼″ is the 3½″ sleeper height, plus the ¾″ bottom thickness, plus the 1″ counter thickness.) The 2″ width of the face rail is taken directly from the elevation view. The door height of 2′5½″ is figured from the top of the toe piece to the bottom edge of the face rail. See Section *M-M*. (3′0″ minus 3″ for the counter and face rail, minus 3½″ for the sleeper, leaves 2′5½″ as the door height.) The distance between shelves is figured by taking the distance of 3′0″ and subtracting the counter thickness, top rail thickness, bottom thickness, and toe space, which makes a total of 6″. Subtracting the 6″ from 36″ leaves 30″. Since the shelf is to be centered in this 30″ space, 30″ divided by 2 equals 15″. Subtracting ½ the thickness of the shelf, or ⅜″, from 15″ leaves 1′2⅝″ as the spacing for the shelf.

The edge of the rod marked C shows the layout for the bottom half of the cupboard. The total depth of the case, 2′3⅝″, is obtained by adding ¾″, ⅜″, 2′1″, ½″, and 1″. The other dimensions are easily determined from Section M-M.

The measurements on the edge of the rod marked D are figured from the measurements given on Section M-M.

PROBLEMS

1. Make the rod layout for a cabinet door, 1′6″ wide, 2′0″ high, and ¾″ thick, with ¼″ 3-ply panel set in a ⅜″ deep groove, the stiles and top rail to be 2¼″ wide, the bottom rail 3¼″ wide, square sticking, mortise and tenon construction.

2. Make the rod layout for a cabinet similar to the one shown in Fig. 1— 2′0″ wide, 2′6″ high, and 1′4″ deep. The face frame to be 1¹⁄₁₆″ thick, with stiles and top rail 1¾″ wide. The door will have 2½″ stiles and top rail, a 3½″ bottom rail, and a ¼″ three-ply panel set in a ⅜″ deep groove. The case is to have two shelves (not counting the bottom) dadoed into the sides with equal spacing between each. A ¼″ three-ply back is to be rabbeted into the sides, top, and bottom. (Three faces of the rod should be used.)

REVIEW QUESTIONS

1. What kind of lumber should be selected for making a rod?
2. Where is the layout generally started?
3. Which dimension is laid off first in making a rod layout?
4. How many faces of the rod are used in making a layout for a door?
5. What three dimensions are used in the layout of a cabinet?

Steel Square Layout

QUESTIONS CHAPTER IX WILL ANSWER FOR YOU

1. *How is the steel square used by the cabinetmaker?*
2. *What kind of a square is best suited to the needs of a cabinetmaker?*
3. *How is the diagonal of a rectangle determined by the steel square?*
4. *How is the edge of a pyramid found by the use of the steel square?*
5. *How are finish rafter-end layouts made?*

INTRODUCTION TO CHAPTER IX

The cabinetmaker has many opportunities to use the steel square in layout problems. The steel square method shortens many of the mathematical computations and makes the worker more efficient.

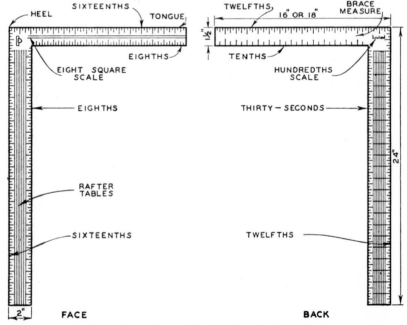

Fig. 1. Steel Square, Showing Location of Scales

Many of the tables found on a steel square are not ordinarily used by the cabinetmaker. However, the better grades of squares all have such tables. For the purpose of cabinetmaking, a good steel square is graduated in tenths, twelfths, and sixteenths of an inch.

The material in this chapter is limited to those problems that are most commonly encountered by the cabinetmaker.

PRINCIPLE OF THE STEEL SQUARE

The steel square has a *body* (sometimes called the blade) 2″ wide and 24″ long and a *tongue* that is 1½″ wide and 16″ long. Some squares have an 18″ tongue, but the square with the 16″ tongue is best for the work of the cabinetmaker. The face, back, heel, and various tables of the square, are shown in Fig. 1.

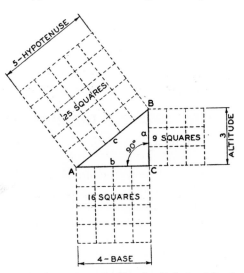

Since the body and tongue of the steel square are exactly at right angles, or 90°, to each other, this tool can be used to solve any hypotenuse problems, basing the solutions on the principle: *the square of the hypotenuse of a right triangle is equal to the sum of the squares of the other two sides.*

Fig. 2. Right Triangle, Showing Relationship of the Three Sides

To illustrate: Find the hypotenuse of an angle that has a 3″ altitude and a 4″ base.

Mathematically, this problem is solved as follows:

3 squared equals 9 (or $3^2 = 9$)

4 squared equals 16 (or $4^2 = 16$)

The addition of 9 and 16 equals 25.

The square root of 25 equals 5 (or $\sqrt{25} = 5$). See Fig. 2.

Using the steel square, the problem is solved as follows:

Measure diagonally across the square from 3″ on the tongue to 4″ on the body. The measurement is exactly 5″.

From this fact, it can be deduced that the measurement from any point on the body to any point on the tongue of the square will give the correct hypotenuse for the right-angle triangle thus formed.

Testing a Steel Square. When using a new square or one that has not been tested, it is best to make sure that the body and the tongue form a right angle. The square is tested in the following manner:

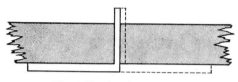
Fig. 3. Testing Steel Square

1. Hold the square against a straightedge, or board that has been planed perfectly straight, as shown in Fig. 3. With a knife or sharp pencil, draw a line along the tongue of the square.

2. Reverse the square as shown, and check to see if the line will coincide exactly with the same outside edge of the tongue. If there is perfect alignment, the tool is square.

HOW TO APPLY THE RULE OF THE RIGHT TRIANGLE

The application of the right triangle rule is illustrated in the following problem:

Find the hypotenuse of a right-angle triangle whose sides are 25½″ and 34″ respectively.

Solution: Since the steel square is not large enough to measure the diagonal of 25½″ and 34″, divide each dimension in half and then measure the diagonal of the smaller triangle, as shown in (A) of Fig. 4. Double the result. The diagonal of 12¾″ and 17″ is 21¼″. The diagonal of 25½″ and 34″ is twice 21¼″, or 42½″, as shown in (B).

HOW TO SCALE A TRIANGLE ON THE STEEL SQUARE

In a similar manner, the hypotenuse of any right-angle triangle can be found on the steel square. In the problem illustrated, the triangle was reduced to one-half scale or to one-half actual size in order to solve it. The hypotenuse of a right triangle whose dimensions are given in feet can likewise be solved by scaling on the steel square. *Each inch represents one foot; each twelfth of an inch represents one inch.* Thus, the hypotenuse of a triangle whose sides are 12′ and 16′ respectively can be found by measuring from 12″ on the tongue to 16″ on the body of the square, resulting in a hypotenuse of 20″, which, reduced to 1″ equals 1′0″, gives the answer as 20′0″.

Only approximate lengths are determined in this manner; a careful reading of the diagonal measurement will, on some jobs such as rafters, give a sufficiently close answer that can be used. *Exact* answers can only be ascertained by mathematical calculations.

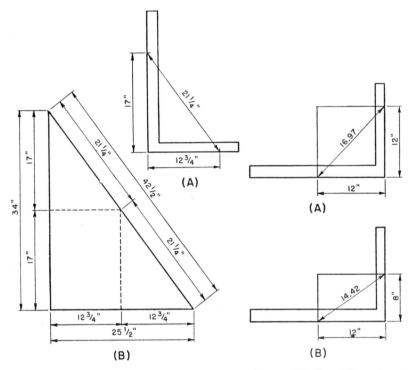

Fig. 4. Illustrating Application of Rule for Finding Hypotenuse of Right Triangle

Fig. 5. Finding Diagonals of Rectangles and Squares with Steel Square

HOW TO DETERMINE THE DIAGONALS OF SQUARES AND SOLIDS

The diagonal of a square or rectangle is found on the steel square by measuring the distance between the two members which represent the dimensions of the rectangle or square as shown in (A) and (B) of Fig. 5. The diagonal of a 12″ square is 16.97″, as shown in (A). For practical purposes this is called 17″. The diagonal of a 12″ square is a *basic dimension* which is used with a number of layout problems, such as on hip and valley rafters.

The diagonal of a rectangular solid can be found on the steel square in the following manner: The diagonal of the base of the rectangular solid and the altitude of one of its edges form a right triangle whose hypotenuse is the diagonal of this solid, Fig. 6.

The length of the edge of a pyramid may be found on the steel square as follows: Half the diagonal of the base of the pyramid and the altitude forms a right angle whose hypotenuse is equal to the length of one of the edges of the pyramid (Fig. 7).

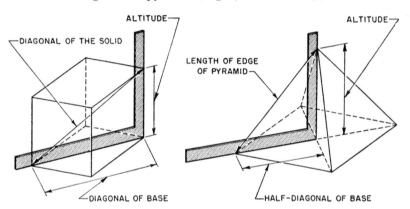

Fig. 6. Finding Diagonal of Rec-   Fig. 7. How to Find Length of Edge of
tangular Solid   Pyramid

Additional problems, which are based on geometrical principles, will be described, covering specific jobs which can be laid out by means of the steel square.

HOW TO HANDLE AND PLACE THE STEEL SQUARE

Shown in Fig. 8 is a method of laying the square on a piece of stock to mark a 45° miter cut. The face is usually placed up, with the body held in the left hand. However, the square may be used in any position to obtain the desired layout, always keeping the measurements on the tongue and body equal.

Sometimes it may be necessary or convenient to use the inside edges. However, *at no time should an outside edge be used with an inside edge,* as the body and tongue are not the same width.

Where successive use of the same angle is necessary, a *fence* made from a slotted piece of wood may be clamped on the square to maintain that angle as shown in Fig. 9. The fence is held against the edge of the board in a similar manner to that of the head of a **T** bevel, while line C, forming the desired angle X, is marked.

To obtain the exact length of hypotenuse D, so as to locate the second position of the square, mark line E along the edge of the blade, running the line to the lower edge of the board. Place the tongue of the square exactly on the starting point of line E for the second position. The third position is started in the same manner.

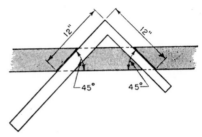

Fig. 8. How To Obtain a 45° Miter Cut

Steel square gages may be used in place of the fence.

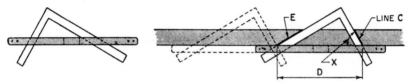

Fig. 9. How To Mark Accurately When Laying Out Successive Angles

RAFTER TERMINOLOGY

The terms *span, rise, run,* and *pitch* (Fig. 10) are used principally in roof framing and stair layout. However, the terms can be applied to any similar situation where the base and altitude of a right triangle are involved.

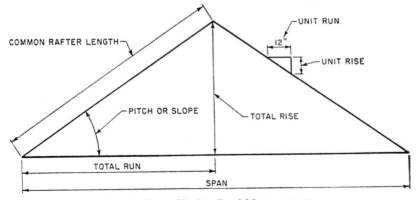

Fig. 10. Terms Used in Roof Measurements

Unit run is a horizontal measure of one foot (12″).

Total run is the horizontal distance over which a rafter passes. In geometry, the base of a right triangle is equivalent to the run.

Span is the total distance across a building or the horizontal distance from common rafter seat to common rafter seat. In geometry, span becomes the base of the equilateral or isosceles triangle. Total run is always half the span.

Unit rise is the vertical measure of rise *per foot of run.*

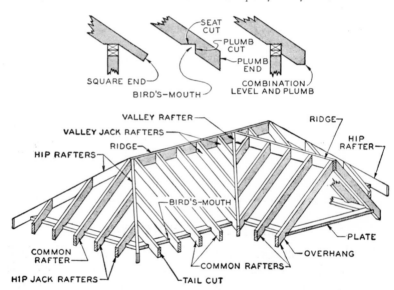

Fig. 11. Roof Framing Terms, Showing Types of Finish for Tail Cuts (*top*) and Names of Various Roof Members (*bottom*)

Pitch is the degree of slope of the rafter. The term can also be defined as the mathematical relationship of the total rise to the span (two times the run).

To illustrate: A roof that has a total rise of 10′ and a span of 30′ is one-third pitch ($\frac{1}{3}$) $= \dfrac{\text{rise}}{\text{span}}$ or $\dfrac{10}{30} = \dfrac{1}{3}$. A roof that has 8′ of total rise and 32′ of span has a $\frac{1}{4}$ pitch. A roof is said to be "equal pitch" when all sloping surfaces are the same slant or pitch.

The various roof members of an intersecting roof are shown in Fig. 11. While the cabinetmaker deals only with the rafter end problem, he should, at least, be familiar with the terminology used in cutting rafters.

RAFTER-END LAYOUT

Millwork plants are called on to lay out and cut rafter ends, sometimes called tail rafters. These are made of finish lumber and extend into the roof from 2½′ to 3′ in order to provide sufficient holding power to the part that extends beyond the building (overhang) and forms the finished cornice. See page 155.

The rise and run of the roof is usually given on the architectural drawings, together with the cornice run and the band-sawed contour design, if any.

A band-sawed rafter end is made with a specified unit run, rise, and cornice run. The terminology is similar to the terminology used in rafter layout.

The bird's mouth, if made at the mill, will have to be laid out so that the top edge of the common rafters and the top edge of the band-sawed tail rafters will be flush when nailed together. The millman need not concern himself with the length of the common rafter. The band-sawed tail rafter is either nailed against the common rafter or to a header cut between the common rafters, as shown in Fig. 12.

Fig. 12. Band-Sawed Rafter Ends

Layout for Common Rafter Ends. In this problem a unit rise of 8″, a standard unit run of 12″, and a cornice run of 10″ is given. The problem is to lay out the seat cut, plumb cut, and the tail cut. The layout is made as follows:

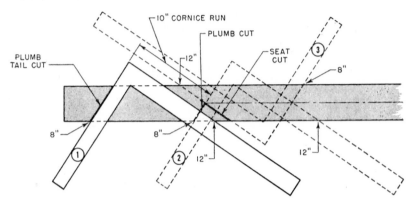

Fig. 13. How To Lay Out the Seat Cut, Plumb Cut, and Tail Cut for Common Rafter Ends

Place the steel square in Position *1*, Fig. 13, with the unit rise of 8″ on the tongue and the unit run of 12″ on the body.

Mark tail cut as shown for a plumb end. Also mark the point locating the plumb cut (cornice run) at 10″ on the body of the square.

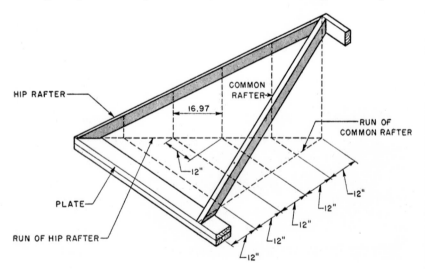

Fig. 14. Unit Run of Hip or Valley Rafter in Relation to Common Rafter Run

Shift the square to Position *2*, placing the tongue on the previously marked 10″ point, thus locating the plumb cut. Mark the plumb cut along the edge of the tongue of the square.

The point locating the level seat cut is usually determined to be at a point half the width of the rafter, but this measurement is conditioned by the pitch of the roof and the width of the rafter. (The amount of stock to leave above the seat cut is indicated by the carpenter and must be the same as the common rafter.)

In this problem, mark a point on the plumb cut at half the width of the rafter. Place the square in Position *3* (12″ on the body, 8″ on the tongue) with the edge of the body on the point so located, and mark the line of the level seat cut along the edge of the body of the square.

Layout for Hip and Valley Rafter Ends. The run of the hip rafter forms the diagonal of a square of which the runs of the common rafters form two of the sides, while the side and the end of the building form the other sides. Since

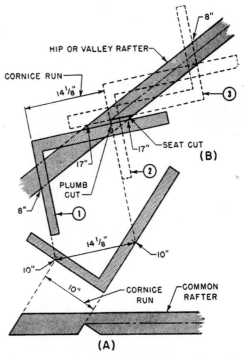

Fig. 15. Layout for Tail and Seat Cuts of Hip or Valley Rafters

the diagonal of a 12″ square is 17″, there will be 17″ of run in a hip rafter to 12″ of run in a common rafter (Fig. 14).

Given a ⅓ pitch (8″ unit rise and 12″ unit run) for the common rafter, and a cornice run of 10″, lay out a hip tail rafter.

Determine the cornice run for the hip rafter by measuring on the steel square from 10″ on the body to 10″ on the tongue, as shown in (*A*) of Fig. 15, which is 14⅛″.

Place the square in Position *1*, as shown in (*B*), at the required unit rise of 8″ and a 17″ run. (There is 17″ of hip run for every 12″ of com-

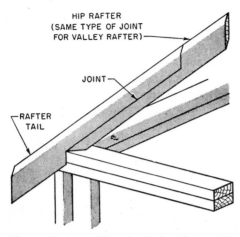

HIP RAFTER
(SAME TYPE OF JOINT
FOR VALLEY RAFTER)

JOINT

RAFTER
TAIL

Fig. 16. Method of Framing Rafter Tail to Hip
or Valley Rafter

mon run.) Mark the plumb tail cut line.

While square is in same position, mark required cornice run for the rafter hip as shown, in this case 14⅛".

Place the square in Position *2* and mark the plumb cut, using **8"** for unit rise and **17"** for unit run. Place the square in Position *3* and mark the seat cut.

Hip and valley tail rafters must be framed to form a continuous straight line (Fig. 16). The usual procedure is to cut the hip or valley tail rafter seat cut as required to match the common rafter, using 17" as the run figure. The half-lap joint is then cut to conform to a similar cut on the hip or valley rafter, using measurements provided by the carpenter.

BRACE LAYOUT

A brace represents the hypotenuse, while the run and rise of the brace represent the other two sides of a right triangle (*1–2–3*, Fig. 17). When the run and rise of a brace are the same length, the brace represents the hypotenuse of a right triangle in which each of the acute angles is 45°. The brace then is a 45° brace.

The layout for a short brace of this type, in which the dimensions do not exceed the size of the square (run or rise 16" or less), is made as follows:

Draw a line along the tongue for the angle of the cut to fit against the top (*A*, Fig. 17). Another line drawn along the blade will give the angle for the cut to fit against *B*.

A line connecting points *1* and *3* will give the length of the outside of the brace as shown.

For long 45° braces, the step method (Fig. 18) may be used. The layout is made as follows:

Lay the square in position near the right end of the piece which is to be used for a brace. The 12″ mark on both the blade and tongue should be exactly on the edge of the piece as shown.

Holding the square firmly in this position, draw lines along the outside edge of both the blade and the tongue.

Next, move the square along the brace toward the left until the 12″ mark on the blade coincides with the same point where the 12″ mark of the tongue was in the previous position. Again draw lines along the outside of both blade and tongue. Continue this procedure until the four steps have been completed. The cutting lines of the brace at the points *1* and *3* will make an angle which fits at top and side. Care should be taken in using this method, as a slight error will spoil the angle cut and cause an imperfect fit of the brace.

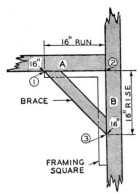

Fig. 17. Layout for a Short 45° Brace

For long braces when the total run is less than the total rise, to find the length of the brace and the angle cuts for the top and side, the total run is divided into as many units as there are feet in the rise. For example, if the total rise is 48″ and the run 36″, since the rise contains

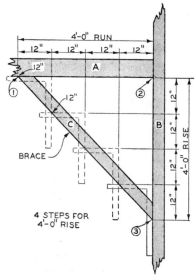

Fig. 18. Method of Laying Out a Long 45° Brace

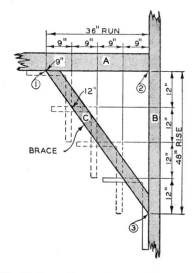

Fig. 19. Brace Layout When Run and Rise Are Unequal

four 12″ units, then the run should be divided into four 9″ units, as shown in Fig. 19.

X Brace Layout for Paneled Doors.   In this problem the total rise of 3′6″ and the total run of 3′1½″ are given, as shown in (A) of Fig. 20. The layout for any similar X brace is made as follows:

Find the unit rise and unit run of the brace. In this case one third of each is 14″ and 12½″. To lay out the corner angles (upper), draw a center line the length of the brace, and mark the plumb and level cuts as shown in (B) with the steel square in positions 1 and 2. The measurements, 14″ on the body and 12½″ on the tongue, are lined up on the center line. Measure the diagonal of the total rise and run to determine the length of the brace; measure this distance on the center line and mark plumb and level lines on the lower end.

The center joint is best laid out on the full-length brace, as this method will mark the location where the short braces butt against the full-length brace.

Find middle point O of the center line already established on the long brace. Through this point, lay off, by means of the steel square, plumb and level lines as shown in (C), with the square in positions 3 and 4, establishing points E, F, G, and H. Draw a line from E to F and from G to H. Set a T bevel to the angle GHF, which gives the angle of the butt cut as shown.

Determine the length of each short brace and mark the corner angles and the butt cut.

It is advisable to check the length of each brace on the door before cutting the second end. This procedure insures a perfect joint.

MITER AND BUTT JOINTS FOR POLYGONS

Polygon miter and butt joints can be laid out by the use of the steel square. The task is simplified by the use of a table of polygon cuts.

Fig. 21 shows how the steel square is used to lay out the miter and butt joints for three types of polygons, using 12″ as a constant. By always using the figure 12 on the body as a constant, there is only one other figure to remember.

Fig. 22 gives the miter cuts for polygons with 3 to 20 sides. The angle may be laid out with a protractor and T bevel, or by taking the figure 12 on one side of the square and, on the other side, the figure indicated for the polygon.

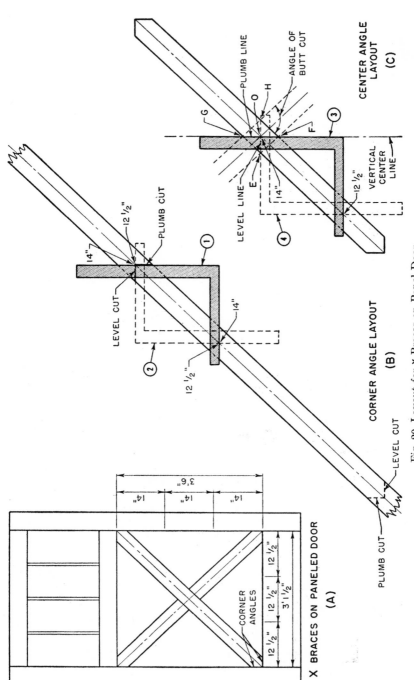

Fig. 20. Layout for X Braces on Panel Door

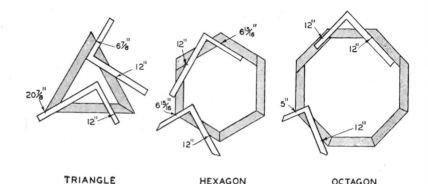

TRIANGLE   **HEXAGON**   **OCTAGON**

Fig. 21. Laying Out Miter and Butt Joints of Polygons with Steel Square

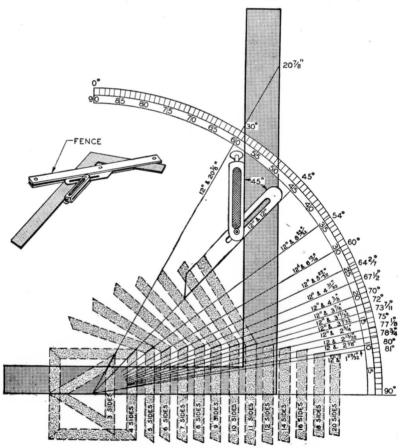

Fig. 22. Miter Cuts for Polygons Using Steel Square

HOPPER JOINTS

Laying Out Hopper Joints. When making a square or rectangular box, the four corners form an angle of 90° and miter joints of 45°. However, the hopper is wider at the top than at the bottom, as shown at (A), Fig. 23. This type of jointing requires a butt joint of more than 90° and a miter cut of more than 45°.

Since the hopper is like a roof turned upside down, the principles of roof framing are applied in laying out the cuts. The run is the distance the top extends over the bottom. This is the same as the run of the common rafter on a roof. The rise is the distance vertically between

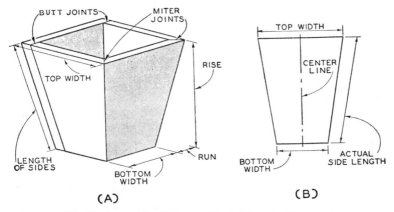

Fig. 23. Layout for Miter and Butt Joints for Hopper

the top and the bottom of the hopper. The length of the side is the same as the length of a common rafter.

The method of laying out the side of a hopper from a center line to get the actual lengths of the joints is shown at (B), Fig. 23. When miter joints are used on square hoppers, all sides will be the same. When butt joints are used, two sides are smaller by the thickness of the material of the other two sides. The layout at left in Fig. 24 will give all necessary figures which are to be used on the framing square, as shown at right, for obtaining the angle of the butt and miter joints.

PROBLEMS

The layouts for the following problems can be made on any kind of stock. When the problem has been checked for correctness, the lumber is planed clean, ready for another problem.

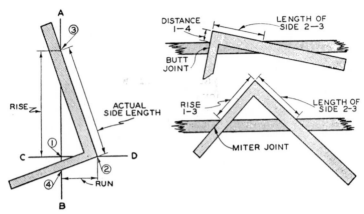

Fig. 24. Method of Laying Out Miter and Butt Joints for Hopper

Common Rafter Ends. Lay out the rafter ends for roofs which have dimensions as given in the following:

Problem	1 Size of Stock	2 Pitch	3* Cornice Run	4* Stock Left above Seat Cut	5* Length into Roof	6 Tail Cut
1........	2 x 4	⅓	14″	2¼″	3′0″	plumb
2........	2 x 4	¼	18″	2″	2′6″	plumb
3........	2 x 4	½	19″	2⅛″	3′4″	level
4........	2 x 6	⅜	16″	3″	2′8″	plumb
5........	2 x 6	⅝	20″	3⅛″	3′2″	plumb and level

* Dimensions in columns 3, 4, and 5 have been selected to provide a varied layout experience. These dimensions are determined by the architect and shown on the blueprint. Tail cuts are made to conform to the design of the building and requirements of construction.

For problems 6, 7, and 8, use the dimensions given in problems 1, 2, and 3, and lay out finish hip-rafter ends.

Brace Cuts and Lengths

9. Lay out a 45° brace which has an over-all length of 22″.

10. Lay out a 45° brace to fit a rise of 4′8″.

11. What is the unit-rise and unit-run of a brace that has a total rise of 5′8″ and a total run of 3′8″?

12. Lay out the **X** brace for a door which has panel dimensions between stiles and rails as follows: width 3′6″, height 4′9″. Brace stock is ¾″ x 3½″.

Butt and Miter Joints

13. Lay out the butt and miter joints for an octagon, using ¾″ x 3½″ stock.

14. Lay out the butt and miter joints for a hexagon, using ¾″ x 3½″ stock.

15. Lay out the butt and miter joints for a pentagon, using ¾″ x 3½″ stock.

16. Lay out butt and miter joints for a hopper having a top 18" x 18", a bottom 14" x 14", and a vertical height of 16".

REVIEW QUESTIONS

1. Name the parts of a steel square.
2. What is the diagonal of a 12" square? Why is this figure important?
3. When is it an advantage to use a fence or gages in working with the square?
4. What is meant by the term *Run? Span? Rise? Unit Rise? Pitch?*
5. What is the pitch of a roof having a rise of 6'0" and a run of 9'0"?
6. What is the rise of a roof having a ¼ pitch and a run of 10'0"?
7. What is a *Bird's Mouth?*
8. Determine the diagonal of the following squares by the steel square method: a, 8"; b, 15"; c, 22'.
9. State the geometrical principle for finding the hypotenuse of a right triangle.
10. What graduations on a steel square are important to the cabinetmaker?

Geometrical Shop Layout Jobs

QUESTIONS CHAPTER X WILL ANSWER FOR YOU

1. *What tools are commonly used for layout jobs in the shop?*
2. *How is the center of a tapered pilaster found?*
3. *How is an ellipse drawn?*
4. *What is a rake molding?*
5. *What is a rule joint?*

INTRODUCTION TO CHAPTER X

The cabinetmaker in his daily work encounters many layout problems that involve the basic principles of geometry. The success of any job depends to a large degree upon the accuracy of the layout. There are any number of layout jobs that can be done quickly and accurately by improvised methods with a minimum of equipment. This chapter outlines some of the commonly used layout methods as used by the tradesman. Each layout is shown as a step-by-step procedure.

SHOP LAYOUT TOOLS

Most of the work that has to be laid out in the shop is too large for the ordinary drafting tools. Triangles are used to advantage on small layout problems, but for accuracy on large work the most effective tools are the *straightedge, dividers, trammel, rule, tape, steel square, try square, combination square, and* **T** *bevel.*

Straightedge.   For regular large scale layout a laminated straightedge of maple and a porous wood such as oak or mahogany, is best suited. The lamination stiffens the straightedge while the maple provides a smooth working edge. Straightedges are used to draw straight lines and to check the straightness and trueness of a surface.

HOW TO TEST A STRAIGHTEDGE

1. Lay the straightedge on a smooth flat surface.
2. With a sharp pencil, carefully mark a line along the straight edge of the tool.

3. Reverse the straightedge by turning it over.

4. Place against the line first made. If the tool is perfect, it will coincide with the line at every point. If there is space between the line and the straightedge, the edge is hollow. If the ends do not touch, the edge is bowed (Fig. 1).

For special layout prob-lems, it may be necessary to joint a long board for the job. Some work may require the use of a chalk line. Fig. 2 shows how to move a straightedge along

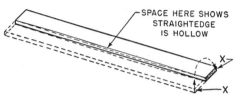

Fig. 1. Testing a Straightedge

another straightedge in order to draw a longer line. (Two steel squares can be used in a similar manner.)

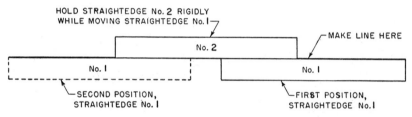

Fig. 2. How To Extend a Line Using Two Straightedges

GEOMETRICAL LAYOUTS

Many of the problems in shop layout work can be solved by the following geometric constructions.

Bisecting a Straight Line. See (A) of Fig. 3. Let ST be the line which is to be divided into two equal parts. From the ends of ST, with any radius greater than half, but less than the length of ST, scribe the intersecting arcs UV and WX. A line drawn through the intersecting arcs will bisect the line at Y.

Dividing a Line into Equal Parts. See (B) of Fig. 3. Let ST be the line that is to be divided into any number of equal parts. Draw the slant line SU to any angle and length. With a compass, step off the required number of equal parts on line SU. Connect the last point with the end of the line ST to form the line TV. Lines drawn parallel to TV from the numbered points will divide line ST into equal parts.

Bisecting an Angle. The method of bisecting angles is shown in Fig. 4. Let angle BAC be the required angle. With A as center and any convenient radius, describe the arc *BC*. With *B* and *C* as centers and a radius great enough to intersect, scribe the arcs *DE* and *FG*. Draw a straight line from *A* through the intersecting point of arcs *DE* and *FG*. This line will be the bisecting line.

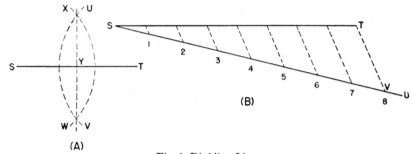

Fig. 3. Dividing Lines

(A) Bisecting a line. (B) Dividing a line into equal parts.

Constructing a Triangle When the Length of Each Side is Given. Given the three sides *AB*, *CD*, and *EF* as shown in Fig. 5, draw the line *GH* equal to *EF*. With *H* as center and a radius equal to the line *CD*, scribe an arc such as *YZ*. With *G* as center and *AB* as a radius, scribe an arc cutting *YZ* as at *X*. *GHX* is the required triangle.

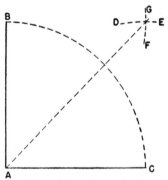

Fig. 4. Bisecting an Angle

Constructing Octagons. See Fig. 6. Draw the circle to the required size which will control the size of the inscribed octagon. Draw the two diameters at right angles as shown. Bisect angle *ABC*. Line *BD* divides the arc *AC* into two equal parts. Set the compass equal to one of these parts and mark off the sides of the octagon on the circumference of the circle. Connect these points to complete the octagon as shown.

Constructing Hexagons. See Fig. 6. Draw the circle to the required size which will control the size of the inscribed hexagon. Draw two diameters at right angles. With a compass set to equal the radius of the circle and, with *A* and *E* as centers, scribe the arcs *CD* and *FG* as shown. Connect points *A*, *D*, *G*, *E*, *F*, and *C*, completing the hexagon as shown.

Constructing Pentagons. See Fig. 6. Scribe the circle to the required size, which will control the size of the inscribed pentagon. Draw

the two diameters at right angles. Bisect the radius line *AB* at *C*. With
C as center and radius *CD*, scribe arc *DE*. With *D* as center and radius *DE*, scribe the arc *EF*. Draw the line *FD*, which is one side of the

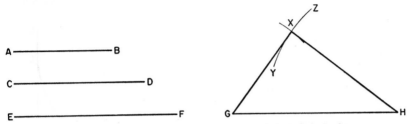

Fig. 5. Constructing Triangle When Length of Each Side Is Given

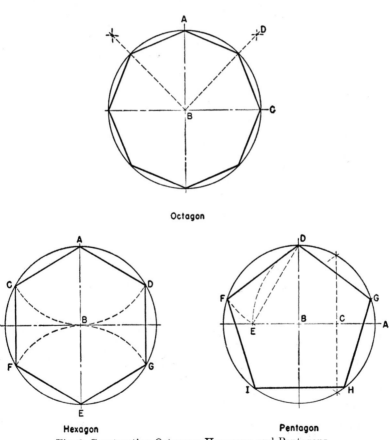

Octagon

Hexagon   Pentagon

Fig. 6. Constructing Octagons, Hexagons, and Pentagons

pentagon. With *FD* as a radius, mark the remaining sides of the pentagon and draw the lines *FI, IH, HG,* and *GD* to complete the pentagon.

Drawing an Arc or a Circle through Three Points. Let *A, B,* and *C* (Fig. 7) be the given points, not in a straight line. With *B* as center,

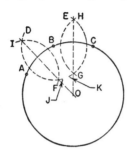

Fig. 7. A Circle Drawn
through Three Points

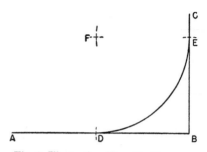

Fig. 8. Illustrating How To Draw an
Arc Tangent to Sides of Right Angle

scribe the arcs *EK* and *DJ*. With *A* and *C* as centers, scribe arcs *IF* and *HG*. Draw the two bisecting lines and extend so as to meet at *O*. This gives the center to scribe the arc or the complete circle.

Drawing an Arc Tangent to the Sides of a Right Angle. Let *ABC* be the right angle, as shown in Fig. 8. Set the compass to the radius of the arc desired and, with *B* as center, strike arcs at *D* and *E*. With *E* and *D* as centers, and with the same radius, scribe intersecting arcs at

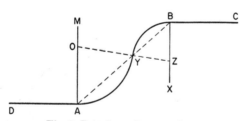

Fig. 9. Drawing a Reverse Ogee

F. With *F* as center, and the same radius, scribe the arc *DE*, which is tangent to the sides of the angle.

Drawing a Reverse Ogee to Connect Two Parallel Lines. Given the parallel lines *DA* and *BC*, and a radius for one of the curves, erect a perpendicular to one of the lines at the point where the ogee is to connect, such as *AM* in Fig 9. Locate the given radius on this line, such as line *AO*. Connect points *A* and *B* with a straight line as shown, and scribe the arc *AY*, using *O* as center, and the given radius *AO*. Erect a perpendicular to line *BC* from the point *B*, such as line *BX*. From point *O*, draw a line through the point of intersection of arc

AY and line AB. Extend this line to meet BX, as at Z. With BZ as a radius and Z as center, scribe the arc YB to complete the ogee.

How to Draw an Ellipse. An ellipse is formed by a plane surface intersecting a cylinder at an oblique angle, as shown in A of Fig. 10. The largest diameter is called the major axis. See (B) of Fig. 10. The shortest diameter, which is at right angles to the major axis, is called the minor axis. Two fixed points called foci (plural of focus) are located on the major axis.

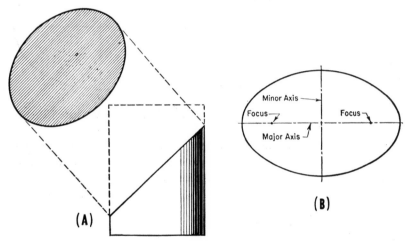

Fig. 10. How an Ellipse Is Produced and the Names Used in Describing an Ellipse

STRING METHOD

Draw the required major and minor axes as shown in Fig. 11. Locate each focus point at a distance from the end of the minor axis equal to one half the major axis. (OX will be equal to YZ.) Drive brads at Q, Y, and Z. Fasten a string to the brad at Q and then pass the string around the brad at Y and fasten to the brad at Z, as shown by dotted lines. Remove the brad at Y and insert a pencil inside the string. Scribe the curved line by keeping the string tight as shown. Scribe each quadrant in the same manner to complete the ellipse.

TWO-RADII METHOD

Draw the required major and minor axes, such as AC and BD in Fig. 12. Draw the line AB, connecting the major and minor axes as shown. Lay off *BE* equal to the difference between *OA* and *OB*. (Swing an arc from *O*, using *OA* as radius. Extend line *OB* to meet this arc. Take the distance from *B* to the arc as the length of *EB*.) Erect a per-

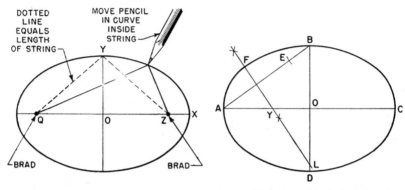

Fig. 11. String Method of Drawing Ellipse

Fig. 12. Two-Radii Method of Drawing Ellipse

pendicular bisector to line *AE;* extend to meet line *BD*, as at *L*. With *L* as center, draw the arc *BF*, using the distance *BL* as a radius. With *Y* as center and a radius equal to *AY*, draw arc *FA*. Complete the other quadrants in the same manner.

Drawing a Spiral. Draw a square which is one-fifth of the required measurement *A* (Fig. 13). With *1* as center, and a radius equal to *1–4*, draw the arc *4X*. With *2* as center, and a radius equal to *2X*, draw the arc *XY*. With *3* as center, and a radius equal to *3Y*, draw the arc

Fig. 13. Drawing a Spiral

YZ. With *4* as center, and a radius equal to *4Z*, draw the remaining arc to complete the spiral. A tangent may be drawn at any required point, such as at *Z* or *C*.

SHOP LAYOUT JOBS

The following shop layout jobs cover a variety of problems. These problems include layouts for tapered pilasters, miter cuts for two unequal width boards, laying out circles when no center is used, laying out an ellipse by means of a trammel, layouts for hip cove brackets, rake molding developments, rafter end contours, and an inclined die on a circular curved counter front.

Problem 1. *How to find the center line of a tapered pilaster.*

A pilaster is an upright architectural member, rectangular in plan and treated as a column shaft with base and capital. Pilasters are often used on the face of a piece of paneling to give the decorative effect of a supporting column. Sometimes the pilaster is smaller at the top, thus requiring a tapered piece of stock. In such cases, a center line is helpful in laying out the work.

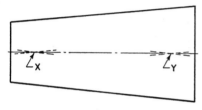

Fig. 14. How To Find Center Line of Tapered Pilaster

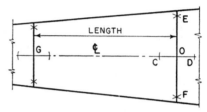

Fig. 15. Squaring Ends of Tapered Pilaster from Center Line

Solution: Draw two short intersecting lines near the ends of the board and parallel to the edges (Fig. 14). The points of intersection as at *X* and *Y* locate the center line of the board. Use a straightedge to connect *X* and *Y*, continuing the center line the full length of the pilaster, as shown in the illustration.

Problem 2. *How to square the ends of a tapered pilaster by means of a compass or trammel.*

Solution: With *O* located on the center line and at the point where the end is to be squared, strike arcs at *C* and *D* (Fig. 15), using the same radius. With *C* and *D* as centers, strike intersecting arcs as at *E* and *F*, using a larger radius. Measure the length as from *O* to *G* and square this end, following the same procedure.

Problem 3. *How to square the ends of a tapered pilaster to the center line by means of a steel square.*

Solution: Hold a straightedge on the center line (position *1*) and place a steel square against it, as shown in Fig. 16. Hold the square firmly and move straightedge to position *2;* remove square, and mark along straightedge.

Measure length of pilaster along center line and repeat the layout on opposite end.

Problem 4. *How to square the ends of a tapered pilaster using a T bevel.*

Solution: Set a T bevel to any angle and place in position *1* (Fig. 17) at the desired point where the end is to be squared, such as *A*. Make a mark at *B*. Reverse the position of the T bevel to position *2*,

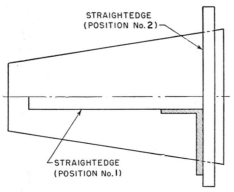

STRAIGHTEDGE
(POSITION No. 2)

STRAIGHTEDGE
(POSITION No. 1)

Fig. 16. Squaring Ends of Tapered Pilaster with Steel Square

with the blade touching point *A*, and make a mark as at *C*. Bisect angle *BAC* and draw the line *AX*, which is the required line at right angles to the center line of the pilaster. Reset the T bevel to angle *DAX* and place in position *3*, marking a line such as *LM*. Reverse the position of the T bevel to position *4* and check accuracy. If the blade does not coincide with line *LM*, the work should be rechecked and the T bevel reset if necessary. Move the T bevel to position *5* at the required length and mark.

Problem 5. *How to find the miter cut of two unequal width boards.*

On many cabinet jobs it is necessary to make a miter cut on two cabinet tops that are of different widths and which form angles of various degrees.

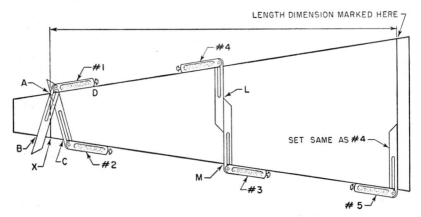

LENGTH DIMENSION MARKED HERE

#4

#1

A

D

L

B

X

C

#2

SET SAME AS #4

M

#3

#5

Fig. 17. How To Square Ends of Tapered Pilaster with T Bevel

Solution: Place one board on top of the other at the desired angle (Fig. 18). Mark the edges at the outside and inside intersection on both boards, separate the boards, and connect the points with a straight line to form the cutting guide lines.

Problem 6. *How to locate the center of an arc to be drawn through three points not in a straight line by means of the steel square.*

This method is useful in the layout of an arc required over a window or door frame where the chord and rise are known.

Solution: Let *A*, *B*, and *C* represent any three points not in a straight line (Fig. 19). Draw lines *AB* and *CB*. Find the center of these lines (by measurement or bisecting) as at *1* and *2*. Place heel of square

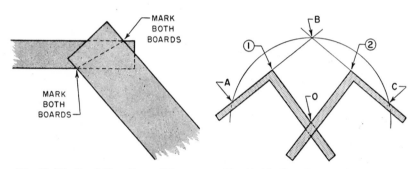

Fig. 18. Finding Miter Cuts of Two Unequal Width Boards

Fig. 19. Finding Center of Arc with Steel Square

on point *1* with the tongue on line *AB*. Draw a line along the blade of the square. Repeat the same procedure at point *2*. The intersection of the lines, as at *O*, will be the center of the arc to be drawn between points *A*, *B*, and *C*.

Problem 7. *How to construct an arc to be drawn through three points not in a straight line by means of a built-up triangle.*

Some jobs require the striking of an arc which cannot be laid out by use of the trammel or steel tape due to obstructions in the building, such as supporting columns. The job is done by means of a built-up triangle.

Solution: (See Fig. 20.) Given points *D* and *E*, draw the line *DE*. Locate the center of line *DE* and draw a perpendicular center line. Locate point *F* on this line at the desired distance from line *DE*. Drive nails at points *D*, *F*, and *E*, which represent the three points to be connected by the arc. Draw a line parallel to line *DE*, such as *FG*. Shape a triangular wooden frame to fit angle *DFG*, as shown in (*A*) of Fig.

20. Nail the frame securely, so it may be moved. Place the frame in position *1*, as shown in (*B*). Hold a pencil at the vertex of the triangle, and then carefully slide the triangle to position *2*, keeping the edges of the triangle against the nails at *D* and *F*. Move the triangle to the position shown at (*C*) and complete the construction.

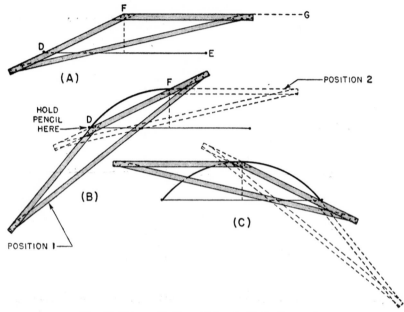

Fig. 20. Using a Built-up Triangle To Scribe an Arc

Problem 8. *How to describe a semicircle by means of a steel square.*

Sometimes it is necessary to describe a semicircle when no center is available. This can be done without difficulty by means of the steel square, providing the diameter of the desired semicircle is not longer than the tongue of the square.

Solution: Drive nails at points *A* and *B*, the required diameter (Fig. 21). Place square in position and move blade and tongue along nails and describe arc *AB* with pencil held at heel of square.

Problem 9. *How to describe an ellipse by means of a wooden trammel.*

The trammel method is practical when laying out a large ellipse where accuracy is necessary.

Solution: Given the longest and shortest dimension of the ellipse, lay out these two dimensions at right angles, as shown in (A) of Fig. 22, with line *FH* representing the longest dimension (major axis) and line *EG* the shortest dimension (minor axis). Fasten two straight-edged pieces of wood at right angles (butt joint) with the two straight edges directly in line with the two axes of the ellipse, as shown in (B). Select a narrow, thin piece of soft wood to make the trammel. The length should be a little longer than half the major axis. Bore a hole at one end so the point of a pencil just protrudes through the wood, as shown by *P*

in (C). Make the distance from *P* to *M* equal to the distance *FO* in (A) and the distance *PN* equal to *GO* in (A). Drive nails at *M* and *N*, allowing the nails to protrude through the wood. Place the trammel on the wooden guide, as shown by the dotted lines of (D). Place a pencil in the hole at *P* and, keeping the nails along the edges of

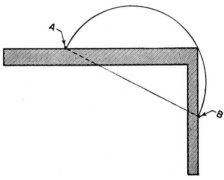

Fig. 21. Describing Semicircle with Steel Square

the guide, scribe one-quarter of the ellipse as shown. Repeat the same procedure for the remaining quarters, changing the guide each time. The guide may be fastened by two small nails in each piece that just protrude through the wood enough to hold the frame from slipping as the trammel is being used.

Problem 10. *How to lay out elliptical hole to permit a round pipe to pass through a board at a given angle and at a given point.*

On cabinetwork involving the installation of pipe, such as a refrigeration unit, it is sometimes necessary to lay out a hole on a flat surface that is on an inclined plane to the vertical axis of the pipe. The hole at right angles to the vertical axis will be round; the hole on the inclined plane will be elliptical.

Solution: Establish the pitch of the pipe to the proper angle as shown in (A) of Fig. 23. Start the layout for the ellipse by drawing a surface with the edge parallel to the line *LM*. At right angles to the line *LM*, project the center point *O* to *O'*. Establish the center lines for the ellipse as shown in (B). Project lines at right angles from the points *L* and *M* to form the major axis of the ellipse in (B). The minor axis is the diameter of the pipe. Lay out the ellipse by any of the previously described methods. Notice at points L and M that there is a difference in the slant distance on the upper and lower sides of the board. To make the hole fit the pipe at these points, the edge of the cut must be parallel to the center line of the pipe.

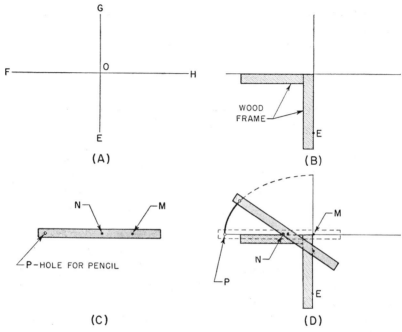

Fig. 22. Describing Ellipse by Means of Wooden Trammel

Problem 11. *How to find the contour of a cove corner bracket for a right-angled room that will correspond to the contour of a wall cove bracket.*

Contractors often order band-sawed cove brackets when constructing a plastered cove ceiling. The regular cove brackets are laid out by setting a compass to the correct radius and marking a quadrant (90° arc) on a block of correct width and which has been properly squared to a 90° angle.

A different layout problem arises on cove brackets which are nailed in the corners of the room. These are called hip-coves as they are laid out on the same fundamental principle as a hip rafter. The shape of the curve is elliptical instead of an arc of a circle.

The radius rise and run of the cove is determined by the architect.

Solution: With R as center, and a radius equal to the radius of the regular cove bracket, scribe the arc AB. (AB is a 90° arc.) Establish the rise and run of the regular cove bracket as shown in Fig. 24 making an elevation of the regular cove bracket. Extend lines from the elevation view of the regular cove bracket as shown. Draw a 45° center line such as CP. Mark the plan for the hip cove as shown (the thickness of the hip cove is the thickness of the board), marking the one end at 90° to the center line and the other end with two 45° angles. (The end with the two 45° angles will fit into the corner of the room.) Project a line from B parallel to the edge of the regular cove to meet line CP, as at D. This completes the plan view for the hip cove. Project lines from points C, D, and P at right angles to the center line CP. From a point such as O,

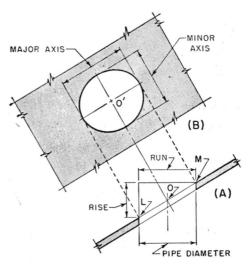

Fig. 23. Layout for Pipe Passing through Board at an Angle

draw a line at right angles to the line CO, such as line OMS. The line OMS establishes the run of the hip mold, and the line OM the major axis for developing the contour of the hip cove. From point O, lay off the distance for the minor axis, which is the same as for the regular cove bracket. From point S, mark the rise of the hip bracket, which has the same rise as the regular bracket. Draw the lines SU, UT, and TL as shown. The elliptical curve LM, which is really a quadrant of an ellipse, may be drawn by any of the previously described methods. The completed hip cove bracket, when fastened in the corner of a rectangular room, will give the proper contour.

Problem 12. *How to find the contour of a rake mold, given the angle of the rake and the face of the horizontal molding.*

A cornice on the exterior of a building is sometimes finished with a crown molding placed horizontally at the eave line of the roof, as shown in (*A*) of Fig. 25. If the roof is gable type, the molding may be continued on the end of the building along the slope of the roof. Molding thus placed in a slanting direction is called a "rake" molding, as shown in (B). This term is applied to any molding placed at an angle other than horizontal or vertical.

A similar type of finish problem is encountered on an exterior entrance such as is illustrated in Fig. 26. The eave line, although very short, is finished with a crown mold placed in a horizontal position. This molding is then fitted on the angle of the pediment. (A triangular frame resembling a gable crowning the front of an entrance.) If the pediment is broken, as in the illustration, the crown molding must also be returned to the wall at the top of the rake.

When a rake molding is mitered to a horizontal

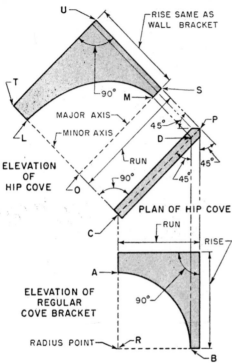

Fig. 24. How To Layout a Hip Cove

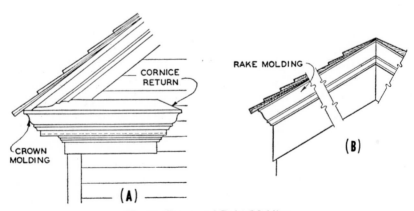

Fig. 25. Crown and Rake Molding

molding, the profile of the rake molding must be "elongated" so that each point of change in the shape of the molding will exactly coincide at the miter.

When the angle of the "rake" changes, a different rake mold pattern must be developed.

To determine the exact shape of the "elongated" section, a layout drawing must be made, using the exact measurements of the horizontal molding and the pitch or slope of the rake

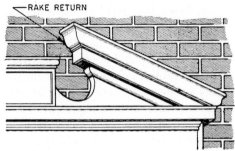

Fig. 26. Front Entrance with Pediment

molding, which is to receive the molding as the basis for the layout. For a front entrance with a broken pediment, *two* elongated patterns are required, as shown in Fig. 27.

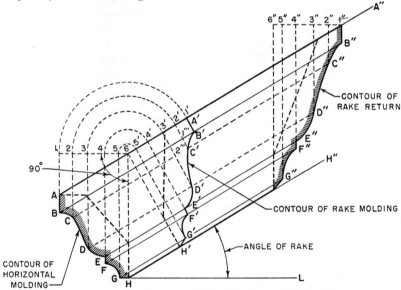

Fig. 27. Laying Out Contour of Rake Molding and Rake Return

Solution: A piece of plywood or drawing paper of sufficient size should be secured on which the layout can be made. The pencil should be sharp and each point of change in the profile of the molding very carefully located. To lay out the contour of a "rake" mold, proceed as follows:

1. Draw horizontal line *GL* to any convenient length.

2. Draw a full-size contour or profile of the horizontal molding as shown.

3. Draw line *HH″* to the exact slope or pitch of the rake mold. (This angle will usually be shown on the blueprint.)

4. Draw line *AA″* parallel to line *HH″*. The two sloping lines now represent the top and lower edges of the rake mold, respectively.

5. Establish points *B* to *H*, inclusive, on the molding profile. These points are located where molding has an inside or outside angle; intermediate points on long curves are located at high and low points on the curve and also at other points as desired. The closer these points are together, the more accurate will be the "stretchout-profile."

6. Extend lines from these points at right angles to line *GL*, as shown.

7. Where extended line *H* intersects line *AA″*, establishing point *6*, draw horizontal line *6–1*, at right angles to *H6*.

8. Using a compass with *6* as the radial point, and a radius equal to the distance *6–1, 6–2, 6–3*, etc., strike arcs to intersect the top edge of the molding to locate points *1′* to *5′* inclusive, as shown.

9. Project lines from points *1′, 2′, 3′*, etc., at a 90° angle to the top edge of the rake molding (line *AA″*), to the lower edge of the rake molding, line *HH″*.

10. Project lines from points *B* to *G*, inclusive, indefinite in length, making them parallel to the top and bottom edges of the rake molding.

11. Locate the intersecting points of these lines with lines *1′ to 5′*, inclusive, and locate points *A′, B′, C′*, etc.

12. Draw a line connecting the points *A′, B′, C′, D′*, etc. This line is the profile or contour of the rake molding and is used by the sticker man as his pattern when grinding a special set of knives for the sticker.

To develop the rake return at the top of a broken pediment, use the same layout drawing as in Fig. 27, but proceed as follows:

1. From any convenient point on the line representing the top edge of the molding, draw line *1″* to *6″* parallel to line *HL*.

2. Lay out points *1″* to *6″*, spaced the same distance apart as points *1* to *6*.

3. From points *1″, 2″, 3″*, etc., draw lines at right angles to line *1″ 6″* and of sufficient length to intersect the lines drawn from *B* to *G* (*Step Ten*).

4. Where lines having the same numbers intersect, such as the line from *1‴–B′* intersects the line from *1″, 2‴–C′* intersects *2″*, etc.,

place marks. Connect these marks to form the contour of the rake return.

Problem 13. *How to lay out the band-sawed contour of a hip or valley rafter-end for an equal pitch roof when the common rafter contour is given. See page 127.*

Some types of architecture require the exposed rafter end of an open cornice to be band sawed on its lower edge to obtain certain decorative effects. The contour or shape of the common rafter (Fig. 28) is designed by the architect, and a full-size drawing is usually furnished. The shape or contour on the hip or valley rafter, however, must be developed by the mill layout man, using the common rafter design as the basis for the new layout.

In the following description, the hip rafter will be illustrated. The procedure is identical for the valley rafter.

The layout job requires an auxiliary development which is not difficult to make. Layout points are established on the common rafter profile as shown in Fig. 28. The exact amount of stock left at *each* of these points is measured on the common rafter and then used on proportionately similar layout points established on the hip rafter pattern to develop the elongated curve.

A clean floor area, or a large piece of plywood, is required on which the layout work can be done. The pencil should be sharp and layout lines carefully and accurately made.

Solution: To lay out a band-sawed hip rafter end, proceed as follows:

1. Draw a full-size outline of the common rafter, including seat and tail cuts. Trace contour of rafter end from full-size detail furnished by the architect. The illustration shown is ⅓ pitch, 8″ rise, 12″ run, and 16″ cornice run.

2. Draw line *1–1′* indefinite in length, as an extension of the plumb cut line or at 90° to the seat cut.

3. Establish line *LM* at any convenient distance above common rafter layout. Draw this line at 45° to the line *1–1′* and intersecting line *1–1′*.

4. Project line *1′–1″* indefinite in length at a 90° angle to line *LM*. (Line *1′–1″* establishes the plumb cut for the hip rafter.)

5. Establish the hip rafter seat cut by projecting a line at 90° to *1′–1″* and parallel to line *LM*.

6. Establish center line of hip rafter at the correct angle for ⅓ pitch roof (8″ rise from the horizontal seat cut at 17″ run).

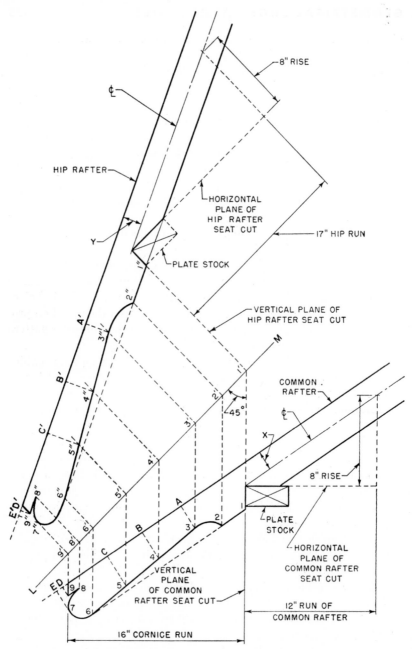

Fig. 28. Laying Out Contour for Hip Rafter End

7. Draw outline of hip rafter parallel to center line with measurement Y equal to measurement X on common rafter.

8. On common rafter, establish points *2* to *9* at key points as shown.

9. From points *2* to *9*, project vertical lines (parallel to line *1–1'*) to intersect line *LM*, thus establishing points *2'* to *9'*. (Point *1'* has been established.)

10. At right angles to line LM, from points *2'* to *9'*, project lines indefinite in length to the body of the hip rafter. At right angles to the line representing the bottom, and where the lines from points *2'* to *9'* intersect, draw lines to the top edge as shown.

11. Measure distance A'–$3''$ at right angles to top of hip rafter equal to distance A–3 on common rafter. Repeat for distance B'–$4''$, etc., to establish points *2''* to *9''*.

Draw angles and curves through the points thus established to form the pattern for the hip rafter.

The seat cut and plumb cut do not always intersect through the center line of the rafter, but vary according to the pitch of the roof

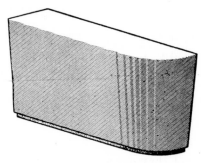

Fig. 29. Sloping Die Counter with Curved End

and the width of the plate stock. The rule is "to get as full (or wide) a seat bearing as possible and yet leave at least one half of the width of the rafter stock above the seat cut."

Problem 14. *How to develop the inclined die of a circular-end counterfront.*

In cabinetmaking, the vertical front face of a counter is called a die.

Modern designers create store fixtures and furniture with slanting and curved surfaces which are usually obtained by bending plywood over a framework foundation, constructed and shaped to the contour desired. Fig. 29 illustrates a counter with a slanting die which terminates in a curved end. The curved end is actually a quadrant of an inverted cone section.

Measurements for the layout are obtained from the architect's plans and specifications, Fig. 30, and must include the angle of the slope, the radius of the curve, and the height of the die.

Solution: The layout problem may be solved by making a full scale layout. A clean floor area should be secured on which the full-size layout will be done. If the job is a small one, a piece of plywood may be satisfactory. To make the layout, proceed as follows:

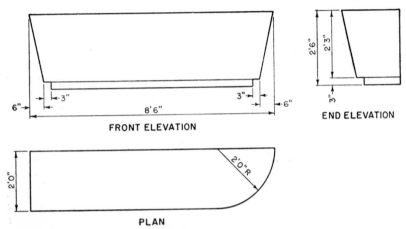

Fig. 30. Architect's Detail of Contour, Showing Measurements Necessary for Layout Work

1. Lay out a full-size end elevation of the curved end of the counter die, using measurements as shown by the architect's drawings, Fig. 30. Line *AD* is equal to the radius of the circular end as shown in the plan view; line *DC* is at 90° to line *DA*, as shown in *Step One* of Fig. 31.

Extend line *AB* and *DC* to intersect at *P*.

2. Draw full-size plan view of the curved end of counter, using radius taken from architect's drawing.

Using a pair of dividers, step off any number of equal spaces on the curve of the quadrant thus formed; in this case, six spaces. (This layout can be done in any available space as it is used only to determine the stretchout length on the curvature of the pattern.)

3. With *PA* as a radius and *P* as center, draw arc *AA'* to any convenient length.

With *PB* as a radius and *P* as center, draw arc *BB'*.

Set a pair of dividers to the distance *1–2* (*Step Two*) and beginning at some convenient distance from *A*, as at *1'*; mark off six spaces. Number these spaces as shown.

Draw the lines *1'–1''* and *7'–7''* by using *P* as a center. The outline as shown in *Step Three* is the pattern for the curved portion of the counter die.

In actual trade practice, the experienced layout man will place the piece of thin veneer or plywood which is to be used for the counter die on top of the full-size layout made on the floor, and then transfer the established layout lines directly on the stock.

Problem 15. *How to lay out a rule joint.*

The rule joint is most generally used to fasten leaves on table tops. Such joints are used in the better grades of furniture, since the joint is neater in appearance than the butt joint.

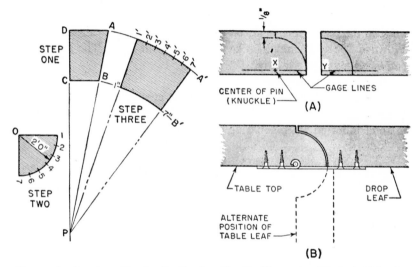

Fig. 31. Laying Out Circular-Enclined Die for Counter Front

Fig. 32. Illustrating Method of Laying Out a Rule Joint

Solution: The layout for the rule joint is made as follows:

1. Mark gage lines as shown in (*A*) of Fig. 32. The gage lines should be located the same as the distance between the center of the pin and the underside of the table top.

2. Set a pair of dividers to a distance that is $\frac{1}{8}''$ less than the distance from the gage line to the top of the table.

3. Using this same setting of the dividers, mark this distance from the edge of the table top as indicated by point X. Scribe the quarter circle as shown, and mark the straight portion of the joint by projecting a line at right angles to the gage line from point X.

4. With the same divider setting and the intersection of the gage

line with the edge of the board as a center such as Y, scribe the arc for the drop leaf. (The divider setting for the drop leaf layout is sometimes increased $\frac{1}{16}''$ to provide better clearance.) The finished joint is shown in (B) of Fig. 32.

Accurate location of the hinge is required for easy operation of the table leaf.

PRACTICE PROBLEMS

Actual shop layouts cannot always be made due to difficulties involved in providing actual materials. However, *the basic principles underlying various layouts* can be learned by doing the layout work on the drafting board.

The drawings should all be drawn to as large a scale as possible. Plywood 36" x 72" may also be used for layout work. The pencil lines can be removed by sanding.

Problems 1, 2, and 3.

Make a scale drawing and develop the center line of a tapered pilaster as dimensioned in the following. Indicate on the drawing the method followed when squaring ends of pilaster.

PROBLEM	PILASTER DIMENSIONS			SQUARING METHOD TO USE
	Top	Bottom	Length	
1	16"	26"	4'0"	Compass
2	14"	20"	6'10"	T bevel
3	11"	15"	8'4"	Steel square

Problems 4 and 5.

Make a scale drawing and develop the miter cut for the two different width boards joined at right angles and dimensioned as follows:

Problem	Width of Boards
4	17" and 23"
5	20" and 34"

Problems 6 and 7.

Lay out semicircles, using the steel square and the dimensions shown.

Problem	Circle Diameter
6	15"
7	13"

Problems 8 and 9.

Secure a small board, and lay out an ellipse by the trammel method, using dimensions shown.

Problem	Major Axis	Minor Axis
8	21″	14″
9	28″	18″

Problems 10 and 11.

Make a scale drawing and develop the shape of the hip cove bracket required to match a regular cove bracket cut to the radius as shown below.

Problem	Radius of Regular Bracket
10	8″
11	11½″

Problems 12 and 13.

Make a scale drawing of a suitable contour design for a common rafter rafter-end. Then develop the hip rafter contour. Pitch of roof and cornice run are indicated below.

Problem	Cornice Run	Pitch of Roof	Square Setting
12	18″	⅓	8 and 12
13	32″	½	12 and 12

Problem 14.

Make a scale drawing and lay out the curved front or die for a sloping counter front, using dimensions shown.

Problem	Vertical Rise of Die	Horizontal Run of Slope	Radius
14	24″	4″	24″

Problem 15.

Lay out a rule joint for a drop-leaf table. The thickness of the top is 1½″.

REVIEW QUESTIONS

1. Name six layout tools.
2. Describe the method of testing a straightedge.

3. What is a pilaster?
4. Describe a rake molding.
5. Describe a crown molding.
6. What is a hip cove bracket?
7. What is a pediment?
8. How is the contour of the hip-rafter end obtained?
9. What is the meaning of the term "die"?
10. Where is the rule joint used?

CHAPTER XI

Lumber, Adhesives, Veneers, and Plywood

QUESTIONS CHAPTER XI WILL ANSWER FOR YOU

1. *What are the principal hardwood trees?*
2. *How is the age of a tree determined?*
3. *What is quarter-sawed lumber?*
4. *What glues are commonly used in cabinetmaking?*
5. *What methods are used in cutting veneers?*

INTRODUCTION TO CHAPTER XI

When America was discovered, much of the land was covered with timber. Since that time, the lumbering industry has been one of the leading industries of America. Today the commercial forest lands of the United States include some 490 million acres. While this figure represents only a fraction of the original forest lands, it is adequate to meet present and future demands, provided, of course, that these demands are reasonable. The conservation of our forests is of utmost importance to the future of our country. Each individual must help in this effort in every possible way. Most states today have adopted reforestation programs that are designed to insure an adequate supply of lumber for future use.

In this chapter you will learn about the varieties of woods, how the lumber is sawed and dried, and other information that will prove valuable in cabinetmaking work. This chapter will also give the beginner an appreciation of the basic material with which he works.

SPECIES OF USEFUL TREES[1]

Of the more than 1,100 varieties of trees in the forests of the United States (Fig. 1), only about 100 have sufficient commercial value to be of broad economic significance.

Of these, about 40 are what the forest industries call *softwoods*, and the rest are *hardwoods*. Of the softwoods, 14 species are extensively used in the manufacture of lumber, plywood, and pulp, and of the hardwoods about 15 species. The term softwood as used in the lumber

[1] Based on material from *Trees for Tomorrow*, a publication by American Forest Products Industries, Inc., Washington, D.C.

163

trade does not necessarily mean a tree the wood of which is soft, nor does hardwood always indicate one the wood of which is hard. In fact, no definite degree of hardness divides the two groups. The custom has developed of calling the coniferous trees softwood and the broad-leaved trees hardwood. Coniferous trees are those with needles or scalelike leaves, popularly called evergreens. Broad-leaved trees are termed de-

Fig. 1. An American Forest
Courtesy of American Forest Products Industries, Inc., Washington, D.C.

ciduous because most of those in the United States shed their leaves each year. Fig. 2 shows the forest regions of the United States.

The principal hardwood trees, in order of their commercial importance as measured by the volume harvested, are: oak (Fig. 3), red gum, maple, yellow poplar, tupelo, birch, cottonwood, beech, basswood, elm, ash, chestnut, hickory, walnut, sycamore, alder, magnolia, willow, pecan, cherry, hackberry, locust, buckeye, cucumber, and butternut.

There are about 250 species of the pine family, which includes the pines, spruces, firs, hemlocks, cedars, and other cone-bearing trees with needle-shaped leaves. The chief softwoods of commercial importance are the southern yellow pines (short-leaf pine, long-leaf pine, loblolly

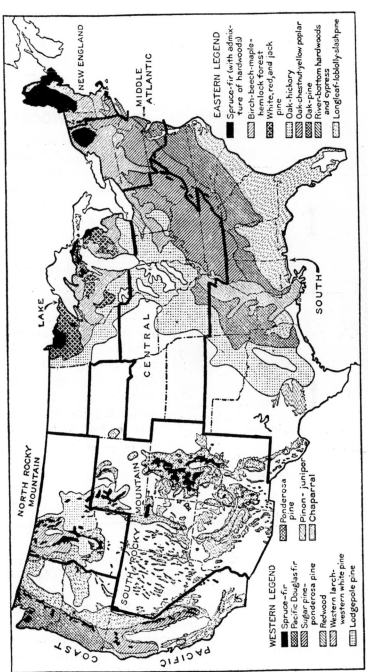

Fig. 2. Forest Regions of the United States

pine, slash pine), Douglas fir (Fig. 4), ponderosa pine, hemlock (Fig. 5), northern white pine, Norway pine, Idaho white pine, cypress, redwood, sugar pine, Sitka spruce, together with the western red cedar, larch, white spruce, and red spruce.

Fig. 3. A Fine Specimen of Southern Red Oak
Courtesy of Southern Hardwood Producers, Inc., New Orleans, La.

IMPORTED WOODS

Although America has an ample supply of wood for her essential needs, imported woods form an important segment of the lumber consumed in the United States.

The furniture, fixture, and novelty factories probably consume the largest share of imported woods.

One of the most useful woods imported is mahogany (Fig. 6). Species of this wood are imported from Africa, Central and South America, and the West Indies. Philippine mahogany (not a true mahogany), known as Red Lauan, and other species are extensively used in the United States.

A great variety of foreign wood is imported for the veneer and plywood industries.

STRUCTURE OF WOOD

Annual Rings. Each year adds a ring of new growth to a tree. In most species of wood, this ring is in two distinct parts. The soft porous section is formed in the spring and is called spring growth. The harder, more dense growth, takes place in the summer and fall and is called summer growth. The two sections form what is called an annual ring.

Heartwood and Sapwood. The annual rings grown just prior to the time the tree is cut down are lighter in color than the inner rings of annual growth. The darker inner rings are known as heartwood and the lighter outer rings are known as sapwood (Fig. 7).

Medullary Rays. Extending radially from the heart of a tree to its outer circumference is a thin, hard growth called medullary rays. These rays are sometimes called pith rays or wood rays as shown by *G* in Fig. 7.

Fibers and Grain of Wood. The growth and arrangement of the fibers which compose the cellular structure of wood (Fig. 8) forms what is known as the grain of the wood. The cellular ducts are called pores.

Quarter-Sawed Wood. When a board is cut parallel to the rays, cutting the annual rings at right angles, the board is said to be quarter-sawed (Fig. 9).

The medullary rays are cut at an acute angle, exposing a flaky, mottled effect scattered over the edges of the annual rings. The distinctive, mottled-grain effect of quarter-sawed white oak, red oak, and sycamore is noted for its beauty, as is the ribbon-grained effect of woods with less pronounced medullary rays.

The term "quarter-

Fig. 4. A Stand of Douglas Fir Near Mineral, Washington

Courtesy of West Coast Lumbermen's Association, Portland, Ore.

sawed" is used mainly with reference to hardwoods. Softwoods, cut similarly across the annual rings, are said to be *edge-grained* or *vertical-grained*. Hardwoods sawed to cut the annual rings at approximately 45° with the face of the board are said to be *bastard-sawed*. The term *rift oak*, or any rift-sawed wood, has the same meaning as quarter-sawed. The term stems from the old Norse word *rive*, meaning to cleave. The rift in a log along a medullary ray is caused by the shrinkage of the wood, hence, rift-sawed.

Plain-Sawed Wood. Lumber, the surface of which is cut from the log tangentially to the annual rings (Fig. 10), is said to be plain-sawed for hardwoods and slash-grained or flat-grained for softwoods. The annual rings are severed at an acute angle, exposing the alternate layers of spring growth and summer growth.

Strength of Wood. In general, close-grained woods are stronger than open-grained or porous woods. The weight and strength of wood

Fig. 5. Mountain Hemlock, Mount Baker National Forest, Washington. Section of Wood Shown at Left

Courtesy of West Coast Lumbermen's Association,
Seattle, Wash.   *Courtesy of United States Forest Service; Photo*
by Bureau of Aeronautics, U.S. Navy

depends upon the thickness of the cell walls. The shape, size, and arrangement of the fibers, the presence of the wood rays, and the layer effect of the springwood and summerwood account for the large difference in the properties along and across the grain.

SEASONING WOODS

Green and Wet Wood. Seasoning is a process or treatment to reduce the moisture content of lumber to a point consistent with the requirements for the manufacture and service condition of a given article. Lumber freshly cut from the log is said to be *green*, which means that it contains the natural moisture grown in the tree. Lumber that has attained a degree of dryness through the process of seasoning and has later been subjected to damp atmospheric conditions or rain and

Fig. 6. Mahogany Tree with Section of Veneer Shown at Left
Courtesy of Mahogany Association, Inc., Chicago, Ill.

has absorbed moisture because of exposure is said to be *wet*.

Moisture in Wood. Green wood contains water which saturates the fibers and fills the pores or cells. The point in the drying or wetting of wood at which the cell walls are saturated and the cell cavities are free from water is called the *fiber saturation point*.

Shrinkage of Wood. Wood, like many other materials, shrinks as it loses moisture. Shrinkage occurs

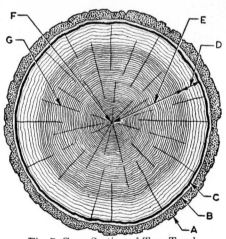

Fig. 7. Cross Section of Tree Trunk
(A) Outer bark, (B) inner bark, (C) cambium, (D) sapwood, (E) heartwood, (F) pith, and (G) wood rays.

when the moisture content is lowered beyond the fiber saturation point; for most woods this point is between 25% and 30% moisture content. Lumber containing 12% to 15% moisture will have shrunk about one-

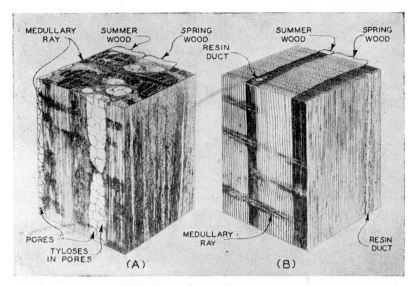

Fig. 8. Magnified Blocks of White Oak (A) and Shortleaf Pine (B)

The top of each block represents the end—cross or transverse section. The left side shows a quarter-sawed section (hardwood) and vertical grain or radial section (softwood). The right side illustrates flat-grain, plain-sawed, or tangential section.

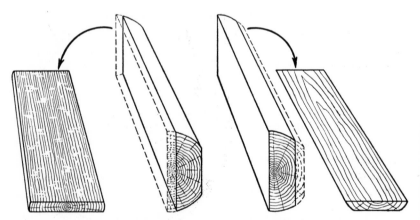

Fig. 9. Quarter-Sawed Lumber   Fig. 10. Plain-Sawed Lumber

half its total possible shrinkage. Wood shrinks most in the direction of the annual growth rings (tangentially). Only a small amount of shrinkage occurs along the grain (longitudinally).

Effect of Shrinkage. Shrinkage often causes checks across the rings of annual growth (Fig. 11). In any log of wood there is always the

possibility of shrinkage in two directions, along the radial lines following the direction of the medullary rays, and around the circumference
of the log following the direction of the annual rings. If the wood
shrinks in both directions at the
same rate, the result will be only a
decrease in the volume of the log,
but if it shrinks more rapidly
around the circumference of the log
than along the radial lines, checks
will be formed. Because of the different thicknesses of the fibers in
wood, a piece of lumber has a tendency to warp as it is being dried
(Fig. 12). Lumber cut from crooked
logs is often cross-grained and has

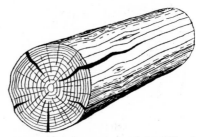

Fig. 11. Checks Caused by Wood
Shrinking More Rapidly around the
Circumference of a Log Than along
the Radial Lines

a greater tendency to warp than lumber with a more uniform structure.
Proper drying conditions and proper stacking will minimize this tend-

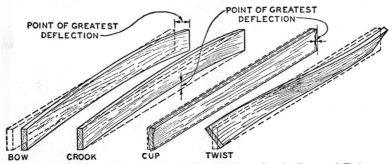

POINT OF GREATEST DEFLECTION

POINT OF GREATEST DEFLECTION

BOW   CROOK   CUP   TWIST

Fig. 12. Various Kinds of Warp in Wood—Bow, Crook, Cup, and Twist

ency. The characteristic shrinkage of various shapes cut from different
parts of a log are shown in Fig. 13.

Air-Dried Lumber.   Lumber stacked under favorable ventilated
conditions (Fig. 14) and allowed a sufficient number of seasons to dry
is called "air dried."

The slow natural process of air drying lumber under proper conditions allows the fibers to knit into a stronger unit and is most suitable
where strength is a requirement.

Kiln-Dried Lumber.   Kiln drying or controlled drying of wood is a
process of artificially and scientifically subjecting the wood to a treatment of heat, moisture, steam, and controlled air in a closed kiln until
the moisture content in the lumber is reduced to the desired point.

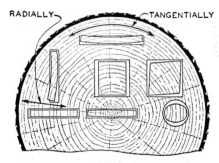

RADIALLY   TANGENTIALLY

Fig. 13. Cross Section of Tree Trunk, Showing Characteristic Shrinkage and Distortion of Flats, Squares, and Rounds as Affected by Direction of Annual Rings

Lumber so treated is designated as *K.D.*, or kiln-dried, lumber and is used in the manufacture of furniture, fixtures, and millwork.

Moisture Variations in Woods. "Woodwork should be dried to a moisture content which will correspond to the average moisture content of the house in which it is going to be installed.

"In localities where home heating is required, we are apt to encounter a large variety of conditions during the winter. Often homes are heated with air conditions that may dry the woodwork to as low as 4% or 5% moisture content. Again, moisture may be added to cause condensation troubles at the windows. (This usually occurs before the woodwork shows distress.) The highest moisture content of woodwork generally occurs during prolonged damp weather in summer. This may reach 13% to 15% but rarely any higher. An average moisture content for woodwork for most of the United States would run between 8% and 11%, Fig. 15. For localities of extreme conditions, the woodwork should be 'tempered' for a few weeks before installation for best results. The smaller the seasonal range of moisture content variation can be kept, the better it will be for the woodwork."[1]

Fig. 14. Stacked Lumber in Yard at Palatka, Florida, for Air Drying. Care Is Taken in Piling To Insure Good Seasoning

Courtesy of Southern Cypress Manufacturers Association, Jacksonville, Fla.

[1] *The Care of Woodwork,* Curtis Companies Service Bureau, Clinton, Iowa. Permission to use is hereby acknowledged with appreciation by the authors

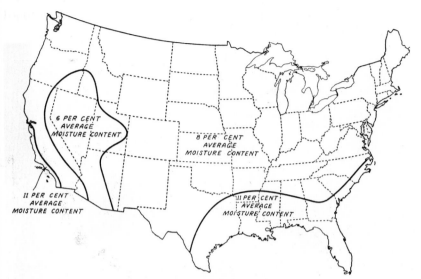

Fig. 15. Recommended Moisture Content Averages for Interior-Finishing Woodwork for Use in Various Parts of the United States
Courtesy of U.S. Forest Service, Forest Products Laboratory Photo

LUMBER GRADING FACTORS

Two main factors are considered in the grading of lumber: (1)
Natural defects inherent in the tree or such damage as may be caused
by natural elements, insects, and fungi beyond the control of man.
(2) Manufactured defects or defects caused by poor manufacture, improper handling, drying, or storage.

Combinations of the above factors considered with respect to the
ultimate use or purpose of the lumber determine the classification of
grade or quality of stock into which a board may fall.

DEFECTS OF LUMBER

Since timber is a natural product developed through many years of
growth in the open air, and exposed continually to varying conditions
of wind and weather, defects of various kinds develop.

Knots. Knots are formed at the juncture of a branch with the main
trunk of a tree. When a branch is broken off near the trunk leaving a
small piece attached to the tree, the tree continues to grow, but the
broken piece of limb dies. As the tree increases in size, the piece of
dead limb becomes imbedded in the trunk. These bits of wood are
called knots. Sound knots are interwoven with the tree by growth and

are the result of some of the fibers of the wood turning aside to follow along a live limb. Encased or loose knots (A) of Fig. 16 are formed

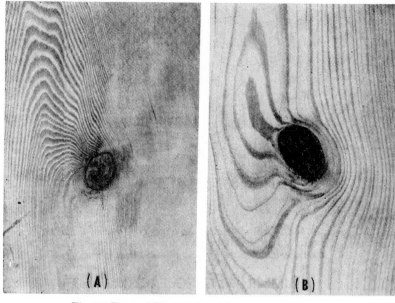

Fig. 16. Encased Knot (A) and Intergrown Knot (B)
Courtesy of U.S. Forest Service, Forest Products Laboratory Photo

around dead or broken limbs. Intergrown knots (B) of Fig. 16, are knots of which the annual growth rings are completely intergrown with those of the surrounding wood. When the limb is sawed at right angles, round knots are produced; when the cut is diagonal, an oval knot is produced. A spike knot occurs where a limb is sawed in a lengthwise direction. Pin knots are less than ½″ in size. Small knots are ½″ to ¾″. Medium knots are ¾″ to 1½″. Large knots are more than 1½″ in size. The size of the knot is measured as shown in Fig. 17.

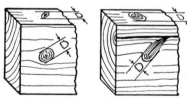

Fig. 17. Measurement of Knots
Courtesy of U.S. Forest Service, Forest Products Laboratory Photo

Pitch Pockets. An opening extending parallel to the annual rings of growth and usually containing pitch in either solid or liquid form is called a pitch pocket.

Checks. A lengthwise separation of the wood caused by shrinkage is called a check.

Splits. A tearing apart of the cells due to improper handling or storage is termed a split.

Heart Shake. Heart shake is a defect at the heart of a tree due to shrinkage in the live tree because of decay (Fig. 18).

Wind Shakes. Defects as the result of wrenching of the live tree by high wind causing the annual rings to separate (Fig. 19), are termed wind shakes.

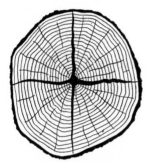

Fig. 18. Heart Shake Caused by Decay Beginning at Center of Trunk and Extending Outward

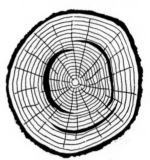

Fig. 19. Wind Shake Caused by Racking and Wrenching of a Tree by the Wind

Pith. The heart of the tree is made up of soft, spongy, cellular tissue called pith, which is considered a defect when it appears in lumber.

Cross Grain. Cross grain is grain not parallel to the length of a board. It may be either spiral, diagonal, or a combination of the two.

Crook. A board in which the edge is convex or concave is described as crooked.

Bow. A board in which the face is convex or concave is described as bowed.

Cup. A curve across the width of a board, either concave or convex, is termed cup.

Twist. A turning or winding of the edges of a board is termed twist.

Warp. Warp is any deviation from a straight line, such as crook, bow, cup, or twist; usually a combination of two or more of these conditions.

Wane. Bark, or lack of wood or bark, on the edge of a board is called wane.

Bark Pocket. A patch of bark partially or wholly enclosed by wood is known as a bark pocket.

Decay. The disintegration of wood from any of a number of causes is termed decay.

Stain. Stain is discoloration caused by fungi or as the result of drying. Fungi stain may be bluish, grayish, or brown. Chemical brown stains occur during the drying processes of certain species of wood.

Worm Holes. Holes caused by insects or beetles are called insect or worm holes.

Imperfect Manufacture. Variations in sawing, torn grain, loosened grain, skip, mismatched material, machine burn, hit and miss surfacing and chipped grain are all classed under imperfect manufacture.

ESTABLISHMENT OF GRADING STANDARDS

Grading rules by which lumber is bought and sold are adapted and revised from time to time by the various lumber manufacturers' associations. The information given here is of a general nature to inform the beginner of the considerations which enter into the grading of lumber.[2]

American Grade Standards for Hardwoods. The rules which are considered standard in grading hardwood lumber in the United States are those adopted by the National Hardwood Lumber Association. In these rules the grade of a piece of hardwood lumber is determined by the proportion of the piece that can be cut into a certain number of smaller pieces of material, clear on one side and not less than a certain size. In other words, the grade classification is based upon the amount of clear usable lumber in the piece rather than upon the number or size of the features that occur in the cutting. This clear material, commonly termed *clear cuttings*, must have one face clear and the reverse face sound, which means free from rot, heart center, shake, and other features that materially impair the strength of the cutting. Some grades require only that cuttings be sound.

The highest grade of hardwood lumber is termed *Firsts* and the next grade *Seconds*. Firsts and Seconds, or, as they are generally written, *FAS*, practically always are combined in one grade. The third grade is termed *Selects*, followed by *No. 1 Common, No. 2 Common, Sound Wormy, No. 3A Common*, and *No. 3B Common*.

A brief summary of the hardwood grades follows. This summary

---

[2] This section is based on *Wood Handbook,* United States Department of Agriculture, Forest Products Laboratory, Forest Research—Forest Service, Madison, Wis.

should not be regarded as a complete set of grading rules, as there are numerous details, exceptions, and special rules for certain species that are not included. The hardwoods, generally termed *Commercial,* are listed as follows:

Alder	Cherry	Magnolia
Ash	Chestnut	Mahogany: African,
Aspen	Cottonwood	Cuban, and San Do-
Basswood	Cypress	minican
Beech	Elm: Rock (or Cork)	Oak: Red, White
Birch	and Soft	Pecan
Blackberry	Gum: Black, Red	Poplar
Box Elder	and Sap, Tupelo	Sycamore
Buckeye	Hickory	Walnut
Butternut	Locust	Willow
Cedar, Red		

Two of the woods included, cedar (eastern red) and cypress (southern), are not hardwoods. Cypress lumber has a different set of grading rules from those used for the hardwoods. All cypress rules are originated by the Southern Cypress Manufacturers' Association and are either used verbatim or with minor changes by the National Hardwood Lumber Association.

Standard Lengths (Feet). Standard lengths are 4', 5', 6', 7', 8', 9', 10', 11', 12', 13', 14', 15', and 16', but not over 50% of odd lengths will be admitted.

Standard Thicknesses (Inches). Standard thicknesses for hardwood lumber are given in Table I.

TABLE I. STANDARD THICKNESSES FOR HARDWOODS

Rough (Inches)	Surfaced 1 Side (S1S)	Surfaced 2 Sides (S2S)	Rough (Inches)	Surfaced 1 Side (S1S)	Surfaced 2 Sides (S2S)
	Inches	*Inches*		*Inches*	*Inches*
$3/8$............	$1/4$	$3/16$	$2\frac{1}{2}$............	$2\frac{5}{16}$	$2\frac{1}{4}$
$1/2$............	$3/8$	$5/16$	3............	$2\frac{13}{16}$	$2\frac{3}{4}$
$5/8$............	$1/2$	$7/16$	$3\frac{1}{2}$............	$3\frac{5}{16}$	$3\frac{1}{4}$
$3/4$............	$5/8$	$9/16$	4............	$3\frac{13}{16}$	$3\frac{3}{4}$
1............	$7/8$	$1\frac{3}{16}$	$4\frac{1}{2}$............	(*)	(*)
$1\frac{1}{4}$............	$1\frac{1}{8}$	$1\frac{1}{16}$	5............	(*)	(*)
$1\frac{1}{2}$............	$1\frac{3}{8}$	$1\frac{5}{16}$	$5\frac{1}{2}$............	(*)	(*)
2............	$1\frac{13}{16}$	$1\frac{3}{4}$	6............	(*)	(*)

* Finished size not specified in rules. Stock usually made in small quantities or on special order.

Hardwood Interior Trim. Hardwood interior trim and molding are generally graded under the rules of the Hardwood Interior Trim Manufacturers' Association. These rules have been adopted by the National Lumber Association. The rules list only a single grade in all species designated as Grade A. This grade provides for practically clear-faced trim except for slight imperfections that vary with the species and are allowed in not more than 10% of a shipment. Kiln-dried material is required with a moisture content not to exceed 10% when shipped from the mill. The design and sizes of trim and molding conform to American lumber standards.

American Standards for Grading Softwoods. Species of softwoods vary with the locality in which they grow. Familiarity with the names and places of origin is important to the woodworker because of the working quality encountered in each species of wood. Table II gives the names that are used to identify the commercial softwoods.

TABLE II. NOMENCLATURE OF COMMERCIAL SOFTWOODS

CEDARS AND JUNIPERS			
Official Forest Service Name Used in This Handbook	Name Adopted as Standard under American Lumber Standards	Other Names Sometimes Used	Botanical Name
Alaska cedar	Alaska cedar	Yellow cedar, Sitka cypress, yellow cypress	*Chamaecyparis nootkatensis*
Alligator juniper	Western juniper	Juniper	*Juniperus pachyphloea*
Eastern red cedar	Eastern red cedar	Red cedar, cedar, juniper	*Juniperus virginiaina*
Incense cedar	Incense cedar	Cedar, white cedar	*Libocedrus decurrens*
Northern white cedar	Northern white cedar	Arborvitae, cedar, swamp cedar, white cedar	*Thuja occidentalis*
Port Orford cedar	Port Orford cedar	Lawson's cypress, Oregon cedar, white cedar	*Chamaecyparis lawsoniana*
Rocky Mountain red cedar	Western juniper	Juniper	*Juniperus scopulorum*
Southern white cedar	Southern white cedar	White cedar, swamp cedar, juniper	*Chamaecyparis thyoides*
Utah juniper	Western juniper	Juniper, white cedar	*Juniperus utahensis*
Western juniper	Western juniper	Juniper, cedar	*Juniperus occidentalis*
Western red cedar	Western red cedar	Red cedar, cedar, western cedar	*Thuja plicata*

CYPRESS			
Southern cypress	Red cypress (coast type), yellow cypress (inland type), white cypress (inland type)	Cypress, tidewater red cypress, Gulf coast red cypress, Louisiana red cypress, bald cypress, red cypress, black cypress	*Taxodium distichum*

TABLE II. NOMENCLATURE OF COMMERCIAL SOFTWOODS—*Continued*

DOUGLAS FIR

Official Forest Service Name Used in This Handbook	Name Adopted as Standard under American Lumber Standards	Other Names Sometimes Used	Botanical Name
Douglas fir	Douglas fir (Coast region), Douglas fir (Inland empire and California), Douglas fir (Rocky Mountain region)	Red fir, Oregon fir, Douglas spruce, yellow fir, Puget Sound pine, Oregon pine	*Pseudotsuga taxifolia*

THE TRUE FIRS

Alpine fir	Alpine fir	Balsam, white fir	*Abies lasiocarpa*
Balsam fir	Balsam fir	Balsam, eastern fir	*Abies balsamea*
Southern balsam fir	Balsam fir	Balsam, eastern fir	*Abies fraseri*
California red fir	Golden fir	Red fir	*Abies magnifica*
Noble fir	Noble fir	Red fir	*Abies nobilis*
Silver fir	Silver fir	Red fir, white fir, fir	*Abies amabilis*
White fir	White fir	Colorado white fir	*Abies concolor*
Lowland white fir	White fir	Yellow fir	*Abies grandis*

HEMLOCKS

Eastern hemlock	Eastern hemlock	Hemlock, hemlock spruce, spruce pine	*Tsuga canadensis*
Mountain hemlock	Mountain hemlock	Weeping spruce, Alpine spruce, hemlock spruce	*Tsuga mertensiana*
Western hemlock	West coast hemlock	Hemlock, hemlock spruce, Pacific hemlock, Alaska pine	*Tsuga heterophylla*

LARCH

Western larch	Western larch	Tamarack, larch	*Larix occidentalis*

PINES

Western white pine	Idaho white pine	White pine, soft pine	*Pinus monticola*
Jack pine	Jack pine	Scrub pine	*Pinus banksiana*
Loblolly pine	Loblolly pine*	Old-field pine, slash pine, shortleaf pine, Virginia pine, sap pine, yellow pine, North Carolina pine	*Pinus taeda*
Lodgepole pine	Lodgepole pine	Scrub pine, spruce pine	*Pinus contorta*
Longleaf pine	Longleaf pine*	Southern pine, yellow pine, hard pine, Georgia pine, pitch pine, heart pine, fat pine, southern yellow pine	*Pinus palustris*

TABLE II. NOMENCLATURE OF COMMERCIAL SOFTWOODS—*Continued*

PINES

Official Forest Service Name Used in This Handbook	Name Adopted as Standard under American Lumber Standards	Other Names Sometimes Used	Botanical Name
Northern white pine	Northern white pine	White pine, cork pine, soft pine, northern pine, pumpkin pine, eastern white pine	*Pinus strobus*
Norway pine	Norway pine	Red pine, hard pine, northern pine	*Pinus resinosa*
Pond pine	Pond pine	Marsh pine, loblolly pine, spruce pine, bull pine	*Pinus rigida serotina*
Ponderosa pine	Ponderosa pine	Western yellow pine, bull pine, Arizona white pine, western soft pine, western pine	*Pinus ponderosa*
Shortleaf pine	Shortleaf pine*	Yellow pine, spruce pine, oldfield pine, Arkansas soft pine, North Carolina pine.	*Pinus echinata*
Slash pine	Slash pine*	Swamp pine, pitch pine	*Pinus caribaca*
Sugar pine	Sugar pine	Big pine	*Pinus lambertiana*

REDWOOD

Redwood	Redwood	Sequoia, coast redwood	*Sequoia sempervirens*

SPRUCES

Red spruce	Eastern spruce	Red spruce	*Picea rubra*
White spruce	Eastern spruce	White spruce	*Picea glauca*
Black spruce	Eastern spruce	Black spruce	*Picea mariana*
Engelmann spruce	Engelmann spruce	White spruce, silver spruce, balsam, mountain spruce.	*Picea engelmannii*
Sitka spruce	Sitka spruce	Spruce, tideland spruce, western spruce, yellow spruce, silver spruce	*Picea sitchensis*

TAMARACK

Tamarack	Tamarack	Larch, hackmatack, red larch, black larch	*Larix laricina*

YEW

Pacific yew	Pacific yew	Yew, western yew, mountain mahogany	*Taxus brevifolia*

* American lumber standards name *Arkansas pine* includes loblolly pine and shortleaf pine; *North Carolina pine* includes loblolly pine, shortleaf pine, and Virginia pine; *Southern pine* includes longleaf pine, shortleaf pine, loblolly pine, slash pine, pond pine, and pitch pine.

General Classification of Softwood. Softwood lumber is graded into three main classifications (Table III):

1. Yard lumber, such as finish boards and dimensional stock.
2. Structural materials, often referred to as timbers, such as beams, purlins, posts, or any weight-carrying structural timber.
3. Factory and shop lumber suitable mainly for manufacturing purposes, such as interior trim, sash, doors, fixtures, and furniture.

Rules for grading softwoods are adapted by the various lumber associations concerned with the particular species involved.

Yard Lumber-Grade Standards. Ordinary building lumber is graded by lumber manufacturers' associations as finish items, select *A*, *B*, *C*, and *D*; boards, No. 1, No. 2, No. 3, No. 4, No. 5; and dimensions, No. 1, No. 2, and No. 3.

Yard Lumber-Size Standards. Standard lengths are multiples of two feet except for the following odd lengths which are allowed:

$$2 \times 4, \ 6 \times 8 \quad \dots\dots\dots\dots\dots \quad 9' \text{ and } 11'$$
$$2 \times 8 \quad \dots\dots\dots\dots\dots \quad 13'$$
$$2 \times 10 \quad \dots\dots\dots\dots\dots \quad 13' \text{ and } 15'$$

Structural Material Grade Standards. Structural material is intended for use where working stresses are required.

The effect of knots, deviations of grain, shakes, and checks on the strength of a timber varies with the loading to which the piece is subjected. Also the effect of seasoning varies with the size of the timber. Consequently, efficiency in grading necessitates classifying timbers according to their size and use. Such a classification is listed below as follows:

Beams and Stringers. Large pieces (nominal dimensions 5″ x 8″ and up) of rectangular cross section graded with respect to their strength in bending when loaded on the narrow face.

Joist and Plank. Pieces (nominal dimensions 2″ to 4″ in thickness by 4″ and wider) of rectangular cross section graded with respect to their strength in bending when loaded either on the narrow face as joist or on the wide face as plank.

Posts and Timbers. Pieces of square or approximately square cross section, 4″ x 4″ and larger, in nominal dimension, graded primarily for use as posts or columns but adapted to miscellaneous uses in which strength in bending is not especially important.

In accordance with American lumber standards, rough (unsurfaced) pieces shall be sawed full to nominal dimension except that occasional slight variation in sawing is permissible. At no part of the length shall any piece, because of such variation, be more than $\frac{3}{16}''$ under the nominal dimension when this dimension is $3''$ to $7''$ inclusive, nor more than $\frac{1}{4}''$ under the nominal dimension when this dimension is $8''$ or greater. The actual thickness of nominal $2''$ material shall not be less than $1\frac{7}{8}''$ at any part of the length. Further, no shipment shall contain more than 20% of pieces of minimum dimension.

Surfacing of joist and plank, whether on one or both of a pair of opposite faces, shall leave the finished size not more than $\frac{3}{8}''$ under the nominal dimension when this dimension is $7''$ or less and not more than

TABLE III. STANDARD THICKNESSES AND WIDTHS FOR SOFTWOOD YARD LUMBER

Product	Rough Green or Nominal Sizes (Board Measure)		Minimum Rough-Dry Dimensions			Dressed Dimensions		
	Thickness	Width	Thickness		Width	Thickness		Width (Face when Worked)
			Standard Yard*	Standard Industrial		Standard Yard	Standard Industrial	
	Inches	Inches	Inches	Inches	Inches	Inches	Inches	Inches
Finish	....	3	....	....	$2\frac{3}{4}$	$\frac{5}{16}$	....	$2\frac{5}{8}$
	....	4	....	....	$3\frac{5}{8}$	$\frac{7}{16}$	....	$\dagger 5\frac{1}{2}$
	....	5	....	....	$4\frac{5}{8}$	$\frac{9}{16}$	....	$\dagger 4\frac{1}{2}$
	....	6	....	....	$5\frac{5}{8}$	$\frac{11}{16}$	....	$\dagger 5\frac{1}{2}$
	1	7	$\frac{29}{32}$	$\ddagger\frac{30}{32}$	$6\frac{5}{8}$	$\frac{25}{32}$	$\frac{26}{32}$	$6\frac{1}{2}$
	$1\frac{1}{4}$	8	$1\frac{3}{16}$	....	$7\frac{3}{8}$	$1\frac{1}{16}$	....	$\dagger 7\frac{1}{4}$
	$1\frac{1}{2}$	9	$1\frac{7}{16}$	....	$8\frac{3}{8}$	$1\frac{5}{16}$	....	$\dagger 8\frac{1}{4}$
	$1\frac{3}{4}$	10	$1\frac{9}{16}$	....	$9\frac{3}{8}$	$1\frac{7}{16}$	....	$\dagger 9\frac{1}{4}$
	2	11	$1\frac{5}{8}$	$*1\frac{7}{8}$	$10\frac{3}{8}$	$1\frac{5}{8}$	$1\frac{5}{8}$	$\dagger 10\frac{1}{4}$
	$2\frac{1}{2}$	12	$2\frac{1}{8}$	....	$11\frac{3}{8}$	$2\frac{1}{8}$	....	$\dagger 11\frac{1}{4}$
	3		$2\frac{5}{8}$			$2\frac{5}{8}$		
Common boards and strips	1	3	$\frac{29}{32}$	$\ddagger\frac{30}{32}$	$2\frac{3}{4}$	$\frac{25}{32}$	$\frac{25}{32}$	$2\frac{5}{8}$
	$1\frac{1}{4}$	4	$1\frac{3}{16}$	....	$3\frac{3}{4}$	$1\frac{1}{16}$	....	$3\frac{5}{8}$
	$1\frac{1}{2}$	5	$1\frac{7}{16}$	....	$4\frac{3}{4}$	$1\frac{5}{16}$	....	$4\frac{5}{8}$
	....	6	....	....	$5\frac{3}{4}$	....	....	$5\frac{5}{8}$
	....	7	....	....	$6\frac{3}{4}$	....	....	$6\frac{5}{8}$
	....	8	....	....	$7\frac{5}{8}$	....	....	$7\frac{1}{2}$
	....	9	....	....	$8\frac{5}{8}$	....	....	$8\frac{1}{2}$
	....	10	....	....	$9\frac{5}{8}$	....	....	$9\frac{1}{2}$
	....	11	....	....	$10\frac{5}{8}$	....	....	$10\frac{1}{2}$
	....	12	....	....	$11\frac{5}{8}$	....	....	$11\frac{1}{2}$
Dimension and heavy joist	2	2	$1\frac{3}{4}$	$*1\frac{7}{8}$	$1\frac{3}{4}$	$1\frac{5}{8}$	$1\frac{3}{4}$	$1\frac{5}{8}$
	$2\frac{1}{2}$	4	$2\frac{1}{4}$	....	$3\frac{3}{4}$	$2\frac{1}{8}$	....	$3\frac{5}{8}$
	3	6	$2\frac{3}{4}$	....	$5\frac{3}{4}$	$2\frac{5}{8}$	....	$5\frac{5}{8}$
	4	8	$3\frac{3}{4}$	....	$7\frac{5}{8}$	$3\frac{5}{8}$	....	$7\frac{1}{2}$
	....	10	....	....	$9\frac{5}{8}$	....	....	$9\frac{1}{2}$
	....	12	....	....	$11\frac{5}{8}$	....	....	$11\frac{1}{2}$

* 20% may be $\frac{1}{32}''$ scant.
† Based on kiln-dried lumber.
‡ 10% may be $\frac{1}{32}''$ scant.

½" under the nominal dimension when this dimension is 8" or greater.

Surfacing of posts and timbers, whether on one or both of a pair of opposite faces, shall leave the finished size not more than ⅜" under the nominal dimensions, when this dimension is 4", and not more than ½" under the nominal dimension when this dimension is 5" or greater.

Only pieces consisting of sound wood free from any form of decay are acceptable.

Factory and Shop Lumber-Grade Standards. Factory and shop lumber is divided into two classes from the standpoint of use, factory plank and shop lumber, each of which has a different set of grades. These grades are based on the percentage of the area of each board or plank that will furnish cuttings of specified sizes and qualities, except in the upper grades of shop lumber of all thicknesses. Factory plank is 1¼" or more in thickness and is used largely for door and sash cuttings.

Shop lumber is used for general cut-up purposes. Shop lumber grades in some woods are available in only 1" stock. Thick stock in these woods for cut-up purposes is bought under factory-plank rules.

Factory and Shop Lumber-Size Standards. Standard lengths of factory and shop lumber are 6' and over in multiples of 1', except the box grade of shop lumber, in which the standard lengths are 4' and over.

Standard widths are 5' and over and are usually shipped in random widths. The thicknesses of factory and shop lumber are shown in Table IV.

TABLE IV. STANDARD THICKNESSES OF FACTORY AND SHOP LUMBER

NOMINAL THICKNESS (INCHES)	FINISHED THICKNESSES S1S OR S2S	NOMINAL THICKNESS (INCHES)	FINISHED THICKNESSES S1S OR S2S
	Inches		*Inches*
1	$2\frac{5}{32}$ or $2\frac{6}{32}$	2¼	2⅛
1¼	$1\frac{5}{32}$	2½	2⅜
1½	$1\frac{13}{32}$	3	2⅝
2	$1\frac{26}{32}$	4	3⅝

IDENTIFICATION OF WOODS

The ability to recognize different kinds of wood can come only from experience. There are, however, a number of factors which will make the recognition of different woods easier. Nearly all woods have characteristics differing from that of others, such as *odor, color, grain, texture, sapwood, defects, working quality,* and *feel.* These characteristics may vary more or less in the same kind of wood. A section of sugar maple wood is shown at the left in Fig. 20. Notice the wavy pattern of the grain; occasionally the grain may be curly or bird's eye.

Fig. 20. Sugar Maple, Pisgah National Forest, North Carolina

Courtesy of Appalachian Hardwood Manufacturers, Inc., Cincinnati, Ohio; United States Forest Service Photo

Color. All woods have their individual color tones which may be a combination of colors and shades. These combinations are described in detail under the heading, *Decorative Features.*

Feel. The sense of touch can be helpful in determining the specie of such woods as mahogany versus Philippine wood, maple versus birch, and fir versus pine. This is true whether the lumber is rough or dressed. The velvety feel of a finished piece of tobasco mahogany or hard maple is pleasing to the touch, but the pieces still have distinct characteristics that help in identifying the wood.

Moisture. Unless scientific tests are made, the *moisture content* of lumber is determined through the senses of smell, feel, sight, weight, or heft, and the springiness of the board. Green lumber has a distinct odor from that of the kiln-dried lumber. Wet lumber feels damp to the touch. The senses of sight and touch can detect the brittle slivers of dry lumber.

Working Qualities of Wood. In selecting wood for a given purpose, the ease with which it may be worked is sometimes a factor, especially when hand tools are to be used. The following classification, Table V, is based on the experience of the Forest Products Laboratory together with the general reputation of the wood.

TABLE V. WORKABILITY OF WOODS WITH HAND TOOLS

SOFTWOODS

Easy to Work	Medium to Work	Difficult to Work
Cedar, incense	Cedar, eastern red	Douglas fir
Cedar, northern white	Cypress, southern	Larch, western
Cedar, Port Orford	Fir, balsam	Pine, southern yellow
Cedar, southern white	Fir, white	
Cedar, western red	Hemlock, eastern	
Pine, northern white	Hemlock, western	
Pine, ponderosa	Pine, lodgepole	
Pine, sugar	Redwood	
Pine, western white	Spruce, eastern	
	Spruce, Sitka	

HARDWOODS

Easy to Work	Medium to Work	Difficult to Work
Alder, red	Birch, paper	Ash, commercial white
Basswood	Cottonwood	Beech
Butternut	Gum, black	Birch
Chestnut	Gum, red	Cherry
Poplar, yellow	Gum, tupelo	Elm
	Magnolia	Hackberry
	Sycamore	Hickory, true and pecan
	Walnut, black	Honey locust
		Locust, black
		Maple
		Oak, commercial red
		Oak, commercial white

Decorative Features. The decorative value of wood depends upon its color, figure, luster, and the way in which it takes fillers, stains, fumes, and transparent finishes.

Because of the combinations of color and the multiplicity of shades found in wood, it is impossible to give detailed descriptions of the colors of the various kinds. The sapwood of all species, however, is light in color, and in some species it is practically white. The white sapwood of certain species, such as maple, makes it preferable to the heartwood for specific uses. In some species, such as hemlock, the true firs, basswood, cottonwood, and beech, there is little or no difference in color between sapwood and heartwood, but in most species the heartwood is

TABLE VI. Color and Figure of Common Kinds of Wood

Species of Wood	Color of Heartwood*	Type of Figure	
		Plain-Sawed Lumber or Rotary-Cut Veneer	Quarter-Sawed Lumber or Quarter-Sliced Veneer
HARDWOODS			
Alder, red	Pale pinkish brown	Faint growth ring	Scattered large flakes, sometimes entirely absent
Ash, black	Moderately dark grayish brown	Conspicuous growth ring; occasional burl	Distinct, not conspicuous growth-ring stripe; occasional burl
Ash, Oregon	Grayish brown, sometimes with reddish tinge	Ditto	Ditto
Ash, white	Ditto	Ditto	Ditto
Aspen	Light brown	Faint growth ring	None
Basswood	Creamy white to creamy brown, sometimes reddish	Ditto	Ditto
Beech	White with reddish tinge to reddish brown	Ditto	Numerous small flakes up to ⅛″ in height
Birch, paper	Light brown	Ditto	None
Birch, sweet	Dark reddish brown	Distinct, not conspicuous growth ring; occasionally wavy	Occasionally wavy
Birch, yellow	Reddish brown	Ditto	Ditto
Butternut	Light chestnut brown with occasional reddish tinge or streaks	Faint growth ring	None
Cherry, black	Light to dark reddish brown	Faint growth ring; occasional burl	Occasional burl
Chestnut	Grayish brown	Conspicuous growth ring	Distinct, not conspicuous growth-ring stripe
Cottonwood	Grayish white to light grayish brown	Faint growth ring	None
Elm, American and rock	Light grayish brown, usually with reddish tinge	Distinct, not conspicuous, with fine wavy pattern within each growth ring	Faint growth-ring stripe
Elm, slippery	Dark brown with shades of red	Conspicuous growth ring, with fine pattern within each growth ring	Distinct, not conspicuous growth-ring stripe
Gum, black and tupelo	Pale to moderately dark brownish gray	Faint growth ring	Distinct, not pronounced ribbon
Gum, red	Reddish brown	Faint growth ring; occasionally irregular darker streaks in "figured" gum	Distinct, not pronounced ribbon; occasionally irregular darker streaks in "figured" gum
Hackberry	Light yellowish or greenish gray	Conspicuous growth ring	Distinct, not conspicuous growth-ring stripe
Hickory	Reddish brown	Distinct, not conspicuous, growth ring	Faint growth-ring stripe
Honey locust	Cherry red	Conspicuous growth ring	Distinct, not conspicuous growth-ring stripe
Locust, black	Golden brown, sometimes with tinge of green	Conspicuous growth rings	Ditto
Magnolia	Light to dark yellowish brown with greenish or purplish tinge	Faint growth ring	None
Maple, black, bigleaf, red, silver, and sugar	Light reddish brown	Faint growth ring; occasionally bird's eye, curly, and wavy	Occasionally curly and wavy
Oak, all species of red oak group	Grayish brown, usually with fleshy tinge	Conspicuous growth ring	Pronounced flake; distinct, not conspicuous growth-ring stripe
Oak, all species of white oak group	Grayish brown, rarely with fleshy tinge	Ditto	Ditto
Poplar, yellow	Light to dark yellowish brown with greenish or purplish tinge	Faint growth ring	None

* The sapwood of all species is light in color or virtually white, unless discolored by fungous or other chemical stains.

TABLE VI. COLOR AND FIGURE OF COMMON KINDS OF WOOD—*Continued*

| SPECIES OF WOOD | COLOR OF HEARTWOOD* | TYPE OF FIGURE | |
		Plain-Sawed Lumber or Rotary-Cut Veneer	Quarter-Sawed Lumber or Quarter-Sliced Veneer
Sugarberry	Light yellowish or greenish gray	Conspicuous growth ring	Distinct, not conspicuous growth-ring stripe
Sycamore	Flesh brown	Faint growth ring	Numerous pronounced flakes up to one-fourth inch in height
Walnut, black	Chocolate brown; occasionally with darker, sometimes purplish streaks	Distinct, not conspicuous, growth ring; occasionally wavy, curly, burl, and other types	Distinct, not conspicuous growth-ring stripe; occasionally wavy, curly, burl, crotch, and other types
SOFTWOODS			
Cedar:			
Alaska	Yellow	Faint growth ring	None
Eastern red	Brick red to deep reddish brown	Occasionally streaks of white sapwood alternating with heartwood	Occasionally streaks of white sapwood alternating with heartwood
Incense	Reddish brown	Faint growth ring	Faint growth-ring stripe
Northern white	Light to dark brown	Ditto	Ditto
Port Orford	Light yellow to pale brown	Ditto	None
Western red	Reddish brown	Distinct, not conspicuous growth ring	Faint growth-ring stripe
White	Light brown with reddish tinge	Ditto	None
Cypress, southern	Light yellowish brown to reddish brown	Conspicuous, irregular growth ring	Distinct, not conspicuous growth-ring stripe
Douglas fir	Orange-red to red; sometimes yellow	Conspicuous growth ring	Ditto
Fir:			
Balsam	Nearly white	Distinct, not conspicuous growth ring	Faint growth-ring stripe
White	Nearly white to pale reddish brown	Conspicuous growth ring	Distinct, not conspicuous growth-ring stripe
Hemlock:			
Eastern	Light reddish brown	Distinct, not conspicuous growth ring	Faint growth-ring stripe
Western	Ditto	Ditto	Ditto
Larch, western	Russet to reddish brown	Conspicuous growth ring	Distinct, not conspicuous growth-ring stripe
Pine:			
Lodgepole	Light reddish brown	Distinct, not conspicuous growth ring; faint "pocked" appearance	None
Northern white	Cream to light reddish brown	Faint growth ring	Ditto
Norway	Orange to reddish brown	Distinct, not conspicuous growth ring	Faint growth-ring stripe
Ponderosa	Ditto	Ditto	Ditto
Southern yellow†	Ditto	Conspicuous growth ring	Distinct, not conspicuous growth-ring stripe
Sugar	Light creamy brown	Faint growth ring	None
Western white	Cream to light reddish brown	Ditto	Ditto
Redwood	Cherry to deep reddish brown	Distinct, not conspicuous growth ring; occasionally wavy and burl	Faint growth-ring stripe; occasionally wavy and burl
Spruce:			
Black, Engelmann, red, white	Nearly white	Faint growth ring	None
Sitka	Light reddish brown	Distinct, not conspicuous growth ring	Faint growth-ring stripe
Tamarack	Russet brown	Conspicuous growth ring	Distinct, not conspicuous growth-ring stripe

† Includes longleaf, loblolly, shortleaf, and slash pine.

darker and fairly uniform in color. A section of white-oak wood is shown at left in Fig. 21. Notice the grain pattern of the wood. Table VI describes in a general way the color of the heartwood and the type of figure found in the more common kinds of woods. Study these tables carefully.

Fig. 21. White Oak, Mount Vernon Estate, Virginia

Courtesy of Appalachian Hardwood Manufacturers, Inc., Cincinnai, Ohio; United States Forest Service Photo

Lumber Abbreviations. A knowledge of abbreviations used in the lumber industry is important to the woodworker as he performs his daily task. Standard lumber abbreviations in common use in contracts and other documents used in the purchase and sale of lumber will be found in a later chapter.

ADHESIVES

While there are a number of adhesives (glues) on the market to-day, the ones most commonly used in woodworking are the animal glues, the synthetic-resin glues, the casein glues, and the vegetable (starch) glues.[3]

---

[3] This section on adhesives is based on material supplied by the Forest Products Laboratory, Madison 5, Wisconsin.

Animal Glues. The term *animal glue* refers broadly to all glues made from the skins, bones, etc., of cattle, goats, sheep, deer, horses, pigs, etc., unless otherwise specified; however, the term usually refers to cattle glue only.

Cattle glues are divided into three main classes: hide glue, sinew glue, and bone glue. Hide glue is the strongest and most reliable of the three. Bone glue, as a rule, is very inferior. Sinew glue is between hide and bone glue in regard to strength and value.

Each class of glue is sold in cake, flake, ground, pearl, shredded, and other forms, but the form of the glue is no reliable indication of quality. The finely divided forms can be dissolved more easily than the cake and flake forms.

The higher grade glues in flake form are usually light in color and nearly transparent. Inferior glues tend to be dark in color and opaque. Color and transparency, however, are not safe indications as to quality, since low-grade glues are sometimes bleached.

Preparing Animal Glue. In preparing animal glue for use, a number of precautions must be observed. The proportion of glue and water must be obtained from the manufacturer, and the glue and the water carefully weighed. Clean cold water should be used, and the mixture thoroughly stirred at once to allow a uniform absorption of water by the dry glue and to prevent the formation of lumps. The mixture should then be allowed to stand until the glue is thoroughly water-soaked and softened. The soaking may take only an hour or two, or it may require overnight soaking, depending upon the size of the glue particles. When the glue has been properly soaked, it is melted over a water bath or in a container where the temperature is never above 150° F. Electric glue heaters, with thermostatic heat control which holds the glue at 150° F., are widely used.

Strict cleanliness of glue pots, apparatus, floors, and tables of the glue room should be observed. Old glue soon becomes foul and affords a breeding place for bacteria, which start decomposition in the glue, exposing each new batch to the danger of becoming contaminated. Glue pots should be washed every day, and only enough glue for a day's run should be mixed at one time. High temperatures and long-continued heating reduce the strength of the glue. The glue pot should be covered as much as possible in order to prevent the formation of scum over the glue surface. Failure to observe these precautions will result in weak joints.

Gluing with Animal Glues. Many factors affect the strength of the joint when animal glues are used. Pressure, length of assembly periods, kind of assembly, temperature of wood, glue and assembly room, amount of spread, grade of glue, and water content all play an important part in gluing practice.

In factory gluing operations, certain factors are generally predetermined by the conditions in the plant. Warm animal glues, as they normally exist in the spreader, are too thin for pressing, and some thickening must occur before pressure is applied. The best consistency for pressing exists when the glue is thick enough to form short, thick strings when touched with the fingers but not thick enough to resist an imprint or a depression readily. Where the pressure must be applied while the glue is very thin, a low pressure, such as 25 to 50 lbs. per sq. in., is best. In using low pressures, the wood surfaces must be smooth and true. If pressure must be applied after the glue has become very thick or has chilled, high pressures of 400 lbs. per sq. in. or more should be used. In no case should the pressure be so great that it crushes the fibers of the wood. In most commercial gluing operations, pressures of 150 to 210 lbs. per sq. in. will give good results.

When the temperature of the room and the wood are around 70° F., the assembly time is from ½ to 1 minute, when the temperature is 80° F., the assembly time is from 3 to 5 minutes, and when the temperature reaches 90° F., the assembly time may be extended to from 10 to 18 minutes. Room temperatures of 70° F. to 80° F. are satisfactory for most work. Where conditions are such that short periods of assembly are required, heated woods, warm rooms, and light glue spreads will give the best results. High-grade glues, which take as much as 2 lbs. of water to 1 lb. of glue, are best under conditions that require short assembly periods.

When gluing single articles in the shop that are not on a production basis, the work must be well planned in advance. All clamps should be adjusted to the proper opening, and blocks should be prepared to prevent marring the work. It is common practice to clamp the pieces together without glue to test all parts for fit, squareness, and proper method of applying the clamps. The clamps must be tightened sufficiently to force the glue into the pores of the wood; chilled glue does not penetrate and makes a poor bond, and such joints come apart when the glue dries and hardens. The surplus glue should be scraped off with a dull chisel after it has set but before it has become hard. The clamps can be removed at the end of 6 hours and the wood worked lightly; longer periods of time insure stronger joints.

Joints made by animal glues lack permanence under moist conditions and are subject to attack by micro-organisms. Joints made with thin, watery glue are weak.

Cold liquid glues made from fish stock—heads, bones, skins—and also some brands of animal glue are on the market today. These glues may be used cold and can be spread without any preparation. Such glues vary widely in strength. Some are so weak as to be suitable for use on paper or cardboard, while others are almost as strong as high-grade dry animal glue. Liquid glues are used to a certain extent in joint work and also for repair work. The use of such glues is limited, because they are expensive and because the better grades are hard to distinguish by the user.

Synthetic Resin Glues. The term *synthetic resin* was first used to describe synthetic chemical compounds that resembled natural resins in their general appearance. At present, the term is applied to a wide group of materials with many uses.

Several of these synthetic resins have found widespread application as woodworking glues. Included in this group is a high temperature or hot press glue (used primarily for making plywood by the hot press technique) and a room-setting temperature glue. The latter group, which includes the plastic-resin types, is used extensively in cabinet-making. The glue comes in powder form ready for mixing with cold water. The glue should be prepared in accordance with the manufacturer's directions, since the various types on the market today all vary somewhat in such factors as storage life, methods of mixing, working life, rate of spread, assembly time, and curing temperatures.

Preparing Synthetic Resin Glues. The majority of resin glues in powder form are mixed with water to prepare the glue for use, following the manufacturer's directions. The glue is ready for use immediately after mixing. Some glues, however, must be mixed by adding alcohol or acetone as the solvent.

Fillers and extenders are often added to the glue. A filler is often furnished by the manufacturer to modify or improve the working properties and performance of the glue to suit the needs of the user. Walnut shell flour is the most commonly used filler, but wheat or rye flour, starch, finely ground resins, Douglas-fir bark, and vegetable and animal proteins have been used.

Extenders are used primarily to reduce the cost of the glue. Ordinary household flour is often used as an extender with certain types of plastic and plastic resin glues. The amount of flour extension varies to some extent with the glue, but it is primarily determined by the type of product being manufactured. The most common range of extension is 25% to 100% (25 to 100 parts of flour to 100 parts of glue).

Gluing with Resin Glues. The working life of room-temperature-setting resin glues depends upon the temperature of the room. Most glues of this type have a working life of 6 to 8 hours at 70° F. At 80° F., this time will be about 3 hours, and at 90° F. 1½ hours. In hot weather it is desirable to keep the glue container in water cold enough to maintain the temperature of the glue around 70° F. Resin glues should not be used in temperatures below 70° F.

Speed is not so important in working with resin-type room-temperature-setting glue, since the glue does not set for 10 or 15 minutes when the members are exposed to the air (open assembly). When the surfaces are in contact (closed assembly), this time may be increased to 20 or 30 minutes.

Pressure must be applied to bring the members into close contact and to hold the members in this position until the glue has set. The minimum pressure time is 4 hours on straight members and 5 hours or longer on curved members. Thin members can be successfully glued with low pressure, such as that supplied by weights. Thicker members require greater pressure, such as that supplied by clamps and presses. In general, pressures lower than those used with animal glues can be successfully used with resin-type glues.

The surplus glue should be wiped off with a clean cloth moistened in hot water before the glue sets. The glue does not stain the wood. The joints made by some types of synthetic resin glues are completely waterproof and will withstand continuous outdoor exposure. The joints are strong and require only moderate pressures.

Casein Glues. The principal ingredient of casein glue is casein. Casein is the curd of sour milk which, when washed and dried, becomes commercial casein. Other ingredients of casein glue are water, hydrated lime, and sodium hydroxide.

Preparing Casein Glues. There are a number of prepared casein glues on the market complete in powder form. The glue is prepared by mixing with cold water following the manufacturer's directions. The powder is always sifted into the water. When specific directions are not available, trial batches of glue with different glue-water ratios may be used. Most prepared casein glues mix well in the ratio of 2 parts of water to 1 part of dry glue (by weight). Ordinarily, the entire amount of water can be weighed in the mixer and the weighed glue powder added gradually to the water with continuous stirring. After all the powder has been added, the stirring is continued until the mixture becomes smooth and free from lumps, or thickens into a stiff, doughlike mass. If the glue does not thicken but mixes into a smooth liquid, free from lumps in a few minutes, it is ready for use. (Large batches require longer periods of stirring.) If the mixture stiffens to a stiff mass, the mixing should be stopped and the mixture allowed to stand for 20 or 30 minutes. At the end of this time, the mixture will have thinned down to the proper working consistency and is ready for use after being stirred for about one minute. Water should not be added to the mixture when it thickens, or the glue, when finally ready for use, will be too thin. The working mixture should have the consistency of cream.

Gluing with Casein Glues. One of the chief advantages of gluing with casein glue is that it can be used on cold wood and in temperatures below 70° F. The glue is satisfactory for all types of cabinet work, but it does not make a completely waterproof joint that will stand up under prolonged periods of dampness. The joints, however, are waterproof for short periods. Because of the strong alkaline in the glue, the glue stains oak, maple, and some other species of wood. The stain can be removed by sponging the affected areas with a solution of 1 oz. of oxalic acid to about 12 ozs. of water. If this is not entirely effective, it may help to sponge the spot first with a solution of 1 oz. of sodium sulphite in 12 ozs. of water and then, while the wood is still moist, with the oxalic-acid solution. There is a type of stainless casein glue, but it is not waterproof.

The assembly time in working with casein glues may be as long as 15 or 20 minutes. The setting of casein glue involves a chemical reaction that is hastened by an increase in temperature. In hot weather, therefore, casein glue will have a shorter working life than in cold weather.

Casein glue should be mixed fresh at least once each day. Casein glues set quickly and produce strong joints that can be machined within a few hours. This practice is not desirable, however. *The best practice is to allow the glue joint to season until the moisture at the glue line has dried out or distributed itself uniformly throughout the wood. Failure to do this often results in sunken joints and a tendency of the wood to change dimensions or shape after the machining.*

The pressures used with casein glues are the same as those used with the animal glues. The surplus glue should be wiped from the joints with a clean, damp rag.

Vegetable Glues. Vegetable glues are used mainly in woodworking for making plywood and other veneered products for interior use. The glue is prepared by the user by heating the vegetable-starch powder with water and then cooling the mixture to room temperature before use. Vegetable glues are room-temperature-setting and develop their strength by loss of water. The joints are strong but have little resistance to moisture and water.

A type of vegetable glue made by grinding the wood of the Cassava plant (a class of woody shrubs) into a fine powder is employed in certain types of production work using mechanical spreaders.

Vegetable glues are not generally used in ordinary cabinet work.

In general, the strength of a glue joint is not so much dependent upon the kind of glue used as it is upon the conditions under which the joint is made. Edge-to-edge joints made with animal, resin, or casein glue under proper conditions produce joints that are stronger than the wood itself.

A number of synthetic resin glues have been developed for bonding wood and wood products to metal and other materials. The cabinetmaker is often called upon to use these adhesives in many types of constructions.

VENEERS

Veneers[4] are thin sheets of wood usually cut from rare and costly logs. The sheets of veneer are glued to more common woods to increase the strength and add to the appearance. When several sheets of veneer or other woods are glued together so that the adjacent grain runs at right angles, the wood is called *plywood*.

Advantages of Veneering. Veneer manufacturers discovered that they were unable to use in solid form many of the most beautiful woods. Burls, crotches, and stumpwood (Fig. 22), which could be so advantageously employed in matched designs, would crack and break if they were not applied to a more substantial base. Rare woods often were not available in large quantities, or, if they were, might be too delicate for solid construction. New adhesive products applied to an old principle, i.e., strength of wood laminations, have opened new frontiers in the veneering field. By using 3, 5, 7, or some other odd number, of plies, each at right angles to the adjacent ply, as a core, a balanced construction results that gives maximum strength and rigidity with minimum weight.

---

[4] Based on material from *Veneers, a Modern Art 3,500 Years Old.* Courtesy The Veneer Association, Chicago, Illinois.

Beauty, too, has kept pace with utility. Skilled designers have combined their talents with those of the production experts. Today veneer is used for furniture, pianos, radios, aircraft, watercraft, railway streamliners, trailers, store equipment, elevator cabs, and air conditioning units.

If logs are sufficiently pliable, they may be cut cold. Often, however, they must be conditioned in large vats, with steam or hot water,

Fig. 22. Walnut Stumpwood
Courtesy of American Walnut Manufacturers Association, Chicago, Ill.

or both. When they are moist and softened, they are removed, one by one, stripped of their bark, and brought to the rotary lathe. Here a single log is fastened and revolved like a great spindle against a stationary knife, which peels off a long, continuous sheet of veneer. This sheet, depending upon the grade required, is clipped at convenient widths or as undesirable defects appear.

An expert decides which of the three methods, namely, slicing, sawing, or rotary cutting, will produce the best results from each particular log. A number of factors enter into his decision, including size and shape of the log, amount of wavy grain or coloring matter in the wood, type of figure desired in the finished veneers, texture of the wood, and thickness required.

Logs that are to be sliced are split open by a saw, stripped of their bark, and placed in large vats for conditioning. When sufficiently soft and pliable, they are further trimmed and taken to the cutting machine. Here a single *flitch* (an entire log or portion of a log prepared for veneer; the strips of veneer are sometimes referred to by the same name) is fixed horizontally in a heavy movable frame. The frame brings the flitch down against the cutting edge of a long stationary knife which shaves off veneers of the desired thickness, anywhere from $\frac{1}{100}''$ to $\frac{1}{28}''$, the standard American thickness for face veneers being $\frac{1}{28}''$. (Commercial veneers are generally $\frac{1}{20}''$ and thicker, although they may be thinner for certain types of work.)

Method of Cutting Veneers. Sliced veneers may be either *flat-cut* or *quarter-sliced*. Flat-cut veneers are produced by cutting straight through the heart of a half section of a log (Fig. 23). This gives a combination of straight grain and heart figure.

Quarter-sliced veneers are obtained by placing a smaller section of a log in the machine in such a way that the knife will cut through at right angles to the annual rings (Fig. 24). This produces a striped effect.

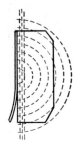

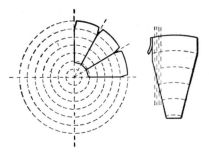

Fig. 23. Flat Cut Veneers Are Sliced through the Heart of a Half Section of Log

Fig. 24. Quartered Veneers Are Sliced from Quartered Flitches. Cut at Right Angles to Annual Rings

Face veneers are generally sliced, unless for some particular reason another method of manufacture is chosen. Slicers vary in size. Some of them are capable of cutting veneer logs 16' in length with each sheet of veneer uniform in thickness, for these machines cut with remarkable accuracy and precision.

Sawed veneers are usually produced with a band or circular segment saw that goes through the log from end to end. This is the oldest method of manufacturing veneers. It is used mainly when veneers are to be comparatively thick or the logs are unusually hard or otherwise difficult to manufacture properly when cut with the knife. Sawing produces very much the same figure as slicing.

A good deal of face veneer is manufactured on the rotary lathe, exactly like commercial veneers. This method is most economical and is satisfactory when the wood does not have too much contrasting coloring matter, or when a more prominent or *wild* figure is desired. Some mills have an electric saw with which they groove the log before it is mounted in the lathe. This eliminates tearing or clipping the veneer as it unrolls. Consecutive sheets are more uniform in size and are easier to match well.

Half round and *back cut* are variations of rotary cutting. The same lathe is used, but the flitch is placed *off center,* so that as it rotates it comes into contact only as the projecting portion reaches the knife. The logs are usually halved first. Burls, stumpwood, and crotches are frequently cut half-round, as are also some types of longwood.

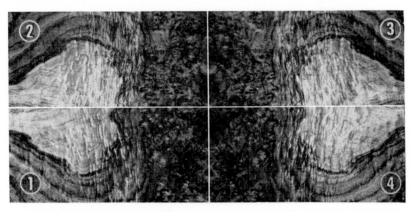

Fig. 25. Combination Book and End Match for Veneers. (1), (2), (3), and (4) Are Book Matches; (1) and (4), and (2) and (3) Are End Matches
Courtesy of The Veneer Association, Chicago, Ill.

Matching Veneers. There is one important final step before the face veneers are finally fabricated into plywood. The art of matching veneers has been developed to such a high degree of perfection that the well-informed designer may obtain almost any desired effect and utilize the full value of every wood. Because face veneers are cut thin, adjacent sheets contain similar grain and figure markings. By utilizing this duplication of pattern, large sheets may be developed (Fig. 25) by following a definite pattern of matching.

After the face veneers that have been selected by the furniture manufacturer are received from the veneer mill, they are carefully redried and kept in the same order as when they were cut. The importance of this step is evident when the matcher begins his work. Depending upon the design, veneers are matched in one of several ways:

1. *Book Match:* Two adjacent sheets of veneer are opened up like a book and then taped together side to side.

2. *End Match:* Similar to book match except that the ends, instead of the sides, of the two sheets of veneer are used as a hinge, and they are taped end to end.

3. *Miscellaneous:* Includes slide match, diamond match, reverse diamond, herringbone, and other effects conceived by the designer (Fig. 26).

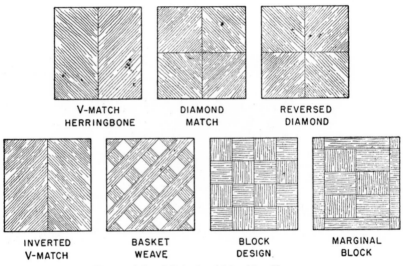

V-MATCH HERRINGBONE	**DIAMOND MATCH**	**REVERSED DIAMOND**
INVERTED V-MATCH	**BASKET WEAVE**	**BLOCK DESIGN**	**MARGINAL BLOCK**

Fig. 26. Other Methods of Matching Veneers

Veneer Woods. The veneers, shown in Table VII, known as *face veneers*, are those used for the exposed surfaces of furniture, fixtures, and architectural panels.

PLYWOOD

Construction of Plywood. *Plywood* is a term generally used to designate glued wood panels that are made up of 2 or more thin layers, with the grain of adjacent layers usually at right angles to each other. Most plywood contains an odd number of layers, 3, 5, 7, or more (Fig. 27).

The Core. The foundation for all plywood is the *core* or center ply. It may be made of lumber or of veneer. The best lumber cores are multiple pieces; that is, they are made up of narrow strips of wood.

TABLE VII. VENEER WOODS*

Commercial Name	Origin	Color Range	Types of Figures Available
Amaranth	The Guianas	Purple	Generally straight grained and plain; occasionally wavy or roey
Ash, Amer.	U.S.A.	White to light brown	Qtd. usually fiddleback if figured; growth rings are pronounced in all types of veneer; a few crotches; some burls
Ash, Jap. (Tamo)	Japan, Korea	White to light brown	Curly, fiddle, mottle, and "peanut"; most veneers cut in U.S. are highly figured
Aspen	U.S.A.	Light straw	Plain to heavy cross-fire; has a velvety appearance; a few crotches
Avodire Longwood	Africa	Milky white to cream	Plain stripe, broken stripe, roll or rope
Crotch	Africa	Milky white to cream	Swirl or feather
Ayous	Africa	Pale straw to yellow	Usually ribbon stripe
Birch	North America	White to light reddish brown	Wavy or curly grained; flat cut, generally figured; rotary, plain; a few burls
Bosse	Africa	Pinkish to light reddish brown	Well figured; roey or curly
Bubinga	Africa	Pale to deep flesh red, with thin dark lines	Plain to well figured; straight stripe, broken stripe, mottle; also shell cut; figure stands out better when finished
Butternut	U.S.A.	Very pale gray-brown	Usually plain; appearance is similar to that of American walnut, except for color
Cedar, Aromatic Red	U.S.A.	Heart: red to pink Sap: cream	Knotty
Cherry (Black)	U.S.A.	Light to dark reddish brown	Slight figure; burl; a few crotches
Ebony, Macassar	Dutch East Indies	Rich, black-brown with medium tan, orange or yellow markings	Contrasting stripes due to pigment coloring

* This table courtesy of the Veneer Association, Chicago, Illinois.

TABLE VII. VENEER WOODS—*Continued*

Commercial Name	Origin	Color Range	Types of Figures Available
Elm, Carp. (Burl)	Europe	Light reddish brown	Varies from small compact figure to wild, grainy figure
Faux Satine (Cypress Cr.)	U.S.A.	Amber to golden	Small, feather-crotch figure
Gaboon (Okoumé)	Africa	Golden to pinkish tan	Plain, wavy, curly, or rope figure; crotch
Gum, Red	U.S.A.	Heart: brown tinged with pink Sap: grayish white	Plain; medium to highly figured with chocolate markings
Harewood Eng. Gray Eng. White	England	Eng. Gray: silver gray, turns to tannish gray Eng. White: cream to white	Plain, curly, fiddleback, finger-roll, or heavy cross-fire
Holly	U.S.A.	White	Plain
Kelobra	Mexico & Central America	Brown, sometimes shaded with reddish tan	Plain striped, large pores; crotch
Koa	Hawaii	Golden brown to red-brown, shaded	Plain, curly, fiddleback; some stumpwood
Lacewood	Queensland, Aus.	Pink to light, leather brown	Small to large "flake"
Lauan (Red and White)	Philippines	Whitish to dark red-brown	Plain, ribbon stripe
Laurel, E.I.	India	Dark brown, with darker streaks	Plain, ripple stripe
Madrone (Burl)	California & Oregon	Light reddish brown	Clean burls and swirls, sometimes spotted with deep red
Mahogany African	Africa	Pale salmon when first cut; darkens with age	Plain stripe, narrow or broad broken stripe, large and small mottle, fiddleback, blister and plum-pudding, rope, and combinations of these figures
Cen. & South America	Cen. & So. Amer.	Light sherry when first cut; darkens with age	Predominantly plain stripe; occasionally same figures as available in African Mahogany

TABLE VII. VENEER WOODS—*Continued*

Commercial Name	Origin	Color Range	Types of Figures Available
Mahogany African Cuban & Santo Dom.	W. Indies	Yellowish white when first cut; darkens to light golden brown, or sometimes a deep, rich, brown-red	Same figures as available in African Mahogany; frequently two or more types of figures are combined
Faux Swirls	. . . .	Light to dark reddish brown	Swirl effect
Crotches & Swirls	. . . .	Light to dark reddish brown	Moon and feather crotch; plain and figured swirl
Maple	No. Amer.	White to light pinkish brown	Plain, curly, bird's-eye, blister, fiddleback; burls Quilted
Myrtle Cluster Burl	California & Oregon	Cream to tan, sometimes with darker burl	Burl or cluster; cluster is mixture of plain wood, cream to light tan, and burl, which varies from tan to dark brown or black
Narra	Philippines	Pale yellow to salmon, to deep red	Stripe, broken stripe, roey, mottle, etc.
New Guinea Wood	Papau, New Britain, Oceania	Brown to light gray with definitive black lines	Plain to highly figured; plain stripe, figured striped, mottled
Oak, Native plain	U.S.A.	Light brown to reddish brown	Figure formed by prominent medullary rays; coarse grain
Qtd.	U.S.A.	Light brown to reddish brown	"Rift sawn," pin stripe, flake (Native Oak also available in Burls)
Oak, Eng. Brown	England	Nut brown to deep brown	Plain or streaked, with a flake figure; burls (incl. Tortoise Shell)
"Oak," Tas. (Yuba)	Australia	Tan	Fiddleback
Oriental wood	Australia	Brown, with lavender gray or greenish gray to salmon cast	Stripe, strong stripe, mottle, fiddleback, roll
Padouk, Afr. Burma Vermilion	Africa Burma Andamans	Golden red to deep crimson	Wide parallel stripe, narrow broken stripe, mottle, finger-roll, fiddleback, curl
Paldao	Philippines	Variable; tan background with brown to black streaks	Stripe and mottle; figure caused by concentric bands; a few crotches

TABLE VII. VENEER WOODS—*Continued*

Commercial Name	Origin	Color Range	Types of Figures Available
Poplar	U.S.A.	White to yellow	No definite figure; a little curly; some blister; some burls
Prima Vera	Cen. Amer. & Mex.	Cream	Broken stripe, mottle, fine feather grain; crotch and swirl
Redwood Burl	California	Reddish brown	True Burl
Rosewood, Brazilian	So. Amer.	Red to brown, streaked with black lines	Wide range of figures caused by pigment coloring; includes "bar" figure; very few crotches
Rosewood, E.I.	India, Ceylon	Variable—purple to straw, striped	Pin and ribbon stripe; a few feather crotches
Sapeli	Africa	Med. to dark brown	Pronounced straight, broken, or ribbon stripe; occasionally a slight cross figure
Satinwood	Ceylon, West Indies	Cream to rich golden yellow	Nearly all more or less figured; stripe, cross-fire, roey, wavy, mottled
Sycamore (Native)	U.S.A.	Tan to pinkish brown	Prominent flake figure; ribbon stripe
Teak	Burma, India	Golden brown, darkening with age	Plain, ripple, mottle; sometimes nicely figured
Thuya (Burl)	Algeria	Deep reddish brown	Figure consists of small, distinctive "eyes"
Tigerwood	Africa	Golden brown	Ribbon stripe; blister; "snail" figure; crotch
Walnut, Amer. Plain Longwood	U.S.A.	Soft gray-brown, sometimes shaded with darker brown	Plain stripe, pencil stripe; typical "flat cut" or rotary figure, without cross-fire
Figured Longwood	U.S.A.	Soft gray-brown, sometimes shaded with darker brown	Mottle, fiddleback, figured striped, rope figure
Stumpwood	U.S.A.	Soft gray-brown, sometimes shaded with darker brown	Plain and figured
Crotches & Swirls	U.S.A.	Soft gray-brown, sometimes shaded with darker brown	Swirl or feather crotch; plain or figured swirls

Commercial Name	Origin	Color Range	Types of Figures Available
Burls	U.S.A.	Soft gray-brown, sometimes shaded with darkerb rown	Burl
Walnut, Claro	California	Light to rich brown, streaked	Characteristic wide black banding; plain, mottle, wavy; crotches
Walnut, Fr., Eng. & Circassian	Europe	Nut brown to dark brown	Various streaked and swirly effects; stumpwood; a few crotches; some burls
Zebrawood	Africa	Creamy yellow, with prominent dark brown or black stripes	Narrow stripes, from $\frac{1}{4}''$ to $\frac{1}{2}''$ apart; some shell cut

Crossbands. Panels of 5, 7, and more plies are made in a similar manner. The extra plies are known as *crossbands*. A 5-ply panel consists of the back, a crossband with the grain running at right angles to that of the back, a core, another crossband parallel to the first, and the face parallel to the back and core.

Face and Back. In constructing 3-ply panels, the *face* and *back* are prepared first. Preferably, they are of identical species, with similar grain. Since they are to be glued to the core, which will support and strengthen them, the face and back need not necessarily be of a very strong wood. Thus, it is possible to select the veneers for beauty rather than strength.

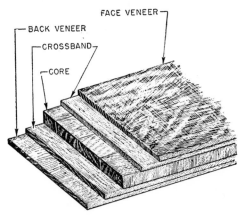

FACE VENEER

BACK VENEER

CROSSBAND

CORE

Fig. 27. Plywood Construction, Showing Core, Cross Bandings, Face, and Back, with Grains of Alternate Plies at Right Angles

Advantages of Plywood. The balanced construction of plywood offers the utmost in strength, lightness, and practicability for the following reasons:

a) Weight for weight, plywood is stronger than steel. Each layer strengthens the next.

b) Plywood is comparatively light in weight.

c) Screws or nails can be driven close to the edge without danger of splitting the plywood.

d) Plywood minimizes the tendency of wood to buckle or twist due to changes in moisture content.

e) Plywood panels can be built to any size, whereas a board must always be less than the width of the tree.

f) Plywood will not shrink or swell.

In plywoods, the strength of sturdy, though not attractive, woods is combined with the beauty of fine cabinet woods by veneering. Since veneers are cut thin enough to insure almost identical patterns on consecutive cuts, they are readily matched to form large attractive sheets.

Curved effects, as found on radios, grand pianos, showcases, and the round corners of modern furniture are made possible through the use of plywoods and veneers which can readily be bent.

MODIFIED WOODS

In recent years considerable research has been done in modifying the properties of wood by various chemical and compression treatments. Some of these treatments involve permeating the wood with synthetic resin-forming chemicals, others take advantage of the plastic properties of *lignin* (lignin is the cementing material that binds the cells of wood together).

Resin-treated woods that are not compressed (*impreg*) and compressed resin-treated wood (*compreg*) have been used to some degree in the making of furniture and wood products. Impreg has been made almost exclusively from veneers.

Compreg is resin-treated wood that is compressed while the resin is being formed within its structure. Untreated compressed wood is preferably called *dense wood* when made from solid wood or *superpressed plywood* when made from veneer.

An important advantage of compreg is that it can be made from a great variety of woods, including such normally inferior species as cottonwood. A high degree of polish can be imparted to any cut surface of compreg by merely sanding the surface with fine sandpaper and then buffing it. This potential polish exists throughout the structure, making it an ideal surface for tables, desks, etc., since all that is necessary to remove marks is to sand and buff the surface. The finish is highly resistant to solvents, such as alcohol and acetone, which destroy most wood finishes.

Compreg is more difficult to work than normal wood and is more brittle. Special saws should be used, such as those for cutting brass or plastics. Machine speeds should, in general, be lower than for cutting normal wood.[5]

REVIEW QUESTIONS

1. Name 6 principal pine trees.
2. Name 10 principal hardwood trees.
3. What is an annual ring?
4. What is the difference between sapwood and heartwood?
5. What determines whether a board is quarter-sawed or plain-sawed?
6. Which is stronger, generally speaking, close-grained woods or open-grained woods?
7. Describe the term "seasoning."
8. When is lumber said to be wet?
9. How is lumber air dried?
10. How is lumber kiln dried?
11. What are the 2 main factors to be considered when grading lumber?
12. What is a pitch pocket?
13. Give 3 main classifications into which softwood lumber is graded.
14. Name 6 factors which may be considered when identifying a piece of lumber.
15. What are some of the advantages of using veneers?
16. Name 3 methods of cutting veneer.
17. Name 2 kinds of sliced veneers.
18. What is meant by the term "matching veneer"?
19. What is plywood?
20. Give 4 advantages of plywood construction.

---

[5] Information furnished by Forest Products Laboratory.

Standards of Construction, Sizes, and Design

1. What is "modular construction"?
2. Why is it important to use standardized items of millwork?
3. What quality glass is used for glazing purposes?
4. What is "obscure" sheet glass?
5. How are nail sizes determined?

INTRODUCTION TO CHAPTER XII

Modern communication and transportation have expanded the limits of markets for manufactured articles. In order to eliminate confusion as to standards of construction, sizes, and design, a spontaneous movement is under way to standardize universally used articles.

The National Association of Manufacturers is working on and has developed, in many cases, standards acceptable to the industry on a national scale. This movement is of great importance to the economy of the nation and in furtherance of improved standards of living. Widely used items can be manufactured in large quantities for wide distribution at a considerable saving in cost.

The information provided in this chapter will acquaint the worker with the various articles that can be purchased as standard items. Such information is valuable in the planning and designing encountered by the cabinetmaker.

MODULAR CONSTRUCTION

Modular construction in the building industry, of which the wood-working industry is a part, means that sections, parts, or units of a building are constructed to conform to a specific unit of measure or multiple thereof. The universally accepted unit (established for this purpose) is a 4″ module (Fig. 1). This does not mean that it is possible to conform to that module in every respect but that, where possible, this unit of measure is used to standardize parts, sections, or units where the principles of modular construction and design can be applied. The following information is taken from the *American Lumberman*.

"In actual construction, the economies in the use of the 4-inch module arise from the fact that products designed on the modular basis can be combined into a finished structure with a minimum amount of costly cutting and fitting on the job, thus permitting savings in both materials and labor. When the exterior wall of a house is modularly designed, and when the modular brick and modular windows are specified, window openings will be exactly right and windows will fit into the wall as though custom made for the openings. There will be little or no trimming and no gaps to be filled." See Fig. 2.

Subdivisions of this 4″ modular are in turn standardized as far as possible but vary with the need of the product. Much remains to be accomplished in this effort to standardize woodwork. Manufacturers have established modules applicable to patented products to facilitate interchangeability of various parts in an effort to conform to the over-all requirement of the 4″ module.

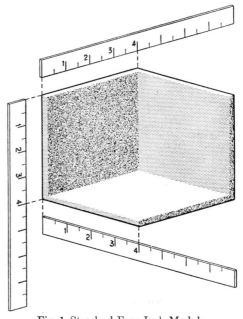

Fig. 1. Standard Four-Inch Module

A module is a unit measurement; it may be any number of inches or feet, and may be applied to width, depth, and height.

STANDARD CONSTRUCTION

Many items manufactured by the woodworking industry are made to order or to "detail" to suit the requirements of a customer. The customer may be an individual requiring a cabinet designed to fit an especially prepared nook in his new home, or he might be the owner of a large department store who has ordered store fixtures which have been designed and constructed to conform to the architectural requirements of the interior of the store.

Woodwork manufacturers have, by common usage, established definite standards of construction and design. These standards include definite dimensions for items which are manufactured as stock to be available on order by large or small manufacturers and contractors.

The standards include certain designs which are the same in practically all states.

Knowledge of the existence of these standards is quite important to the learner and apprentice. Catalogs are available for many types of cabinet work, which will enable him to know *in advance* the design and dimensions of items of woodwork.

Fig. 2. Unco-ordinated and Co-ordinated Window Frame and Masonry

Unco-ordinated window and masonry require cutting of bricks (left). Co-ordinated window and masonry eliminate cutting and save cost (right).

The use of standards in terms of design, construction, sizes, and dimensions enables a cabinetmaker to move from one locality to another and immediately carry on his daily work in the new location with little difficulty of adjustment as far as technical problems are concerned.

The setting up and establishing of standards has been of inestimable value to architects everywhere. Now an architect can design a building with full assurance that numerous building items are easily procurable in standard shapes and sizes. The architect has contributed to standards of design based largely on the principle of modular construction applied to proportioning designs for pleasing effects.

STANDARD MATERIALS

Many materials, such as lumber, plywood, etc., which the woodworker uses, are standardized to facilitate their purchase or sale and to meet requirements of the trade.

Local and national associations of firms manufacturing these materials are formed and set up standards of sizes, grades, and quality enabling the purchaser to know from the specifications what kind of merchandise he will receive when he places an order.

Lumber produced in any one section of the country is adaptable, with limitations, to the various millwork items manufactured in any area, and the products are suited for use over the whole of the United States.

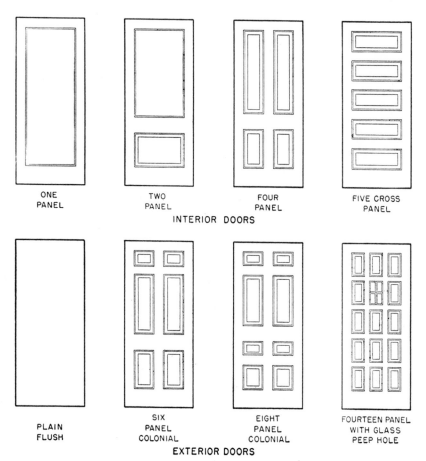

Fig. 3. Door Designs

STANDARDIZED MILLWORK

Individual factories, large factories with branches, local groups, and National Associations of Millwork Manufacturers have come to accept certain standards of sizes, quality, and design in millwork. These standards were based originally on common shop practices, then carried by journeymen workers from shop to shop and from district to district.

Standards of *measure* are, to some degree, based on the necessity of conforming cabinet construction to established sizes of lumber.

Standardized items of millwork are easily obtainable, making it possible to construct a building without resorting to specially ordered woodwork. It must be emphasized that these stock items cannot be utilized unless the planner carefully works out the building dimensions so that the standardized items will fit in place when delivered to the job.

Doors. Standard door *sizes* are now obtainable universally. The *designs* which one will find difficulty in improving have been handed down from the old masters. Methods of construction have changed somewhat as a result of modern equipment and glues. The shape or design of interior and exterior doors is shown in Fig. 3. The construction is either mortise and tenon or dowel. The common sizes are shown in Table I; thickness in 1⅜″ or 1¾″ are available.

TABLE I. AVAILABLE DOOR SIZES

Popular Sizes				
1-6 x 6 -6	2-0 x 6-8	2-4 x 6-8	2-6 x 6-8	2-8 x 6-8
1-6 x 6 -8	2-0 x 7-0	2-4 x 7-0	2-6 x 7-0	2-8 x 7-0
2-0 x 6 -0	2-4 x 6-0	2-6 x 6-0	2-8 x 6-0	3-0 x 6-8
2-0 x 6 -6	2-4 x 6-6	2-6 x 6-6	2-8 x 6-6	3-0 x 7-0

Windows and Sash. Standards are set up for stock sizes of windows, the thickness and width of the wood frame, number and shape of lights, size of the rabbet which holds the glass, and the kind of joints to use to hold the frame together. These standards will vary in some parts of the country but are generally consistent in any given community or district.

The *shape* or *design*, Western Standards, is shown in Fig. 4, and the National Door Manufacturers' Association Standards are shown in Fig. 5. The *construction* is mortise and tenon or dowel. The

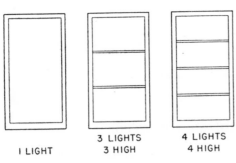

I LIGHT   3 LIGHTS   4 LIGHTS
           3 HIGH   4 HIGH

Fig. 4. Western Standards for Casement Sash

sizes, Western Standards, are shown in Table II and the Eastern Standards in Table III. The thicknesses are 1⅜″ or 1¾″.

TABLE II. WESTERN STANDARDS—WINDOW SIZES

Stock Window Sizes			Stock Sash Sizes			Stock Sizes in Pairs of Casements		
1-6 x 2-0	1-6 x 3-6	1-6 x 4-6	1-0 x 1-6	3-0 x 2-0	1-6 x 4-0			
2-0 x 2-0	2-0 x 3-6	2-0 x 4-6	1-6 x 1-6	3-6 x 2-0	2-0 x 4-0	2-6 x 2-0	2-6 x 3-6	2-6 x 4-6
2-6 x 2-0	2-6 x 3-6	2-6 x 4-6	2-0 x 1-6	4-0 x 2-0	2-6 x 4-0	3-0 x 2-0	3-0 x 3-6	3-0 x 4-6
3-0 x 2-0	3-0 x 3-6	3-0 x 4-6	2-6 x 1-6	1-0 x 3-0	3-0 x 4-0	3-6 x 2-0	3-6 x 3-6	3-6 x 4-6
1-6 x 2-6	3-6 x 3-6	3-6 x 4-6	3-0 x 1-6	1-6 x 3-0	3-6 x 4-0	4-0 x 2-0	4-0 x 3-6	4-0 x 4-6
2-0 x 2-6	4-0 x 3-6	4-0 x 4-6	3-6 x 1-6	2-0 x 3-0	4-0 x 4-0	2-6 x 2-6	2-6 x 4-0	2-6 x 5-0
2-6 x 2-6	1-6 x 4-0	1-6 x 5-0	4-0 x 1-6	2-6 x 3-0	1-6 x 4-6	3-0 x 2-6	3-0 x 4-0	3-0 x 5-0
			1-0 x 2-0	3-0 x 3-0	2-0 x 4-6	3-6 x 2-6	3-6 x 4-0	3-6 x 5-0

TABLE III. EASTERN STANDARDS—WINDOW SIZES

Popular Sizes

1-8 x 3- 2	2-0 x 6- 6	2-4 x 6- 6½
1-8 x 3-10	2-4 x 3-10	2-8 x 3-10
1-8 x 4- 6	2-4 x 4- 6	2-8 x 4- 6
2-0 x 3- 6	2-4 x 4-10	2-8 x 4-10
2-0 x 3-10	2-4 x 5- 2	2-8 x 5- 2
2-0 x 4- 6	2-4 x 5- 6	2-8 x 5- 6
2-0 x 4-10	2-4 x 5- 6½	2-8 x 5-10
2-0 x 5- 2	2-4 x 5-10	2-8 x 6- 6
2-0 x 5-10	2-4 x 6- 6	2-8 x 6- 6½

Frames.   Opening sizes of door and window frames are based on stock sizes of sash and doors. Typical construction is established to cope with the elements, to meet the requirements of building construction, and is adapted to the materials from which the building is constructed.

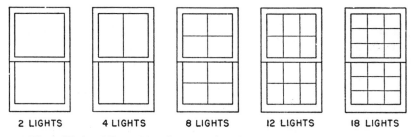

2 LIGHTS   4 LIGHTS   8 LIGHTS   12 LIGHTS   18 LIGHTS

Fig. 5. National Door Manufacturers Association Standards for Windows

The *shape* or *design* is based on the shape or design of the sash or door. A frame will, therefore, be a standard size and shape if the sash or door is standard. Otherwise, the frame will be nonstandard and will require special milling.

The *sizes* are the same as the door and sash sizes shown in Tables I and II.

Interior and Exterior Trim. Molding of both old and modern designs, used for casing openings, for baseboard, for picture moldings and other ornamentation purposes, are available in all modern mills.

Exterior trim includes such items as cornice, belt course, porch columns, etc. These items change with the style and construction of the building, but certain designs of moldings and basic construction needs are typical and stock items are available which can be adapted to almost any need.

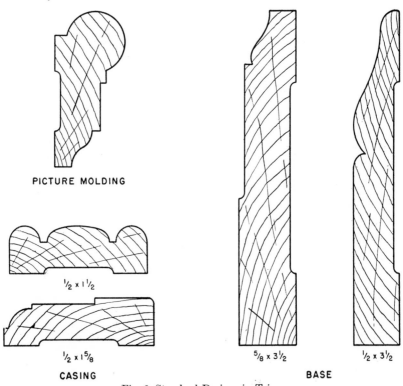

PICTURE MOLDING

$\frac{1}{2}$ x 1 $\frac{1}{2}$

$\frac{1}{2}$ x 1 $\frac{5}{8}$

CASING

$\frac{5}{8}$ x 3 $\frac{1}{2}$

$\frac{1}{2}$ x 3 $\frac{1}{2}$

BASE

Fig. 6. Standard Designs in Trim

The shape and design of various interior or exterior trim items is basically the same throughout the United States. The shapes are always some variation of a geometric curve. A few standard trim items are shown in Fig. 6.

The sizes of the various trim items naturally vary, but each item is usually standardized on the basis of the nominal rough sizes of the lumber available.

Cabinet Work. A catalog of standardized cabinets and mantels is a "must" for all architects, as the dimensions of certain parts of the building are adjusted to conform to a standard piece of millwork which is to be fitted into this part of the building. Fireplaces, for instance, are planned so that the over-all measurements will conform to a selected standard size mantel shelf.

The term *built-in cabinets* is generally applied to cabinets required in the four or five-room residence. They can be classified into groups such as kitchen cabinets, linen closets, broom closets, bookcases, mantel shelves, medicine cabinets, soap cabinets, etc. Many factories specialize in these items.

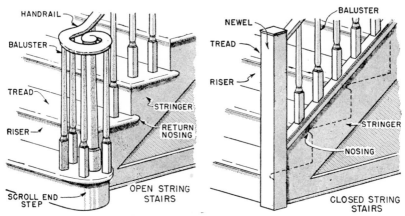

Fig. 7. Stairway Construction

Paneling. A large surface of wood enclosed in a narrow wooden frame is called a panel. Paneling refers to one or more such sections as may be found in walls, ceilings, etc. Paneling does not conform to a standard item which a mill can carry in stock. However, the *design* of a piece of paneling can be selected from a book of designs. Likewise, the methods of construction are usually stated. Hence, an owner or an architect, during the planning stages of a building, can determine how the panel is to be constructed.

Stairs. The dimensions of a stairway cannot be determined until the building is actually constructed, as this millwork item must be built to fit *exactly* into the dimensions of the space allowed for it. However, there are established standards of stairway construction and design which are utilized on stairways of high quality.

The shape of the stairway, the curve of the handrail, the number of balusters to be used, the shape of these balusters, the shape and design of the newel posts (Fig. 7)—all of these construction details can be determined in advance because standards for stairway construction have been established by the cabinetmaking industry.

Store Fixtures.   Store fixtures can be roughly divided into two groups: (1) those that are movable, such as benches, counters, and showcases (Fig. 8); and (2) those that fit into the wall spaces provided, known as wall cases.

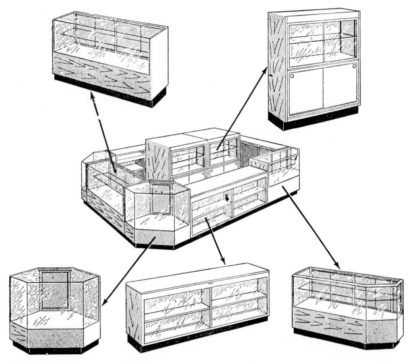

Fig. 8. Group of Movable Display Fixtures

Movable cases are constructed as a stock item by showcase manufacturers. The standardization is divided into the types of cases, such as drug, food, meat, drygoods, etc. It should be obvious that each of these types of showcases must be designed to fit the requirements of the merchandise which is to be displayed. Modern meat display cases require lighting and refrigeration; a drygoods case needs lighting only. Naturally, the design of these specialty cases is planned to meet the requirements of good salesmanship.

Wall cases are sometimes constructed in standardized sections, a group of which can be placed on the wall of a store independent of the exact dimensions of the building. Or, if an exact dimension must be adhered to, the fixture manufacturer can follow standardized construction and still do a "tailor-made" job.

Fixture factories manufacture store fixture items on a modular design basis so that the various parts are interchangeable. Thus, a drawer case may quickly be converted into a shelving case (Fig. 9).

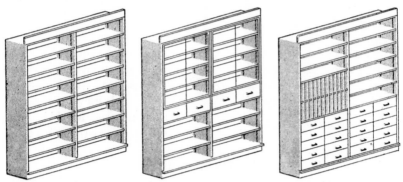

Fig. 9. Modular Wall Cases That Are Used for Both Drawer and Shelving Cases

FASTENERS

Screws. Screws are standardized as to size, shape, and material. Wood screws are made in about 200 different stock lengths and thicknesses, ranging in length from $\frac{1}{4}''$ to $5''$. The diameter, or screw gage, is indicated by a number. The sizes range from 0 to 24. The higher the number the greater the diameter of the screw. This is the reverse of the wire gage used to indicate the nail diameter where the smaller the gage number the thicker the nail. The types of screws most commonly used are the flathead, roundhead, oval head, drive screw, and Phillips Recessed Head (Fig. 10). While the latter requires a special type of screw driver, the screw has the advantage of giving a neater appearance to the finished job. This screw also has a greater drawing power with less damage to the head when being driven into place. Screws are made principally of steel, although some screws are made of brass, copper, and bronze. The brass, copper, and bronze screws are used where corrosive action from moisture, chemical solution, or fumes requires this type of screw. To meet the demand for decorative as well as utility values, screws are also made in the following finishes:

Nickel   Galvanized   Spartan
Cadmium   Hot tinned   Statuary bronze
Chromium   Japanned   Antique copper
Silver plate   Parkerized   Sand brass
Gold plate   Lacquer   Steel blued

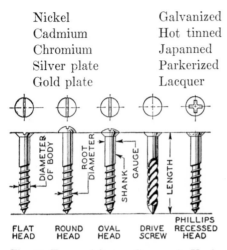

Fig. 10. Types of Screws Commonly Used
in Cabinetmaking

Bolts. Bolts are used in woodwork where great strength is required or where wood is fastened to metal or masonry. Carriage bolts, (A) of Fig. 11, are especially useful since the squared portion, when driven into a bored hole of proper size, will dig into the wood and prevent the bolt from turning. Machine bolts (B) are sometimes used for fastening wood members and joints. Stock sizes in both types are from $\frac{3}{4}''$ to 20" long and from $\frac{3}{16}''$ to $\frac{3}{4}''$ in diameter.

Lag bolts, (C) of Fig. 11, range in size from 1" to 16" in length and from $\frac{1}{4}''$ to 1" in diameter. Lag bolts or screws are used for heavy work where great strength is required.

Handrail bolts, shown in (D), are used for fastening handrails for stairs, curves, and straight runs to make one continuous piece.

Nails. The penny system is used to indicate the length of the most commonly used nails, ranging in length from 1" to 6". The abbreviation for penny is d. The five most commonly used nails are shown in Table IV, which shows the

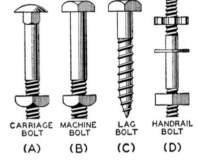

Fig. 11. Types of Bolts Commonly
Used in Cabinetmaking

length, gage, thickness, and the number of nails per pound, since nails are purchased by the pound.

Other types of nails frequently used in the cabinetmaking trade are shown in Fig. 12, which also shows the sizes. An 8 oz. tack, for example, is $\frac{1}{2}''$ long. Dowel pins are used to fasten mortise and tenon joints in sash and door work.

Fig. 12. Types of Nails Commonly Used in Cabinetmaking

CABINET HARDWARE

Hardware such as hinges, locks, catches, etc. (Fig. 13), are not installed by the cabinetmaker on cases that are installed on the job by a carpenter, but he does install them on finished movable fixtures, and should be familiar with the various types of hardware.

GLASS

The following information, which is an excerpt from *Sash and Door Catalog* No. 48,[1] has been included to provide the cabinetmaker and sash and door worker with pertinent information concerning glass.

Glass plays an important part in any structure. It is a most vital factor in the millwork business. Due to the importance of glass in the millwork picture, and the fact that the average layman has a very limited knowledge of glass in general, this section is presented with the hope that a better understanding of this item will be conducive to a generally better understanding among the millwork operator, the architect, the builder, and the consumer. It is compiled from data secured from representative manufacturers and jobbers of glass and is submitted to avoid the common errors and abuses which have appeared in the absence of a strict and definite description of quality and kind.

The approximate production of clear window glass is as follows: 2 to 3%—"AA" quality; 27 to 34%—"A" quality; 65 to 70%—"B" quality; and 3 to 4%—"C" quality.

It is readily seen that "AA" and "C" quality cannot be considered, due to the small percentage produced and the consequent inability to obtain any marketable amount of these two grades.

[1] Published by Southern California Retail Lumber Association, Los Angeles, California. Permission to use is acknowledged with appreciation by the authors.

Table IV. Commonly Used Nails, Their Size, Gage, and Number per Pound

Penny Size	Length in Inches for Common, Box and Finish*	Common Nails			Box and Casing Nails		
		 Common			Box  Casing		
		Gage	Thickness in Thousandths	Number per Pound	Gage	Thickness in Thousandths	Number per Pound
2d	1	15	.072	876	15½	.069	1010
3d	1¼	14	.083	568	14½	.078	635
4d	1½	12½	.102	316	14	.083	473
5d	1¾	12½	.102	271	14	.083	406
6d	2	11½	.115	181	12½	.102	236
7d	2¼	11½	.115	161	12½	.102	210
8d	2½	10¼	.131	106	11½	.115	145
9d	2¾	10¼	.131	96	11½	.115	132
10d	3	9	.148	69	10½	.127	94
12d	3¼	9	.148	63	10½	.127	88
16d	3½	8	.165	49	10	.134	71
20d	4	6	.203	31	9	.148	52
30d	4½	5	.220	24	9	.148	46
40d	5	4	.238	18	8	.165	35
50d	5½	3	.259	14	—	—	—
60d	6	2	.284	11	—	—	—

Penny Size	Length in Inches for Common, Box and Finish*	Coated Nails			Finish Nails		
		Coated			Finish		
		Gauge	Thickness in Thousandths	Number per Pound	Gauge	Thickness in Thousandths	Number per Pound
2d	1	16	.065	1084	16½	.062	1351
3d	1¼	15½	.069	848	15½	.069	807
4d	1½	14	.083	488	15	.072	584
5d	1¾	13½	.088	364	15	.072	500
6d	2	13	.095	275	13	.095	309
7d	2¼	12½	.102	212	13	.095	238
8d	2½	11½	.115	142	12½	.102	189
9d	2¾	11½	.115	130	12½	.102	172
10d	3	11	.120	104	11½	.115	121
12d	3¼	10	.134	77	11½	.115	113
16d	3½	9	.148	61	11	.120	90
20d	4	7	.180	37	10	.134	62
30d	4½	6	.203	29	—	—	—
40d	5	5	.220	21	—	—	—
50d	5½	4	.238	16	—	—	—
60d	6	3	.259	13	—	—	—

*Coated Nails ⅛ inch shorter.

Note: Flooring nails are similar in appearance to the casing nail but are about 1½ gage thicker for each size. They are made in sizes from 6d to 20d. Wire nails are gaged by the old standard Birmingham wire gage.

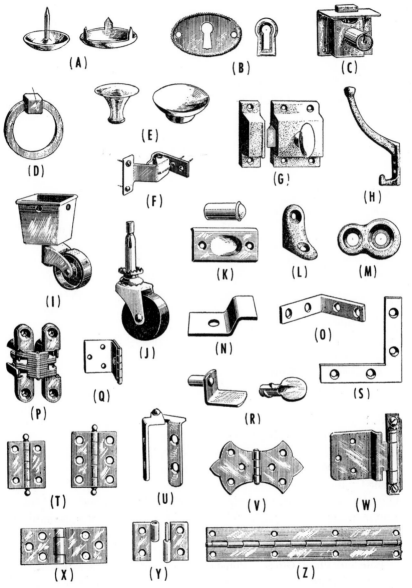

Fig. 13. Hardware Commonly Used in Cabinetmaking

(A) Furniture glides, (B) escutcheons, (C) drawer lock, (D) modern knob, (E) turned knob, (F) noise-less catch, (G) cupboard turn, (H) coat hook, (I) socket caster, (J) swivel caster, (K) bullet catch, (L) corner brace, (M) desk-top fastener, (N) table-top fastener, (O) corner brace, (P) invisible hinge, (Q) cabinet hinge, (R) shelf supports, (S) corner plate, (T) ball-tip butt hinge, (U) semi-invisible pivot hinge, (V) surface cabinet hinge, (W) semiconcealed cabinet hinge, (X) table-leaf hinge, (Y) loose-joint hinge, (Z) continuous hinge.

"A" Quality. This is the highest grade of sheet glass obtainable in commercial quantity. In this market it is specified and used, as a premium priced article, in public schools, government work, and residences of the higher price brackets. In this area the consumption is approximately 10% of the total of sheet glass used.

"B" Quality. This grade is known as the standard glazing quality and is used for all glazing purposes with entirely satisfactory results. In apartment houses, hotels, courts, dwellings, and medium-priced structures, "B" quality should be specified.

The above "A" and "B" qualities are available in single and double strength, weighing 18 to $18\frac{1}{2}$ ozs., and 25 to $25\frac{1}{2}$ ozs. respectively, to the square foot.

Heavy Window Glass. Heavy window glass is generally referred to and known as *Crystal Sheet*. Many have the impression that "Crystal Sheet" is similar in quality to plate glass but lighter in weight. This is erroneous. The word "Crystal" is a trade name, and it has no reference to quality. Crystal Sheet is used as a substitute for plate in cheaper types of work or where extra heavy window glass is required. Heavy drawn, $\frac{3}{16}''$ Crystal Sheet, "B" quality, is more commonly used in this market. It is also available in limited amounts in the following: $\frac{3}{16}''$ thick—"A" quality; $\frac{7}{32}''$ thick—"B" quality; and $\frac{1}{4}''$ thick—factory run.

Obscure Sheet Glass. This is a flat glass in which the vision is more or less obscured by the roughened surface on one side of the sheet. The effect is accomplished by the rolling process in manufacture. Glass of this type is supplied in but one quality. However, a wide variety of surface finishes is available. Obscure sheet glass is made in $\frac{1}{8}''$, $\frac{3}{16}''$, and $\frac{1}{4}''$ thickness in sheets up to 48" x 132".

Obscure Wire Glass. This is rolled flat glass having a layer of meshed wire incorporated in approximately the center of the sheet. This glass is produced in maximum sheets 48" x 130", and is $\frac{1}{4}''$ thick. A limited amount of $\frac{3}{16}''$, $\frac{1}{2}''$, and $\frac{3}{4}''$ thicknesses are obtainable in the same surface pattern as $\frac{1}{8}''$ obscure glass. Sizes up to 54" wide and 144" long are available.

Polished Plate Glass. Polished plate glass is a transparent, flat glass, having polished surfaces and showing no distortion of vision when one is viewing objects through it at an angle. Plate glass is made by rolling large continuous sheets. The sheets are then cut, ground, and polished. Standard plate, for glazing purposes, is $\frac{1}{4}''$ thick, with a permissible tolerance of $\frac{1}{32}''$ (plus or minus) considered as standard for the 1/4". Extremely limited quantities and sizes are available in the following thicknesses: 1/8", 3/16", 3/8", 1/2", 3/4", 1", 1 1/4", and 1 1/2".

Mirrors. The silvering solution which forms the reflective property of a mirror may be applied to glass of any description. Therefore, the quality of a mirror is governed by the grade of glass used in its production.

PLATE MIRRORS

Plate mirrors are made from a grade of plate glass known as *Selected Silvering Quality*. The glass is repolished before the silvering solution is applied. This procedure produces a first quality mirror.

CRYSTAL MIRRORS

Mirrors of this quality are produced by silvering 3/16" Crystal Sheet or heavy window glass. This process does not produce a first quality mirror, since the glass is usually wavy.

SHOCK MIRRORS

These mirrors are made from silvered window glass. The mirrors are thin and contain the characteristic defects of window glass. Not recommended as satisfactory.

REVIEW QUESTIONS

1. What is the universally accepted unit of measure for modular construction?
2. Name three standard sizes for doors.
3. What is meant by sash?
4. How are the sizes of door and window frames determined?
5. What is trim?
6. What is paneling?
7. What are the common types of screws?
8. What governs the quality of a mirror?
9. What are the common types of nails?
10. Name ten articles of hardware used in cabinetmaking.
11. What is meant by term 21 oz. glass?

Layout and Construction
of Cabinet Work

QUESTIONS CHAPTER XIII WILL ANSWER FOR YOU

1. *What is the distinction between cabinet work and casework?*
2. *What are the basic parts of a cabinet?*
3. *How are the parts of a cabinet laid out and constructed?*
4. *How is casework laid out and constructed?*
5. *What are some typical examples of cabinet work and casework?*

INTRODUCTION TO CHAPTER XIII

Cabinets were formerly made by an individual craftsman, the *cabinet-maker*. With the advent of modern milling machinery, he "shares honors" with the *millman* who machines stock and prepares joints for the *sub-assembler* or *glueman*. Sometimes called a *benchman*, the cabinetmaker takes over when hand tool skills are required in making joints, in fitting and assembling pre-manufactured parts, and in preparing the wood for finish. The information in this chapter, therefore, concerns the millman as much as the cabinetmaker.

The simplest and broadest definition of a cabinet is: *a chest or a case, such as a set of drawers, or cupboard, fitted with shelves or drawers, sometimes both, to be used as a depository for various articles* (Fig. 1). The depository space is usually enclosed. The general term *casework* or *case-goods* is often used instead of the term *cabinet*. The distinguishing feature of cabinet work when the term *casework* is applied is that it is three-dimensional, not flat, like a partition, a wainscoting, a mantle, a railing, or a panel. These latter millwork items are cabinetwork but not casework. Although cabinets vary greatly in size and appearance, the principles of their construction and layout are basically similar and may be applied, with some variations, to any type of cabinet design. The material of this chapter is divided into two parts:

1. The layout and construction of cabinet parts.
2. The layout and construction of casework.

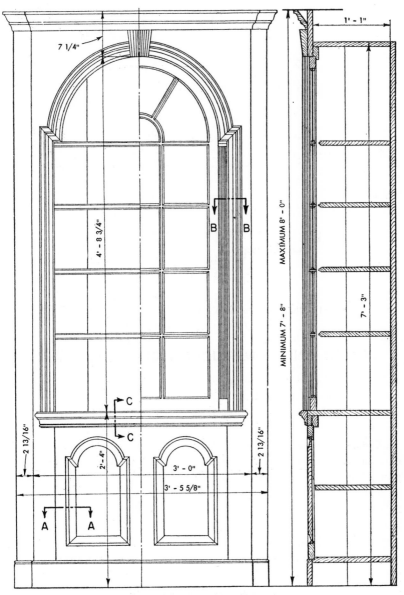

Fig. 1. Typical China Cabinet
Courtesy Curtis Companies Service Bureau

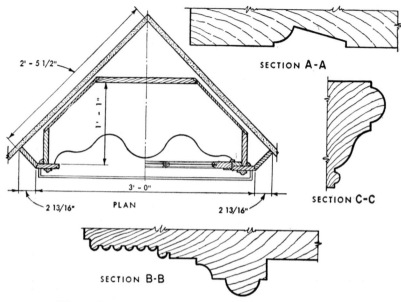

Fig. 1a. Plan and Section Views of China Cabinet in Fig. 1
Courtesy Curtis Companies Service Bureau

LAYOUT AND CONSTRUCTION OF CABINET PARTS

A finished cabinet is composed of several different parts. Some of these parts are machined and go directly into the casework; others are assembled as separate units, then fitted and assembled together to form the cabinet.

Ends. A *cabinet end* (Fig. 2) is sometimes called a *jamb* or, if exposed, a *return* or a *side*. A cabinet end may be made of solid edge-glued lumber, of plywood, or of stiles and rails with panels. It may be lock mitered (Fig. 2A), rabbeted (Fig. 2B), or butt jointed (Fig. 2C) to the face frame, or it may be rabbeted or grooved for a back or left square edged. It may also be dadoed to receive the top, the bottom, stationary shelves, drawer guides, skeleton frames, or dust panels. If a cabinet with a paneled end is to be scribed to the wall, allowance is necessary on the width of the end, or on the width of the back stile. If a paneled end is butt jointed to the face frame, the front stile is made narrower than the back stile to compensate for the thickness of the face frame. See Figure 2C. The layout and construction of a paneled end usually follows the standard practice for cupboard doors.

Posts or Legs. Posts forming legs for casework such as counters, drawers, chests, and desks serve as stiles for the ends as well as the front (Fig. 3). Therefore, a different problem of construction is presented. The paneling of the end may be a single piece of plywood or a full bound panel that is doweled or grooved into the legs. It may also be formed by the top and bottom rails being mortised or doweled into the legs. The panel is then grooved into the rails and legs. Such a piece of casework is usually *free standing* and, as such, should be rabbeted flush at the back or paneled like the ends. In this type of work the skeleton frame extends to the face and forms the dividing rails between the drawers. Sometimes these dividing rails are mortised or doweled into the legs. The drawer runners are then tenoned into a slot on the inside edge of the dividing rails. See Fig. 42. The top of the case may

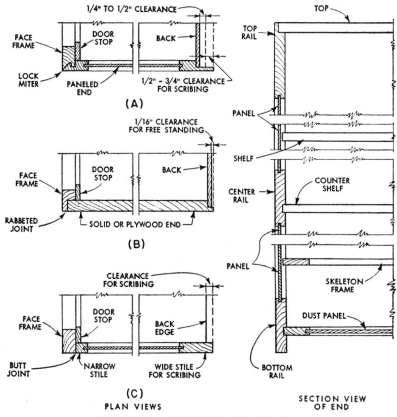

Fig. 2. Various Cabinet End Constructions

be fastened by means of cleats, desk-top fasteners, a skeleton frame (Fig. 41), or it may be angle-screwed.

Divisions and Sleepers. Divisions, sometimes known as *standards* or *partitions,* are usually of solid glued-up stock (Fig. 4). They are usually dadoed into the top and bottom shelves or skeleton frames to allow a full length tie between the top and bottom of the cabinet. The division is dadoed to match the layout of the opposing end or division. The bottom shelf is supported by sleepers, thus extending support to the floor. If there is a difference of layout in the lower part of the cabinet, such as having a skeleton frame on one side and a solid shelf on the other, the division between the two parts must extend continuously to the floor. This construction relies on the face and back to act as a tie between the ends of the cabinet.

Glue Block. A glue block is used to reinforce a right-angled butt or dado joint in hidden construction to make the cabinet rigid (Fig. 4). It is two to five inches long, its face width depending on the space available and the strength required. A glue block is sometimes applied by making a rubbed glue joint, or it may be glued and nailed into place.

Tops. The top of a piece of cabinetwork may be constructed in several ways:

1. If the top is above the line of vision, it is usually made of solid glued-up stock. It may be dadoed into the ends and made flush with the top end of the side (Fig. 2).

2. If the cabinet measures from floor to ceiling, the top may be lowered to allow clearance between the ceiling and the top of the cabinet. The top may act as a door stop if it forms a rabbet with the bottom edge of the top rail (Fig. 5).

3. An exposed top may be scribed to the wall with a rabbet (Fig. 6).

4. A counter top, sometimes called a counter shelf, may be located at a height of 36″ to 40″ from the floor. It is dadoed into the cabinet ends when the latter are continuous. It may also be located to form a rabbet with the face rail and act as a door stop (Fig. 7), or it may extend flush with the face, the front edge being rabbeted for the doors (Fig. 8).

5. A counter ledge may be constructed with a mitered strip around the front and ends of a straight-faced case (Fig. 7). A counter ledge may extend fully to the back of the cabinet or finished with a mitered return (Fig. 8).

6. Tops for counters and cases take many other forms, such as:

a. Drain board with sanitary cove and splash (Fig. 9).

b. Banded plywood covered with synthetic materials (Fig. 10).

c. Veneered stock with veneered edges (Fig. 11A) or with banded edges (Fig. 11B). The banded edge is used when a molded edge is required.

Other forms and variations of tops are based on these types.

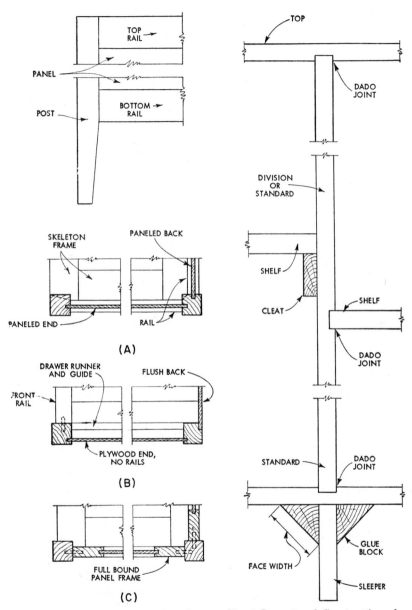

Fig. 3. Layout and Construction of
Cabinet Posts

Fig. 4. Layout and Construction of
Division and Sleeper

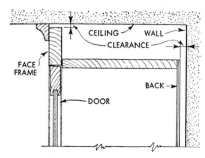

Fig. 5. Ceiling and Wall Clearance for Top

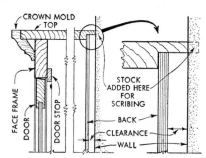

Fig. 6. Rabbeted Top for Cabinet Scribed to Wall

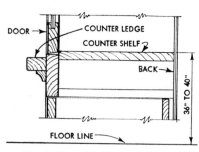

Fig. 7. Top with Planted Counter Ledge

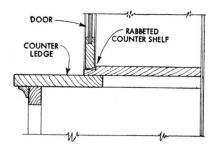

Fig. 8. Top with Rabbeted Counter Shelf

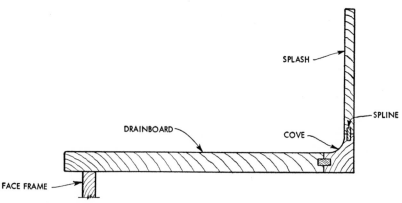

Fig. 9. Drain Board with Sanitary Cove and Splash

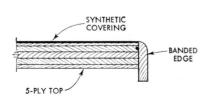

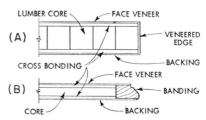

Fig. 10. Banded Plywood

Fig. 11. Veneered Stock with Veneered and Banded Edges

Bottoms and Toe Boards. The bottom of a cabinet is usually made of solid glued material and located to form a rabbet with the top edge of the bottom rail, thus acting as a door stop (Fig. 12). If a drawer section adjoins a cupboard, the bottom of the drawer section should be made flush with the top edge of the bottom face rail (Fig. 13).

Figure 14 shows the bottom of a cabinet in which no rail is used. The door or drawer is made to cover the edge. In this case, a toe board

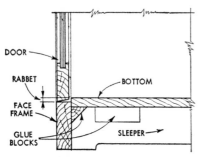

Fig. 12. Rabbeted Bottom and Toe Board

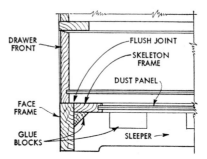

Fig. 13. Skeleton Frame Flush with Bottom Rail

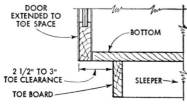

Fig. 14. Bottom and Toe Board Forming Toe Space

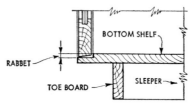

Fig. 15. Rabbeted Bottom with Toe Space

is placed to close the space between the floor and the bottom and to provide toe clearance. Sometimes the bottom is rabbeted to receive the door (Fig. 15).

Skeleton Frames and Dust Panels. The skeleton frame is a machined-and-assembled unit which is fitted into the interior of a cabinet (Fig. 16). Its purpose is threefold:

1. In a horizontal position to serve as a support for drawers.

2. To tie the case together under a counter top and provide a means of fastening the top.

3. To act as a *vertical* standard when a solid division is not required.

A skeleton frame usually consists of stiles and rails only. However, it is sometimes paneled to make each compartment in the cabinet dust proof. Such panels are called *dust panels*. The stiles give support to the ends of the skeleton frame when dadoed into the ends or divisions.

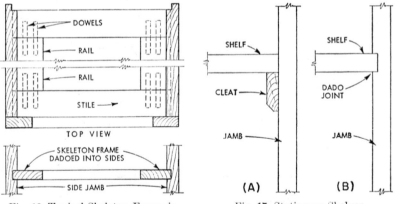

Fig. 16. Typical Skeleton Frame in Cabinet

Fig. 17. Stationary Shelves

Shelves, Cleats, and Ratchets. Shelves are usually made of solid glued-up stock and fitted into the cabinet so that they are either stationary or adjustable. *Stationary* shelves are supported on wooden cleats (Fig. 17A) or are dadoed in (Fig. 17B). *Adjustable* shelves are supported in two ways:

a. With wooden ratchet strips (Fig. 18).

b. With metal shelving standards and supports (Fig. 19).

On open-faced shelves or behind glazed doors, the front edge is faced with a strip of the *same material* as the other exposed parts of the cabinet. The width of a shelf is measured between the back, if any, and the inside face of the door, making allowance for the door stop if such is provided. The length of a dadoed shelf is equal to the sum of the depths of the dadoes, usually ¼″ each, plus the inside distance between the ends.

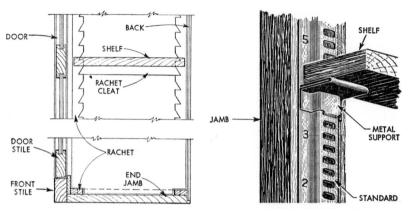

Fig. 18. Adjustable Shelf on Wood Ratchet and Cleats

Fig. 19. Metal Standard for Adjustable Shelves

Face Frames and Stops. A face frame (Fig. 20) is a pre-assembled unit consisting of stiles, rails, mullions, and muntins, forming an opening into which doors and drawers are fitted. Mullions extend from the bottom to the top rails. Great accuracy is required in laying out and making a face frame to make it conform to the layout of the *carcase* or shell of the cabinet and to facilitate the making and fitting of doors and drawers. The frame is usually made square on the inside edges using a mortise and tenon (Fig. 23A) or doweled construction (Fig. 22A).

The manner of joining a face frame to the cabinet ends is shown in Figure 2. If one of the stiles is to be scribed to the wall, ½″ or more is added to the width of the stile, and the end is set in ½″ to ¾″ to provide clearance, as shown in Figure 43.

The design of the openings in a case sometimes creates the problem of where to make the joints in the face frame. In general, the rule is to make the stiles equal to *the full height of the cabinet front* and the top and bottom rails equal to *the full length between the stiles*. The design determines whether the intermediate rails, if any, should be made full length between the stiles, or whether a full length mullion should be installed.

It is important that the finish thickness of a face frame be made at least $\frac{1}{16}''$ more than the finish thickness of the doors to be fitted in it. This is to provide a clearance and to prevent the doors from binding against the door stop (Fig. 21). Note also that the face of the door is recessed slightly below the face frame.

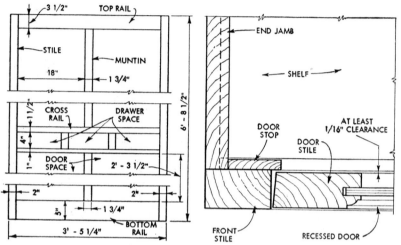

Fig. 20. Typical Face Frame

Fig. 21. Recessed Door Clearance
Between Door and Stop

Cupboard Doors and Sash. Doors used in cabinets of any description are commonly called *cupboard doors*, when paneled or flush, and *cupboard sash* when glazed. In some sections of the country, the terms *c.c. door* and *c.c. sash* are used, the letters *c.c.* being an abbreviation of *china closet.* This term may be used even though the cabinet is not used for chinaware.

Standard shop practice usually determines the size and construction of door stiles and rails. Cupboard doors and sash are listed according to *width, height,* and *thickness,* in that order. It is important that this order be followed, as a door made with the stiles in a horizontal position is not acceptable. Specially designed cupboard doors are made according to the detail drawings furnished with the order.

The thickness of a door should be at least $\frac{1}{16}''$ less than the face frame to provide clearance behind the door and to allow a slight recess below the face frame after the door is fitted. Typical constructions of cupboard doors and sash are shown in Figs. 22B and C, and Figs. 23B and D. Typical sash constructions are shown in Figs. 22D and 23C.

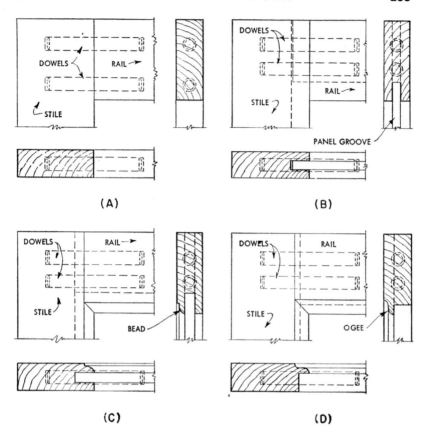

Fig. 22. Typical Door and Sash Doweled Constructions

(A) Dowel butt with square sticking (B) groove and doweled stub tenon with square sticking (C) groove and doweled stub tenon with bead sticking (D) doweled and coped with rabbeted ogee sticking.

DRAWERS AND TRAYS

Drawer Dimensions. The dimensions of a drawer are based on the opening into which it is to be fitted. The measurements are given as *width, height,* and *depth,* in that order. The width of a drawer is the horizontal distance across the face opening; the height is the vertical distance across the face opening; the depth is the distance from the face to the back of the cabinet minus the clearance at the back.

In some shops it is common practice, when ordering drawers, to issue factory orders and to list the drawer dimensions only. The

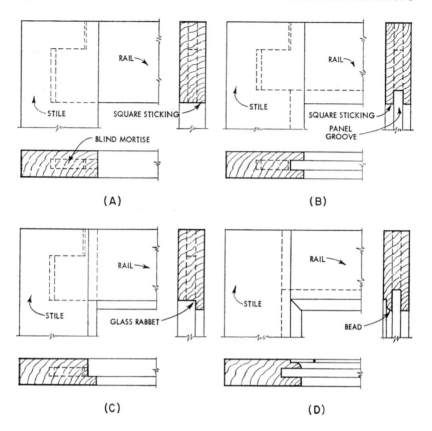

Fig. 23. Typical Door and Sash Mortise and Tenon Constructions
(A) Blind mortise and relished tenon with square sticking (B) blind mortise and relished tenon, grooved, with square sticking (C) blind mortise and relished tenon, rabbeted for glass (D) groove and stub tenon, coped shoulder, bead sticking.

drawer material is then billed according to the dimensions and the type of drawers to be made. Except in detail work, a standard method of construction is used.

Drawer Design. Drawers are usually classified as either *flush front* or *lip front* drawers. A flush front drawer is fitted flush with, or recessed slightly below, the face of the case (Fig. 24A), while a lip front drawer extends over the opening at the top and ends (Fig. 24B).

The thickness of the parts of a drawer varies according to the material, the design, and the type of construction employed (Fig. 25). The front is usually made ¾″ thick except in very large drawers. It may be of plywood or of solid stock. Drawer sides and backs are usually $\frac{3}{8}''$ to $\frac{5}{8}''$ thick when made of softwood and $\frac{7}{16}''$ to $\frac{1}{2}''$ thick when made of hardwood. The bottom is usually made of $\frac{1}{4}''$ plywood, except in small drawers where $\frac{1}{8}''$ or $\frac{3}{16}''$ hardwood plywood is used. The bottoms should be cut to allow a $\frac{1}{16}''$ clearance in the grooves into which the bottom piece fits. The front of the drawer may be raised, paneled, or molded to harmonize with the design of the casework.

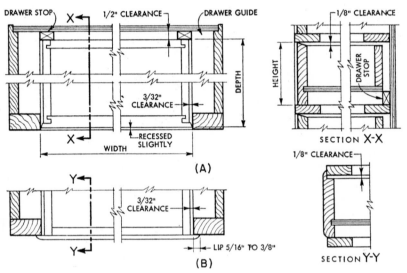

Fig. 24. (A) Flush Front Drawer (B) Lip Front Drawer

Drawer Clearance. The width of the sides and the back of a drawer should be $\frac{1}{8}''$ *less than the net height* of the opening into which it is to be fitted. The *over-all width* of the drawer should be $\frac{3}{16}''$ *less than the net width* of the drawer opening. The drawer will thus have a clearance of $\frac{1}{8}''$ in height and $\frac{3}{16}''$ in width, assuring free running and providing room for expansion in damp weather (Fig. 24). A *flush drawer* front is made equal to the full size of the face opening if it is to be fitted by hand. The depth of a drawer should be about $\frac{1}{2}''$ less than the space between the face and the back of the case to provide clearance for adjusting the drawer front with the face of the case.

Drawer Construction. The standard construction used in many detail woodwork plants is shown in Fig. 25. Notice that the tongued shoulder construction is used to join the sides and front while the dado

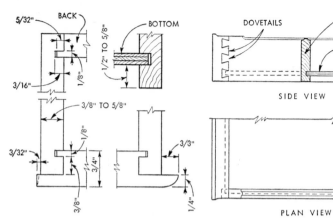

Fig. 25. Standard Drawer Details of Flush Front Drawer (top) and Lip Front Drawer (bottom)

Fig. 26. Typical Mass-Production Drawer

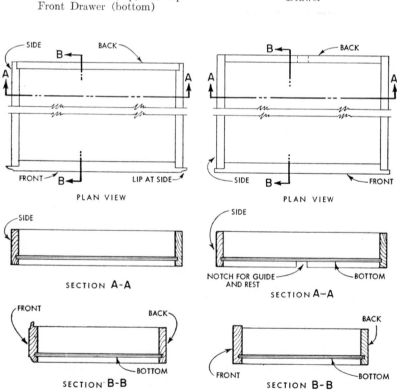

Fig. 27. Typical Kitchen Drawer

Fig. 28. Typical Standard Stock Drawer

and lips are used to join the sides and back. The sides and front are grooved to receive a $\frac{1}{4}''$ plywood bottom. The back measures from the top of the groove to the top edge of the drawer sides.

Figure 26 shows a type of construction employed in the mass production of high-grade furniture and fixtures. The drawer is machine-dovetailed at all corners. The top edge of the front is shaped to meet the narrowed sides. The sides are shaped to provide clearance at the top. The full width of the side at the back of the drawer will prevent it from tilting down when pulled out.

Figure 27 illustrates a type of drawer which is commonly used in kitchen cupboards and cabinets. The drawer has a rabbeted corner at the front and back. The lips protrude only at the top and sides of the drawer front. No lip is made on the bottom edge. If properly made, this drawer is easily fitted. The lip hides the clearance at the edges of the drawer opening, and it also adds to the design.

Probably the cheapest kind of drawer that can be made is shown in Figure 28. This drawer may be made by hand out of standard drawer stock which has been milled on a molder from standard lengths of lumber. Such drawers are often made on the job by the carpenter. The ends of the drawer front are rabbeted to receive the sides. The back is usually fitted to the side with a butt joint. Sometimes the sides are rabbeted or dadoed to receive the back. The foregoing method is also used in cheap cabinet construction.

If the specifications for a cabinet call for a section of trays, the section is usually concealed by a door. Each tray is actually a drawer except that the front and the front portion of the sides are made narrower to permit easy access to the contents (Fig. 29). The trays are constructed in a manner similar to the construction of drawers previously described. The type of corner joint used is determined by the specifications of the job

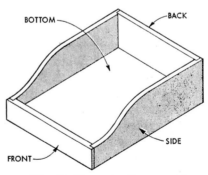

Fig. 29. Tray-type Drawer with Narrowed Front

or, if the work is done in a small shop, by the equipment available. Tray bottoms are sometimes rabbeted flush with the bottom edge of the sides.

Another type of drawer is made by nailing the bottom to the sides, back, and rabbeted front, extending the 3-ply bottom $\frac{5}{16}''$ beyond the drawer sides. This extension serves as a support for the drawer in a corresponding groove made in the body of the cabinet or table (Fig. 30). This type of construction is used only on very small drawers.

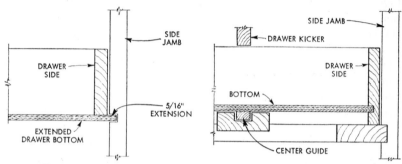

Fig. 30. Drawer with Extended Bottom   Fig. 31. Drawer with Center Guide

Drawer Guides. In fine cabinet work, the method used to guide the drawer as it slides in and out is important and receives very careful attention. A very satisfactory guide is a carefully machined hardwood tongue and groove construction at the center of the drawer (Fig. 31). A simpler method is to install a single bar which projects above the lower rail of the drawer opening and on which the drawer is supported. A notch is cut in the lower edge of the drawer back which acts as the guide. Figure 32 illustrates other types of guides. Variations and combinations of the different types are employed, depending on such factors as design, construction, space, and the quality of the job.

Drawer Kickers. When the design of the case is such that there is a space above the drawer, it becomes necessary to install a drawer kicker to prevent the drawer from tilting down when it is pulled out. The kicker is installed at the center of the drawer (Figs. 31 and 33).

Drawer Stops. On lip front drawers, the lip usually acts as a stop. When a heavily filled drawer is slammed shut, the lip may be torn off. To prevent this, a stop is fastened to the side guide (Fig. 34), to the back end of the drawer side (Fig. 36), or to the runner near the back (Fig. 35). Light flush drawers may be stopped by fastening a stop on the skeleton frame rail directly behind the drawer front (Fig. 36).

Pull-Out Leaf. The bread board in a kitchen cabinet and the work board of a desk or counter are examples of pull-out leaves. They are usually made with flush cleats glued to the end grain (Fig. 37).

Ornamentation. A cornice may be added to the face and ends of a cabinet to give it an architectural finish. Sometimes a cabinet is designed with fluted or beaded plasters set on a base and finished at the top with caps. The china cabinet shown in Figure 1 is a good example of the use of ornamentation.

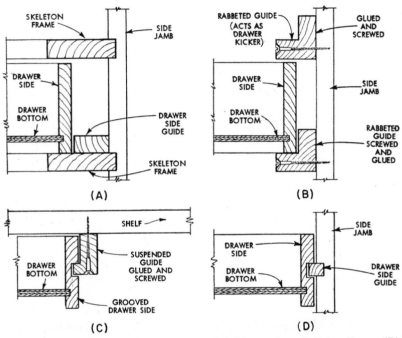

Fig. 32. Various Types of Drawer Guides (A) Mounted on Skeleton Frame (B) Screwed to Side (C) Suspended on Shelf (C) Grooved into Side

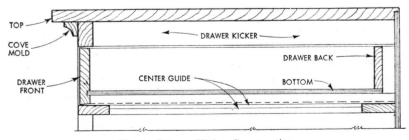

Fig. 33. Drawer Kicker Construction

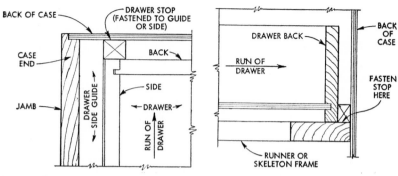

Fig. 34. Drawer Stop Fastened to Side or Guide

Fig. 35. Drawer Stop Fastened to Runner

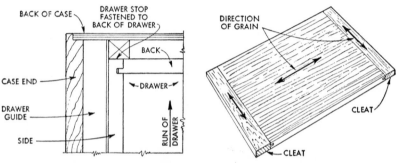

Fig. 36. Drawer Stop Fastened to Drawer Back

Fig. 37. Pull-Out Leaf

LAYOUT AND CONSTRUCTION OF CASEWORK

The term *casework* includes all the parts that constitute the finished cabinet, such as doors, drawers, and ornamentation. The term *carcase* refers to the basic shell or foundation structure. A study of the preceding section of this chapter dealing with the parts that make up a cabinet, their construction and functions, should clarify the following illustrations.

Boxes, Crates, and Chests. Since simple boxes and chests may be considered as cabinets, a description of their construction will clearly illustrate the basic principles of casework. The names of the parts and dimensions of a box are illustrated in Figure 38. The top may be hinged. The grain in the ends and sides runs horizontally. The thickness of the stock depends on the use and size of the box or chest.

Although an ordinary shipping crate is the cheapest of boxes, it should be precisely cut to insure an accurate and strong assembly. The stock may be of common grade from ½″ to ¾″ thick. Occasionally a box or crate will be made with cleated ends to increase its strength and to prevent it from splitting when it is loaded and lifted (Fig. 39). The bottom of the crate is usually made to the *outside dimensions* of the job and screwed or nailed to the sides and ends.

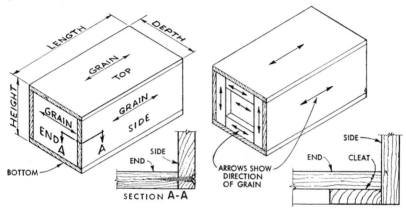

Fig. 38. Construction of Simple Box   Fig. 39. Box with Cleated Ends

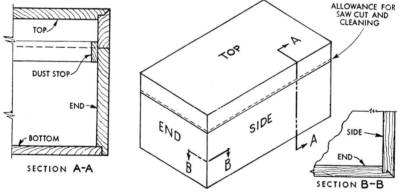

Fig. 40. Chest with Boxed Lid

The simplest form of corner joint used in a box or chest is the butt joint. For better work, the rabbeted joint is used. To prevent end grain from showing on a cedar chest or jewelry box, the lock miter or spline miter is used. For extra sturdiness, the dovetail joint is used.

The top of a box or chest is made to the exact *outside dimensions* and may be screwed, nailed, or hinged on, depending on the use of the box or chest. A chest is made with a boxed lid and is usually constructed as a single case. The lid is cut open after the pieces are assembled (Fig. 40).

Chest of Drawers. Figure 41 shows a chest of drawers with paneled ends grooved into the legs and rails. The drawers are flush with the front, of standard construction, and are guided by center guides. A solid division between the two top drawers is faced with a vertical muntin.

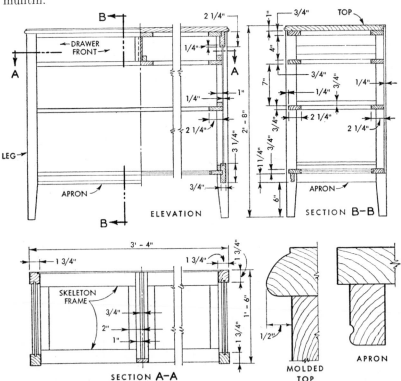

Fig. 41. Chest of Drawers with Paneled Ends

In furniture making where mass production warrants careful layout and machining, the effect of a skeleton frame is obtained by making the drawer guides as integral parts of the case, thus saving material and labor. Figure 42 shows a chest of drawers with the front rail fastened to the front legs. The drawer guides are fastened to the legs with the side guides added.

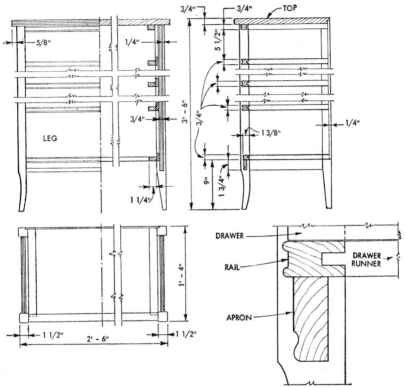

Fig. 42. Chest of Drawers with Front Rail Fastened to Legs

Cabinets. The dimensions of a cabinet are usually given as the *width, height,* and *depth of the case, exclusive of molding or ornamentation.* Figure 43 shows the plan view of the manner of constructing a linen case to be scribed to a wall. The specifications are as follows:

One linen case 3'4" x 8'4" x 1'6", white pine, paneled doors and end, square sticking, mortise and tenon construction, flush drawers with center guides, ¼" plywood back.

Standard construction practices would cover any information which may be lacking in the drawing.

Counters. Figure 44 shows a counter with a flush die mitered at the front corners, one section having drawers, the other having sliding doors. The top is banded to give a heavier appearance and the base (plinth frame) is recessed 3" for toe space.

Figure 5, Chapter I, illustrates the construction and layout of a modern wood and glass office partition.

Figure 45 shows a typical construction of a custom-built tile top sink case.

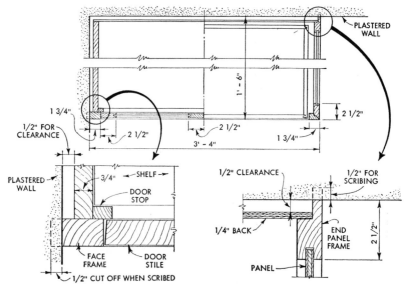

Fig. 43. Plan of Linen Case Scribed to Wall

REVIEW QUESTIONS

1. Name at least four factors which should be considered in determining the type of joints to be used in cabinet work.

2. Make sketches of the following types of joints: butt, spline, tongue and groove, rabbet, dado, doweled, and miter.

3. Name ten standard parts which are used in cabinet work.

4. Under what conditions should the width of a cabinet end be increased at the back end of the jamb?

5. What is the usual method of fastening a division onto a bottom shelf or skeleton frame?

6. What is the name of the part of the cabinet which is placed under a partition to extend support of the cabinet to the floor?

7. What is the location and purpose of a toe board?

8. What is a counter top?

9. What are two common methods for supporting adjustable shelves?

10. Under what conditions should the front edges of shelves be faced with the same material as the exposed parts of the cabinet?

11. Name three parts of a face frame.

12. How much thicker should a face frame be than the door which is fitted into it?

13. Give the correct sequence in the listing of drawer dimensions.

14. Sketch a flush front and a lip front drawer.

15. How much vertical clearance should be allowed between the sides of a drawer and the face frame opening?

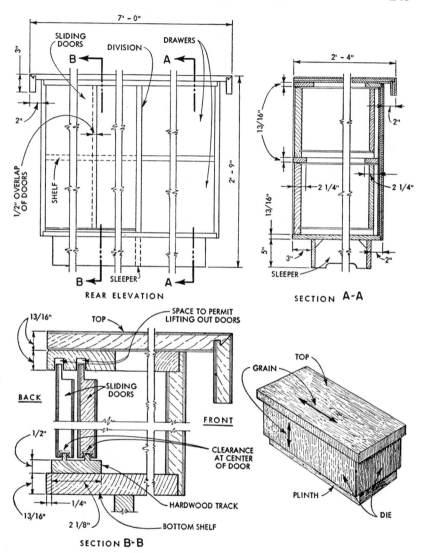

Fig. 44. Counter with Flush Die

16. The construction of a paneled cabinet end is similar in method to what other commonly used part in cabinet work?

17. What is a drawer kicker?

18. Name two types of drawer guides.

19. What is meant by the term *carcase?*

20. Make a sketch of a flush front and a lip front drawer.

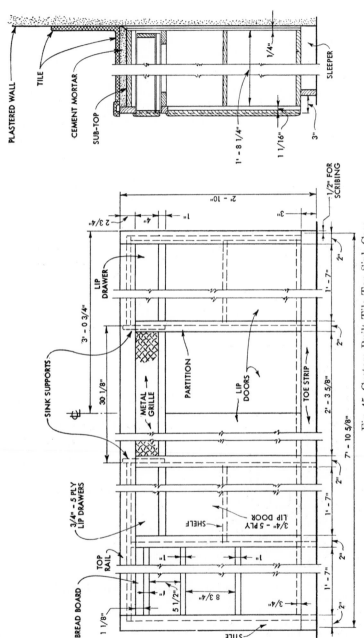

Fig. 45. Custom-Built Tile Top Sink Case

Doors

QUESTIONS CHAPTER XIV WILL ANSWER FOR YOU

1. *What are the typical kinds of doors that are manufactured?*
2. *What are the basic parts of a door?*
3. *What are the typical methods of joining door parts?*
4. *What are the layout methods for stock and standard doors?*
5. *What are the layout methods for detail doors?*

INTRODUCTION TO CHAPTER XIV

The doorways of primitive habitations probably consisted of skins or cloth. In Syria, doors of stone have been found that were in use during the fourth century. Wooden doors originally consisted of a single plank swung from pintles (pivot pins) fastened in the mantel (head jamb) and threshold of the doorway. In the twelfth century highly ornamental hinges came into use, decorating the doors of important buildings. Doors with double planking and bound with iron were built to withstand inclement weather. Later, paneling was introduced to lighten the weight and to add to the decorative effect (Fig. 1).

Paneled doors were made of solid narrow stock to minimize shrinkage. The choice of design was limited, but a number of the original designs are still manufactured in large quantities, including the standard 4 panel, 5 cross panel and 6 panel doors (Fig. 3, Ch. XII, p. 209).

With the advent of water-resistant glues and the mass production of plywood, the scope of design widened to include the 1 panel, 2 panel, 2 vertical panels, 3 cross panels, and the slab doors (Fig. 3, Ch. XII, p. 209).

CLASSIFICATION OF DOORS

Doors may be classified according to their use, such as *exterior, interior, garage,* and *cupboard doors.* The design of a door refers to the arrangement and size of its component parts such as stiles, rails, panels, moldings, glass, and carvings.

The sizes of doors have been standardized by popular demand, enabling the manufacturer to mass-produce certain sizes at a great saving to the consumer. Specially designed or odd sized doors are made individually at considerable cost.

In general, the manufacturer classifies doors on the basis of their price and the problems of their manufacture.

Fig. 1. A Paneled Oak Door
Courtesy of Southern Hardwood Producers, Inc.

Standard Design. This design may not always be carried in stock. However, with the specifications on hand and the facilities for getting out the work quickly, it is easy to manufacture these standard design doors.

Standard Sizes. Sizes of doors that may or may not be carried in stock. The layout and facilities for their manufacture are standard and ready for immediate manufacturing.

Stock Sizes. Standard designs and sizes that are normally carried in stock and are available for immediate shipment.

Odd Sizes. Standard designs of doors made in intermediate sizes: extra large, extra small, or odd combinations of width and height.

Special or Detail Design. Items that require unusual or special set-ups for their construction regardless of whether they are standard or odd sized. A standard design with one manufacturer may not be standard with another. A factory or a dealer may have a large assortment of stock sizes while another has a limited stock of doors.

DEFINITION OF PARTS

It is essential for the millman who is working on any phase of door manufacture to understand the terms designating the various parts of a door. Most of the following terms have been established by general use throughout the woodworking industry (Figs. 2, 3, 4, etc.).

Stile. The outside vertical member of a door usually extending the full height (Fig. 2).

Rail. Any horizontal member extending the full width between stiles such as top rail, bottom rail, lock rail, frieze rail, cross rail and intermediate rail (Fig. 2).

Mullion. A vertical member extending the full length between the bottom and top rails (Fig. 2).

Muntin. A short, light bar or rail in a sash or door, either vertical or horizontal, but not extending the full height or width.

Bar. Any light member extending either horizontally or vertically; usually in glazed openings (Fig. 2).

Panel. The member of a door filling the space between stiles and rails or muntins, usually grooved or rabbeted into the stiles and rails (Fig. 2).

Raised Panel. A thick panel whose edges are molded and shaped to fit in the grooves of stiles and rails (Fig. 5).

Reveal. The offset measurement from the face of a stile or rail to a recessed panel surface (Fig. 3).

Light. A pane of glass or the opening into which a pane of glass is to be set (Fig. 2).

Face. The exposed side, portion of a side, or flat surface of a door member (Fig. 6).

Sticking. The molded inside edge of a stile or rail, such as bead and cove sticking (Fig. 5).

Opening:

1. The size of the frame into which a door, window or sash is to be fitted.

2. The space in a door, window, or sash into which a pane of glass is to be placed.

Daylight Opening. That portion of an opening in a door or sash through which daylight may pass.

Glass Opening:

1. The measurement of an opening across the width and height to the bottom of the rabbet.

2. The size of the glass for an opening plus clearance.

Rabbet. A rectangular cut made in the face or edge of a board to receive another member, such as a panel or pane of glass.

Groove. A rectangular cut in the edge of a board, such as a trough, to receive another member, such as a panel or spline (Fig. 4).

Core. The base or center of a veneered piece of stock formed by short pieces of wood glued together (Fig. 3).

Crossband. The layer of veneer next to the core in a piece of 5-ply plywood with the grain running at right angles to the core (Fig. 9).

Face Veneer. The exposed finish layer of veneer on the face or faces of a piece of plywood (Fig. 9).

Backing. The exposed layer of veneer constituting the back side of a piece of plywood.

Edge Strip, Banding, or Facing. A piece of finished material matching the face veneer, and glued to the edge or edges of the core or crossband of a piece of plywood (Fig. 3).

Planted Molding. A separate piece of molding nailed or glued into place after a door is assembled (Fig. 13).

Flush Molding. A planted molding flush with, or below the face of the stile or rail (Fig. 5).

Raised Molding. A planted molding raised above the face of the stile or rail; usually rabbeted to lap over the edge of the reveal (Fig. 5).

Spline. A strip of wood fitted into the opposed grooves of two pieces of wood which are to be joined (Fig. 21).

Relish. That part of a tenon which is cut out to form the haunch of the tenon (Fig. 7).

Haunch. The shoulder formed by relishing a tenon (Fig. 6).

Ripping Size. The rough-ripped width of a piece of stock preparatory to milling and sizing (Fig. 4).

Finished Size. The over-all dimension of a finished piece of stock including the molded inside edge (Fig. 4).

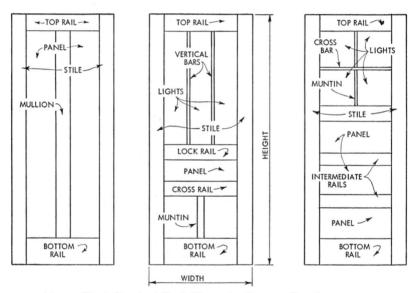

Fig. 2. Standard Trade Terms for Doors or Paneling

LISTING DOORS

Sequence of Measurements. Doors are listed in the following sequence of measurements: *width, height,* and *thickness.* This rule is always followed even though the door may be wider than high, in cupboard doors, garage doors or, less frequently, in interior sliding doors.

The *sequence-of-measurements procedure* is very important as it affects the construction of the door. The wrong arrangement of the stiles, rails, panels, and the direction of the grain of the wood, would make the door useless.

Methods of Listing Doors. The width and height are always listed in feet and inches, and the thickness is always given in inches. A complete description should follow the thickness dimension.

Example 1:

1 Int. Dr. 2′8″ x 6′8″ x 1⅜″, fir, 5 x pan, raised panels, cove and bead sticking.

If no further information is given the method of construction and the width of the stiles and rails will be determined by the standards of the factory accepting the order. The door described above would be a stock item with most factories which carry stock doors.

Example 2:

If the door is a stock item described with specifications in a catalog, it is simply ordered by catalog number and the kind of wood wanted, as follows:

1 Dr. 2/8 x 6/8 x 1⅜. W. P. # N. D. 107[1]

This standard method of listing doors shortens the statement, makes it clear, and saves time.

The digit designating feet is separated from the digit designating the inches by the diagonal. The above order is read as follows:

One door, two-eight, six-eight, one and three-eighths, white pine, number N. D., one hundred seven.

Information Required When Listing Doors. The following information must be obtained from the plans and specifications furnished by the architect. He should be consulted if full information is not provided in his drawings. Each item should be described and made clear.

Quantity. Give the number of doors or number of openings and the number of doors per opening such as:

1 door

1 pr. doors to fill one opening

Size. Give the dimensions as width, height, and thickness in that order. State whether one or more doors are required to fill an opening. If accordion doors are needed with half doors at one or both ends, state these requirements.

[1] National Woodwork Manufacturer's Association stock number.

Wood. Specify the type of stock desired, whether the stiles and rails are to be of solid or veneer stock, and whether the panels should be solid or plywood. If different veneers are desired for each side of the door, specify which side each veneer is to go on.

Panels. State the number and arrangement of the panels, whether raised or flat, and whether of plywood or banded.

Glass. State the number and arrangement of lights of glass and whether the door is to be glazed or open. If glazed, specify whether the glass is to be bedded in putty and whether putty or glass bead is to be used. Specify the kind and grade of glass.

Sticking. Specify the kind or shape of sticking desired, such as, ovolo (Fig. 3), or cove and bead (Fig. 4).

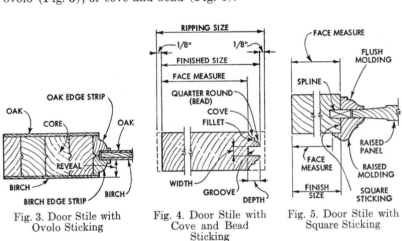

Fig. 3. Door Stile with
Ovolo Sticking

Fig. 4. Door Stile with
Cove and Bead
Sticking

Fig. 5. Door Stile with
Square Sticking

Molding. Specify the kind of planted molding desired, whether flush or raised. If a special design is needed, furnish a detail drawing (Fig. 5).

Construction. Specify a non-standard construction, such as mortise and tenon or half lap, and furnish a detail drawing.

Glue. If a special glue is required, state the kind and the glue manufacturer's type or number.

Special or Odd Doors. If a special or odd door is specified, provide a detail drawing with all the necessary information. If the size, design, and molding requirements of the door are specified in detail, the manufacturing problems are usually left to a shop which is experienced in these matters.

CONSTRUCTION OF DOORS

The basic parts of a door are the stiles, the rails, and the panels. Stiles and rails may be of solid or veneered stock, and panels may be of solid stock or plywood. Panels are flat, raised, or molded. The basic types of door construction are the mortise and tenon joint and the dowel joint.

MORTISE AND TENON CONSTRUCTION

Blind Mortise and Tenon. A blind mortise and tenon joint is one that does not show when the joint is assembled. Figure 6 illustrates how this is achieved. Several factors determine the location and size of a mortise. The following discussion will consider the problems encountered in doors of all types, and to any type of paneled work where the mortise and tenon construction is used.

Width of the Mortise. The width of a mortise is the measurement of the mortise across the face edge of a stile or rail. It is referred to as the *size of the mortise*, regardless of the depth or length, and determines the size of the mortising tool used. It is usually the smallest dimension of a mortise.

Three factors determine the size of the mortising tool to be selected for a job:

1. The thickness of the stiles and rails: For strength proportional to the thickness of the stock, a mortise that is about ⅓ the thickness of the stock is recommended, unless other factors interfere. The following is a table showing recommended mortise sizes for different thicknesses of stock.

TABLE I. STOCK THICKNESS AND MORTISE WIDTH

Thickness of Stock	Width of Mortise
⅝″ to ⅞″	¼″
¾″ to 1¹⁄₁₆″	⁵⁄₁₆″
⅞″ to 1⅜″	⅜″
1⅜″ to 2″	½″
2″ to 2½″	¾″

2. Thickness of the panel: When possible, the size of the mortising tool should correspond to the thickness of the panel. This also allows the haunch of the tenon to fit in the panel groove (Fig. 6).

The thickness of a raised panel is determined by adding the raised

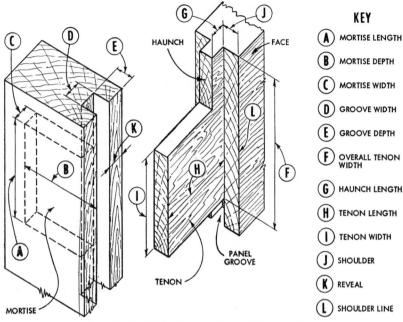

KEY

A MORTISE LENGTH

B MORTISE DEPTH

C MORTISE WIDTH

D GROOVE WIDTH

E GROOVE DEPTH

F OVERALL TENON WIDTH

G HAUNCH LENGTH

H TENON LENGTH

I TENON WIDTH

J SHOULDER

K REVEAL

L SHOULDER LINE

Fig. 6. Blind Mortise and Tenon Construction

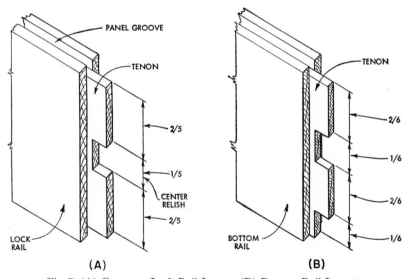

Fig. 7. (A) Center or Lock Rail Layout (B) Bottom Rail Layout

part of the panel to the width of the groove which has been determined by the size of the mortise.

3. The depth of the reveal: If a deep reveal is specified on one side of a door or on the face of paneled work, the size of the mortise may be reduced to line the mortise up with the groove or rabbet.

Location of the Mortise.   The mortise is made on the edge of a stile or rail, and its location depends on the design of the sticking and the amount of reveal desired. On standard doors the mortise is centered and the molded reveal is the same on both sides. In special work the mortise may be lined up with a design having a deeper reveal on one side. Where possible, the mortise is located in line with the rabbet or groove to facilitate relishing and to eliminate difficulties in coping.

The location of the mortise on the inside edge of the rail is also determined by the finish cut of the detailed sticking. The inside end of a mortise should align exactly with the bottom of the groove or rabbet. This rule applies whether the mortise is in line or straddled with the groove or rabbet. In the case of straddling, the tenon must be trimmed, and an extra groove must be cut for the haunch.

When square or sash sticking is involved, the inside end of the mortise aligns exactly with the inside edge of the rail.

Depth of the Groove or Rabbet.   The depth of the groove or rabbet should be determined before a mortise layout is started. Standard shop practice is followed in all cases where a special design or detail does not otherwise specify. Aside from design factors, three rules should be considered:

1. A groove $\frac{3}{8}''$ deep is considered sufficient for plywood panels which shrink very little.

2. A groove $\frac{1}{2}''$ deep is sometimes made to compensate for shrinkage in a large solid panel.

3. A groove $\frac{9}{16}''$ deep is made to permit a $\frac{1}{2}''$ tenon when a stub tenon is used with or without dowels.

Length of the Mortise.   The length of the mortise is determined by the width of the rail. For the strongest job about two-thirds of the over-all width of the tenon is best. See Figure 6.

When laying out a mortise for a standard width center rail, muntin, or mullion, the length of the mortise is ordinarily the same as the over-all width of the tenon.

For wide lock rails or bottom rails the mortise is interrupted at intervals to prevent the weakening of the stile by a long mortise (Fig. 7). Proportions similar to those on a standard top rail should be used.

Depth of the Mortise. The depth of the mortise is determined by the width of the stile. Three rules should be remembered:

1. In general, the depth of the mortise should be at least two-thirds the width of the stile.

2. In a narrow stile the mortise should be as deep as possible and yet leave enough stock on the outside edge of the stile for fitting without cutting into the mortise.

3. In a wide stile the limitations of the mortising equipment may determine the depth of the mortise.

Size of the Tenon. The size of the tenon is decided on only after the size and location of the mortise, as described above, have been determined.

To prevent the end of the tenon from butting into the bottom of the mortise, the tenon should be not more than $\frac{1}{4}''$ shorter than the depth of the mortise. If the tenon strikes the bottom of the mortise before the shoulder touches the stile, an "open" joint will result.

On the other hand, if too much space is left between the bottom of the mortise and the end of the tenon, shrinkage may cause a depression on the face of the stile. This may occur especially when a thin wall is left between the side of the mortise and the face of the stile.

The haunch of the tenon should be made about $\frac{1}{32}''$ shorter than the depth of the groove to allow a tight joint on the face of the rail.

Through Mortise and Tenon Construction. A *through mortise,* as the name implies, extends through the stile, and the end of the tenon shows on the outside edge of the assembled door. This type of joint was formerly used exclusively in doors made by hand for exterior use. The joint was coated with white lead and wedges were driven into the outside end of the tenon to increase sturdiness. This method is still occasionally specified where cost is not a major consideration. However, modern equipment and modern glues make this type of construction unnecessary except for special purposes.

The layout for this kind of mortise is similar to that of the blind mortise except for the depth. In this case, however, the mortise should be carefully laid out on both edges of the stile as the mortise must be cut from both edges, to prevent the tearing of the grain.

DOWELED CONSTRUCTION

The development of modern multiple spindle boring equipment permits an economical method of door construction which is particularly applicable to mass production. However, the limitations of multiple spindle boring equipment determine to some degree, the spacing of the dowels. The center-to-center distance between dowels cannot be less than the adjusting limits of the machine. The dowels are centered according to the thickness of the stile and rail. The thickness of the panel used has no bearing on the diameter of the dowel.

The ends of the door rails are coped over the molding on the stile with a stub tenon which fits into the panel groove.

Location of Dowels. If only one dowel is used in a rail it is centered along the width of the rail between the bottom of the panel groove and the outside edge.

Where two or more dowels are used the inside dowel is centered not less than one dowel diameter from the bottom of the groove in the rail.

The outside dowel should be centered not less than two dowel diameters from the outside edge of the rail. This permits the fitting of the door without cutting into the dowel. A center dowel should be spaced halfway between the other two dowels. See Figure 8.

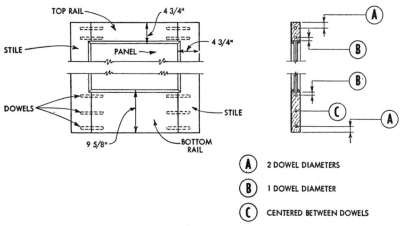

Fig. 8. Doweled Construction

The minimum spacing between the centers of dowels must conform to the spacing capacity of the spindles on the boring equipment. Where adjustment permits, the spacing should not exceed $3\frac{1}{2}''$.

Size of Dowels. The diameter of a dowel is determined by the thickness of the door. It should be not less than $\frac{3}{8}''$ for a door $\frac{3}{4}''$ thick, and not less than $\frac{1}{2}''$ for doors $1\frac{1}{8}''$, $1\frac{3}{8}''$, or $1\frac{3}{4}''$ thick.

The length of the dowel is determined by the width of the door stile.

The dowels should be approximately 5″ long for doors 1⅛″, 1⅜″, or 1¾″ thick.

On standard width stiles half the length of the dowel should extend into the stile and rail each. On narrow stiles the dowel should extend into the stile not less than two-thirds of the stile width, but should not extend so far that it will be exposed when the door is fitted.

VENEERED PANELED DOORS

The lumber for the interior finish of a residence, bank, office, school, or library varies according to the owner's requirements and the architect's design.

Beautiful hardwoods can be selected for the interior trim, doors, wall paneling, cabinets, fixtures, stairways, and other pieces of cabinet work. In order to match the interior woodwork, doors should be made of the same kind of hardwood. However, it is not practical to make hardwood doors out of solid material because of the tendency of hardwood to warp. Hence veneered door stiles and rails are made to meet the matching requirements. Otherwise, the layout procedure is as if the door were made of solid stock. All the exposed edges of a built-up door stile or rail are banded or edged with a piece of hardwood which matches the veneer. This built-up stile or core is then veneered with carefully selected veneers which match the room in which the door is to be hung.

VENEERED FLUSH DOORS

A flush door is one in which the two faces of the door form a flat surface. Built-up cores, either solid (Fig. 9), or hollow (Fig. 10), are manufactured as the base for the flush door. A hollow core door is lighter, easier to handle, and yet is just as durable as a solid core door. The two exposed edges of the core are banded with hardwood; the two faces of the door are veneered with carefully matched veneer to give the effect of one piece of hardwood.

LAYOUT OF DOORS

In door construction layout work involves much more than just an understanding of construction methods and an ability to solve arithmetical problems. A knowledge of wood and its characteristics is also

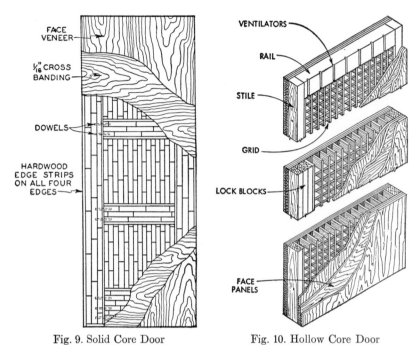

FACE VENEER

1/16" CROSS BANDING

DOWELS

HARDWOOD EDGE STRIPS ON ALL FOUR EDGES

VENTILATORS

RAIL

STILE

GRID

LOCK BLOCKS

FACE PANELS

Fig. 9. Solid Core Door   Fig. 10. Hollow Core Door

necessary. The direction of grain is particularly important so that when the wood is machine-molded the cutters will cut with the grain. Twisting, bending, and other defects of wood should be noted and understood so that unsuitable stock may be rejected before the job progresses so far as to make the article useless because of a flaw in one piece. Minor defects can sometimes be adapted in such a manner that the usefulness of the article will not be affected.

The layout man should check every piece of door stock for direction of grain, twist, bend, bow, and for natural defects that may require it to be rejected.

Face Marking. In layout work, a system of face marking the stock is followed throughout the industry. Face marking serves four main purposes:

1. To designate the working face of every member: This is done so that the same side is used against the fence or table in the various operations. The parts are assembled with the face marks all on the same side, so that the joints on the face of the door will be flush.

2. To designate the most suitable side of the material for a face

side: This involves laying out the stock so that it is milled with the grain. The characteristics of the grain such as color, direction, and design should make a harmonious blend of the various members. This is particularly important in achieving natural or stained finished effects in hardwood. The locating of minor defects, so that they may be eliminated in milling, or so that at least one side of a finished door will be nearly perfect, should be considered, and the stock face marked accordingly.

3. To designate the most suitable edge to mold or use as a face edge.

4. To pair the stiles and other members which are so shaped that, when milled, they may be used only in one position, such as right, left, top, or bottom.

Several methods of face marking are used throughout the industry, each being defended by its users as being the best. One effective method is illustrated in Figure 11. Start with a loop which resembles a figure "6," or a reverse "6," and draw the tail so that it points to and ends at the face edge. This sign indicates with one stroke the face side and face edge and enables the machine operator to know this at a glance.

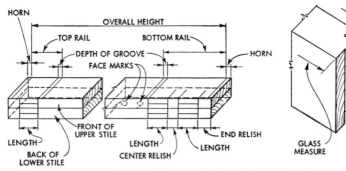

Fig. 11. Layout and Marking of Stiles for Mortise and Tenon Joint

Fig. 12. Sash Door Rail to Match Rabbeted Stile

LAYOUT AND MARKING OF MORTISE AND TENON AND DOWELED DOORS

The layout is done on the back side of a stile or rail, that is, on the side opposite to that which is face marked. Layout involves the establishment of the length and height, the overall width of rails, the depth of grooves or rabbets, and the length of mortises and width of tenons.

The marking is done on the edge of the stile and only those lines locating the mortise are transferred to the edge.

The between-shoulders length of a door rail and the length of the tenon are measured and marked on the back of one rail only. The stops on the tenoner are set to make duplicate lengths on all rails.

The doweled construction requires the laying out of only one stile if a multiple-spindle boring machine is used. This permits the duplicating of dowel holes without marking.

Laying Out a Mortise. The procedure for laying out and marking stiles for a mortise is as follows (Fig. 11):

1. Face mark and "pair" the stiles.
2. Lay off the over-all height (finished length) on the back of one stile leaving horns at each end.
(A horn is the extra length of stile from ⅜″ to ½″ at each end. It protects the corners of a door during handling and shipping. The door fitter trims it off when hanging the door.)
3. Measure from the top mark of the finish height and mark the width of the top rail.
4. Measure from the bottom mark of the finish height and mark the width of the bottom rail.
5. Lay off from the inside edge of the top and bottom rails a distance equal to the depth of the groove.
6. Measuring from the bottom of the groove, proportion the remaining width of the top and bottom rails for the desired length of mortise.
7. Place the stiles in a paired position and mark the face edge with only those lines which indicate the length of the mortise. Any number of stiles of the same layout may be marked from one stile pattern.
8. Intermediate rails are located according to the door detail. The length of the mortise is equal to the width of the intermediate rail, minus the depth of the two grooves. On wide rails a center relish may be required. See Figure 7A.

Laying Out Stiles for Dowels. The procedure for laying out stiles for dowels is as follows (Fig. 8):

1. Follow steps 1–5 above which describe the layout for a mortise.
2. Mark the center line of the dowels as described previously under *Location of Dowels*, or follow the practice of the shop in which the work is to be done.
3. Place the stiles in a paired position and mark the back side of each mate.

LAYING OUT GLAZED DOORS

Doors requiring the use of glass instead of wood panels are called *glazed* or *glass doors*, or more specifically, *sash* or *French doors*. The construction of a door to receive panes of glass necessitates the rabbeting instead of grooving of the edges of the stiles and rails. The glass is held in place by means of a mold called a glass bead or glass stop.

The laying out of glass doors sometimes requires that the shoulders of each tenon be offset; that is, the distance between the shoulders on a rail which is to receive glass should be longer on the rabbeted side (Fig. 12). The layout should be carefully done as many errors may occur. The machine man may rabbet the stile on the wrong face, or he may make the offset shoulder of the rail on the wrong face so that it does not match the rabbeted stile. Follow all the layout steps given for the mortise and tenon construction but observe the special instructions for rail layouts given above.

LAYING OUT A PAIR OF DOORS

When a pair of doors are hinged in the same door frame or door jamb, there should be no light passing through the crack between the doors. There are two methods of solving this problem:

1. Use a T-astragal molding for the stiles that meet (Fig. 13).
2. Use a rabbeted joint for the stiles that meet (Fig. 14).

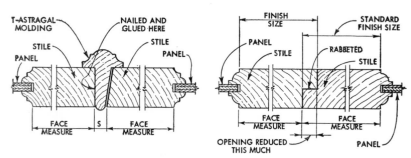

Fig. 13. Pair of Doors Using T-Astragal Mold   Fig. 14. Stock Doors Rabbeted in Pairs

The job specifications, which should take into account the conditions of use, determine the method of laying out a door:

1. When an astragal molding is desired (Fig. 13), either of two methods may be used:
a. Make the door frame wider by the amount of space that will be taken up by the astragal mold. This permits the use of stock size doors.
b. Reduce the between-the-shoulders length on each door rail by one half the space that will be taken up by the astragal.

2. If the edges of stock size doors are rabbeted, the door frame must be reduced in width to account for the fact that the meeting stiles will overlap an amount equal to the depth of the rabbet (Fig. 14).

3. If the face measure of the four stiles must be equal, a stock door cannot be used. The width of both meeting stiles must be increased an amount equal to the depth of the rabbet. The between-the-shoulders length of the rails must be reduced by an amount equal to one-half the depth of the rabbet. A bead should be run on the exposed part of the rabbet to balance the face measure of the stiles (Fig. 15).

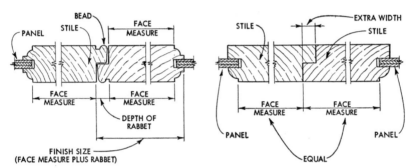

Fig. 15. Pair of Doors with Beaded Rabbet

Fig. 16. Rabbetted Pair of Doors Exposed on One Side Only

4. If a pair of meeting doors are exposed on one side only, as with a closet, a flush rabbet may be used. This requires an increase in the width of one stile only by an amount equal to the depth of the rabbet. After the rabbet is made, the face measure of the meeting stiles will be equal (Fig. 16). The rails are constructed normally.

LAYING OUT FOLDING OR ACCORDION DOORS

Folding doors are made with half doors at one or both sides of the opening depending on whether the doors are to be folded to one or both sides of the opening. The half door is hinged to the door jamb while the full doors are hinged to the half door and to each other. They are hung on an overhead pivot that slides in a metal track. See Figure 17. A careful check must be made of the hardware to be used. If instructions and layout diagrams are furnished by the hardware manufacturer, they should be followed closely by the mill layout man.

The half door measures one half the width of a full door minus an amount equal to the distance A between the center of the door thickness and the center of the hinge pin.

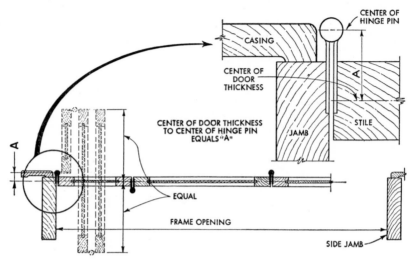

Fig. 17. Layout of Folding or Accordion Doors

Example:

1. Assume that a door frame opening which is 27'0" wide is to be filled with 8 full doors and 2 half doors. Distance A in Fig. 17 is given as $1^{11}\!/_{16}$". Find the width of each full and half door.

Solution:

a. 8 full doors and 2 half doors total 9 full doors.

b. Each half door will be equal to one-half the width of a full door minus $1^{11}\!/_{16}$". Therefore, add twice this amount to the opening space:

$$27'0'' + 3\%'' = 27'3\%''$$

c. Divide this total by 9 to get the width of one full door:

$$(27'3\%'') \div 9 = 3'0\%''$$

d. Subtract $1^{11}\!/_{16}$" from one-half the width of a full door to get the width for a half door:

$$(3'3\%'' \div 2) - 1^{11}\!/_{16}'' = 1'4\frac{1}{2}''.$$

DETAIL DOORS

Detailed doors may be said to include any door that deviates in design from a standard stock door. Stock or standard designs in odd sizes are called *odd stock*. Stock doors that deviate from the straight-line construction are sometimes called *detail doors*.

The number of designs feasible in detail doors makes it impossible to consider every particular design. Standard methods of construction and layout are employed in their manufacture. When special methods have to be used the job is generally given to an experienced craftsman who can devise ways and means of completing the job. Figure 18 shows a common example of detail door construction.

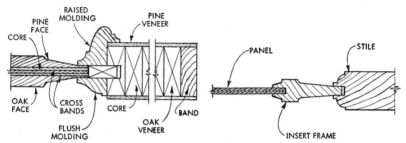

Fig. 18. Detail Door with Flush and Raised Molding

Fig. 19. Detail of Insert Panel Frame

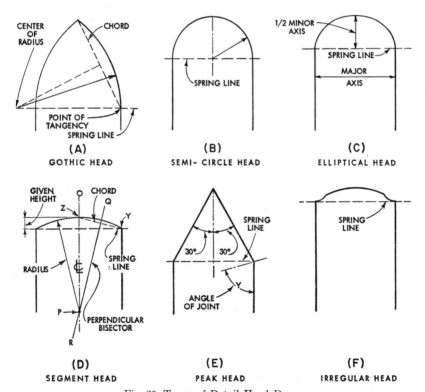

Fig. 20. Types of Detail Head Doors

Detail of Insert Panel Frame. Figure 19 illustrates a stock design that is sometimes used in a detail door. The corners of the insert frame are mitered, glued, and fastened with clamp nails.

Detail Head Doors. Detail head doors may be classified into two general types:

1. The square top type with curved panel or glass lines.

2. The curved top type with parallel curves in the panel or glass lines.

Each of the general types may be broken down into the Gothic, circle, elliptical, segment, peak, and irregular head types (Fig. 20).

Laying Out a Detail Head. All detail heads are laid out geometrically. The architect usually shows on his plans the exact shape of the detail head. The cabinetmaker should check the architect's drawings carefully and determine the type of detail required. In most cases the plans show the radius centers on which the layout work is to be based. The center of an arc is usually shown on the horizontal spring line which the draftsman established when making the drawing.

THE SPRING LINE IN DETAIL HEADS

The term *spring line,* or *springing line,* is defined in architecture as a line, usually horizontal, from which an arc springs, as in an arched doorway. The center of the arc which springs from the line must be located on the line, as in the Gothic, semicircle, and elliptical heads; or it may be located off the line, as in the segment and irregular heads. In all cases, the spring line connects the points of intersection formed by the side and top members of the door.

RULES FOR LOCATING THE SPRING LINE

The over-all width and height of a door is always given on the architectural plans. The height of the side members only varies with and depends upon the type of detail head indicated. The layout for each of the detail heads shown in Figure 20 is described below.

Gothic Head. In the standard layout of the Gothic head the width of the opening is equal to the radius of the members forming the top. To determine the location of the spring line of a Gothic head door it is necessary to make a full size layout and measure the vertical distance from the spring line to the peak of the door.

To find the radius for a Gothic head after the spring line has been established, construct a perpendicular bisector to the chord which connects the extremities of the arc at the peak and the point of tangency at the side of the door. The intersection of the bisector and the extended spring line is the center of the required radius. See Fig. 20A.

Semi-circle Head. The radius of a semi-circle head is half the width of the door. The spring line is, therefore, located at a distance from the top equal to half the width of the door. See Fig. 20B.

Elliptical Head. In the laying out of an elliptical head, a good proportion can be obtained by making the rise equal to one-third the width of the door. The rise is the vertical distance between the spring line and the peak. If the spring line is shown on a blueprint, the rise will be equal to half the minor axis of the ellipse, while the width of the door will be equal to the major axis. See Fig. 20C.

The ellipse may be laid out by any standard method, or as illustrated in Figures 11, 12, and 22 of Chapter X. If the string or trammel method is used it is necessary to scribe the inside line, which establishes the inside edge of an elliptical rail, parallel to the first line laid out, which established the outside edge. If two elliptical arcs were laid out by the string or trammel method using the inside and outside dimensions of the rail, the two lines would not be exactly parallel at all points. Hence the necessity for scribing the second line.

Most layout men prefer to use the two- or three-radii method of drawing an ellipse. In this method parallel arcs may be drawn from the established centers to form the elliptical door head and the casing of the frame.

Segment Head. The radius of a segment head door is usually, but not always equal to the width of the door. The center of the segment is located on the vertical center line of the door. The spring line may be located by measuring the amount of rise required from the top of the door to the spring line. See Fig. 20D.

To lay out the segment:
1. Draw the vertical center line of the door (line OP).
2. Draw a line connecting a point of tangency and the peak of the door (line YZ).
3. Draw a perpendicular bisector QR to YZ and intersect it with OP.
4. Lay out the segment using P as the center and Y and Z as points in the segment.

Peak Head. A peak head is usually laid out at an angle of sixty degrees. To find the height of the spring line make a full size layout.

When the spring line is given, the simplest method to lay out the angle is to make a full size layout. The steel square is very useful here. To determine the angle Y which joins the peak head to the stile, bisect the angle of intersection.

Irregular Head. The irregular head door may take any combination or kind of geometrical shapes and no specific rule can be given covering its layout and construction.

Layout and Construction of Detail Head Doors. The layout of detail head doors is similar in all respects to the layout of an ordinary door except for the location of the spring line and the methods used to join the detail head to the stiles.

There are two standard methods used in constructing a detail head door:

1. The slot and spline method used in curved heads.

2. The mortise and tenon method used in square-top detail head doors.

Slot and Spline Construction Method. Figure 21 illustrates the construction used in a Gothic head. The segments of the head are fitted to a full size and accurate layout pattern. They are then slotted at the top to receive a spline and also at the bottom to receive the tenoned ends of the stile. This construction is applicable to all detail heads shown in Figure 20. The slots are made as deep as possible and the tenons which act as splines, are relished to fit the slots.

Mortise and Tenon Construction. Figure 22 shows a layout for a square-top detail head. Note that the inside edge of the stile is exactly aligned with the curved part of the rail, but that the square shoulders of the rail are recessed into the stile about one-half inch. This is to gain support for the sticking at the point of tangency.

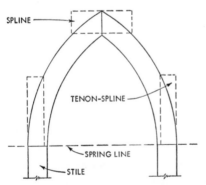

Fig. 21. Slot and Spline Construction for Detail Head

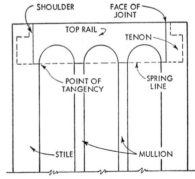

Fig. 22. Mortise and Tenon Joint for Detail Head

DOOR STANDARDS

The *National Woodwork Manufacturers Association* (*U.S.A.*), composed of many leading manufacturers throughout the United States, has published a door-standards catalog outlining the requirements of materials, workmanship, and construction which should be adhered to by their members. Both the cabinetmaker and the millman will find this catalog useful.

REVIEW QUESTIONS

1. Give a definition for the following door terms: *standard design, standard size, stock size, odd size, special* or *detail design.*

2. Define the terms *stile* and *rail.*

3. What is the difference between a mullion and a muntin?

4. What is a reveal?

5. What is the difference between the ripping size and the finished size of a door?

6. In what order are measurements given when a door is listed?

7. Name the two basic methods used for fastening door rails to door stiles.

8. What factor determines the length of a tenon?

9. What factor determines the depth of a mortise?

10. How does the layout man prevent a tenon from causing an open joint?

11. Why should door stiles be laid off in pairs?

12. What procedure may be followed to avoid showing a crack between the doors when a pair of doors is being laid out?

13. Name six types of detail heads.

14. What is meant by the term *spring line?*

15. What is the mathematical relationship between the radius of a circle head and the width of the door?

Windows and Sash

INTRODUCTION TO CHAPTER XV

Among the most important items in the construction of modern buildings are windows and sash. This statement is true even though the development of air conditioning engineering now permits the construction of buildings without windows.

A window is simply an opening in the wall of a building for admitting light and air, and for permitting the occupants of the building a view to the

Fig. 1. A Picture Window
Courtesy of Curtis Companies, Inc.

exterior (Fig. 1). However, the construction of a window requires considerable knowledge and skill. What shape is the window to be? What are its dimensions? How will it open if it opens at all? What kind of glass is it to have? What shape will the panes of glass be? How is the wood frame to be constructed? Fig. 1 shows a well-designed picture window.

WINDOW DESIGN

The shape and size of a window and how it is to open are determined by the architect and the owner. The design of windows should receive very careful consideration as it affects the proportion, line, and form of a building, and sizes must conform to building code requirements. Windows must also withstand all kinds of weather conditions.

The following pages provide essential information for the woodworker who has a part in the manufacture of windows and sash, and who should have an understanding of the trade terminology. Figures 2 and 3 illustrate some basic sash and window constructions and terminology. Figure 20, Chapter V illustrates in detail the basic parts of a double-hung window frame.

SASH TERMINOLOGY

Opening. The window or sash frame set in a wall to receive a sash or window, also the measurement of the sash or window frame at the points where a sash or window is fitted.

Sash. A single frame, movable or stationary, rabbeted to receive one or more panes of glass.

Stile. The outside vertical member of a sash.

Rail. The top, bottom, or center horizontal member of a sash.

Bar or Muntin. A vertical or horizontal member in a sash which divides the sash frame into light openings.

Lug. An extension of the stiles beyond the meeting rails of a sash, usually ogee-shaped.

Light. A pane of glass; also an opening in a sash for receiving a pane of glass.

Sticking. Molding and rabbet used on the inside edge of sash members to secure the panes of glass and to add a decorative effect. Ogee molding is standard although some manufacturers use ovolo sticking.

Bedding. The application of putty in the rabbet before the glass is set to provide a *bed* for the glass.

Face Puttying. The filling of the rabbet with putty after glazing to make a water-tight joint on the sash exterior.

Back Puttying. The forcing of putty between the glass and the rabbet after glazing to fill any voids due to the unevenness of the glass.

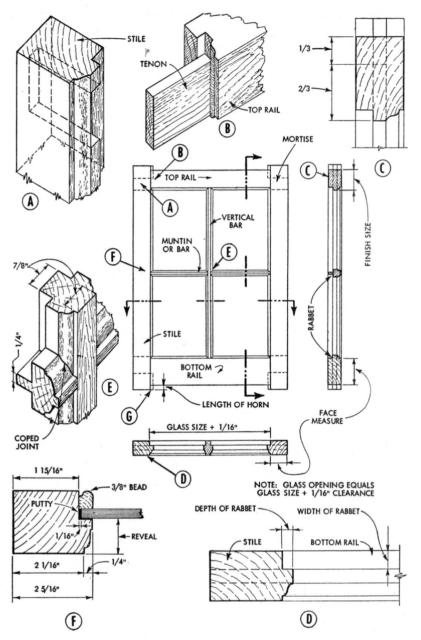

Fig. 2. Sash Construction and Layout Terminology

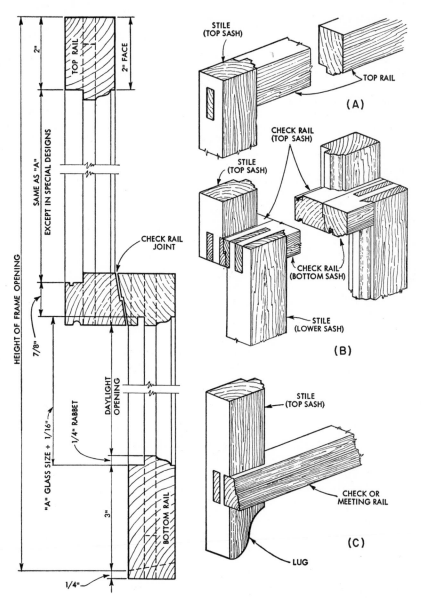

Fig. 3. Double Hung Window Construction and Layout Terminology

Double-Hung or Check Rail Window. Two separate sash made to fill one opening. Each is made to slide vertically and is separated from the other by a parting stop or bead.

Check or Meeting Rail. The middle horizontal member of a double-hung window formed by the bottom rail of the top, and the top rail of the bottom sash.

Triple Hung Window. Three sash made to slide vertically in one opening.

Plain Rail Window. Two sash similar to a double-hung window except that the meeting rails are made as thick as the stiles and no parting stop is installed.

Plain Rail. Meeting rails of a plain rail window, and distinct from *check rail*.

Transom or Cottage Window. A double-hung window whose upper sash is shorter than the lower sash.

Transom Sash. A single sash made to fill an opening over a door or window, and separated from it by a *transom bar*.

Casement Sash. One or more sash made to fill an opening, to swing in or out, and hinged at the side, the top, or at the bottom.

French Windows. Casement sash extending from 6″ to 8″ off the floor to door height, usually hinged in pairs, with door-type locks.

Cellar, Barn, or Utility Sash. A single sash, hinged or stationary, made to fill an opening in a cellar, barn, or utility building.

Storm Sash. A single sash fitted outside a window frame to provide insulation against cold weather. The air space between the storm and the regular sash provides additional protection.

Open Sash. A sash frame in which glass has not been installed.

Glazed Sash. A sash frame in which glass has been installed by means of glazing points and putty, or by means of glass stops or beads.

Screen. A removable frame, usually of wood, and covered with screen mesh, and which is placed outside a window frame to keep out insects.

CONSTRUCTION SPECIFICATIONS

Opening Dimensions. Dimensions of sash, windows, and casements should be stated as over-all opening sizes and expressed in feet and inches, the width, height, and thickness being given in that order. The over-all dimensions are based on even and odd sizes of glass. Fractional inch sizes may result when bars are inserted to divide the glass opening into more than one light.

The standard over-all width of a two-light double-hung window is four inches greater than the width of an even inch pane of glass, while the standard height is six inches greater than the total height of the two lights. Thus the over-all size of a window with two 24″ x 24″ lights is 2′4″ x 4′6″.

A one-light sash requires four inches to be added to the width of the pane of glass and five inches to be added to the height. Thus, a one-light sash 2′4″ x 4′6″ will require a pane of glass 24″ x 49″.

Standard and stock windows and sash are made 1⅜″ or 1¾″ thick (pp. 210–11) while storm, barn, utility, and plain rail sash are usually made 1⅛″ thick. Windows and sash 1¾″ thick or thicker are usually made to order only. Pre-fit windows and sash are made ⅛″ narrower and ¹⁄₁₆″ shorter than the nominal sizes specified on the plans to provide operating clearance.

Too much care cannot be exercised in ordering a list of windows and sash, or in laying them out for manufacture. Dimensions should be given in the correct sequence and conform to the frame measurements.

It is customary to list sash dimensions without using feet (′) or inch (″) symbols. It is important to note that the thickness is always given *last*.

Thus, one window two feet four inches wide, three feet ten inches high, and one and three-eighths inches thick is listed:

1 Win. 2/4 x 3/10 x 1⅜.

Number of Lights. The number of lights specified usually refers to the *total* required for a given opening. For instance, the number of lights specified for a pair of casements is the total number of lights required in both sash.

If more than one light is required for a given sash, the number of lights wide or high should be stated.

Examples: 1 Trans. 2/8 x 1/4 x 1⅜, 4 lt. wide.
1 Pr. casmt. sash 3/6 x 4/0 x 1⅜, 16 lt. 4 high.

In this case "16 lt. 4 high" means that each sash will be cut 2 lights wide and 4 lights high.

Double-hung windows have a minimum of 2 lights, one in each sash. However, the top sash may be cut up into more than one light or both sash may be cut up into an equal number of lights. The specifications should leave no doubt of what is meant.

Examples: 1 D.H.W. 2/0 x 3/6 x 1⅜, 2 lt.
1 D.H.W. 2/0 x 3/6 x 1⅜, 2 lt.; top sash cut 3 lt. 1 high.

Thickness and Quality of Glass. Single strength "B" quality glass is normally used in all sash unless otherwise specified, except for some larger sizes which can be had only in double strength. However, it is usual to specify the thickness and kind of glass wanted.

Examples: 1 D.H.W. 2/0 x 3/6 x 1⅜, 2 lt. S.S.B.
             1 Pr. casmt. 4/0 x 3/6 x 1⅜, 2 lt. D.S.A.

S.S.B. means *single strength "B" quality glass,* and *D.S.A.* means *double strength "A" quality glass.*

SASH LAYOUT

Figure 2 shows the layout and terminology of the basic sash members.

Horns.   Because of possible slight irregularities in the layout and mortising of a stile, an extra length called a *horn,* is left on each end of a stile and trimmed off after assembling (Fig. 2G). This is usually done on the job unless it is made pre-fit at the factory. It is not to be confused with the ogee lug which protrudes beyond the check rail of a double-hung window and is *not* trimmed off. See Fig. 3C.

Size of Sash Members.   Unless otherwise specified, the width of the stiles and rails follows the standard practice of the factory where the order is placed. This is true for stock and odd sizes, as well as for special designs. However, if it is necessary to specify the width of the sash frame members, it should be stated whether it is to be over-all finish size or face measure size.

To-Rabbet Size.   The *to-rabbet size* of a member is the width exclusive of the rabbet (Fig. 3). If the depth of the rabbet on a stile is ¼″, the finish size must be ¼″ greater than the to-rabbet size. If the depth of the rabbet on a bar is ¼″, the finish size must be ½″ greater than the to-rabbet size.

Between-Glass Size.   The face measure of a bar or muntin is often referred to as the *between-glass size.* Eastern Standards call for a 3⁄16″ deep rabbet on stock sash.

Glass Size Clearance.   Window glass comes from the glass manufacturer accurately cut to the specified sizes. However, when glass is cut, the edge may break with a slight bevel or somewhat irregularly. For this reason it is common practice to make the glass opening in a sash 1⁄16″ greater than the glass that is to fit in that opening (Fig. 3A).

If a sash is to be cut up into a number of lights, allowance is sometimes made on the outside stiles and rails to compensate for the bars and to allow clearance for additional lights. In this manner standard size glass may be used. On odd size sash the glass opening is divided as required and the glass is cut to fit.

Daylight Opening. The opening between sash members through which light passes is called the daylight opening. If standard size glass is used, the size of the opening must conform to the size of the glass. For a $\frac{1}{4}''$ rabbet, the daylight opening should be $\frac{7}{16}''$ less than the glass size, which has $\frac{1}{16}''$ clearance (Fig. 3). For a $\frac{3}{16}''$ rabbet the daylight opening should be $\frac{5}{16}''$ less than the glass size.

Between-Shoulders Measurements. The *rails* of a sash are tenoned to fit the mortises in the stiles, the *shoulder* of the tenon being fitted to the bottom of the rabbet for the glass. Hence when laying out a sash to glass size the *between-shoulders* measure of the rail is the size of the glass *plus* $\frac{1}{16}''$ for clearance.

When laying out rails to over-all frame opening size, the between-shoulders measure of the rails will be the over-all measure less the face measure of the stiles.

Rabbeting for Plate Glass. Sash made to hold *plate glass* are usually $1\frac{3}{4}''$ thick and should have a $\frac{3}{8}''$ deep rabbet (Fig. 2F). The rabbet should accommodate the extra thickness of glass and provide more room for the glass stop. It is common practice to bed the plate glass in putty for waterproofing and to fasten it in the rabbet with a wood stop or glass bead because of its weight.

Because of its extra thickness, plate glass may leave an irregular edge when cut. For this reason it is common practice to allow $\frac{1}{8}''$ clearance in the frame in addition to the glass size, hence the $\frac{3}{8}''$ rabbet.

Mortise and Tenon Sizes. In sash layout the mortise is usually cut in the stile and the tenon is cut on the rail (Figs. 2A and 2B). The thickness of the sash determines the size of the mortise, which in turn determines the size of the tenon which fits into it. Since the mortise is centered on the thickness dimension of the sash, it also determines the width of the rabbet, except when rabbeting is being made for plate glass.

The length of the mortise is determined by the width of the rail and is usually made about two-thirds to three-fourths the width of the tenon. For a $2''$ face measure top rail the tenon is generally made $1\frac{1}{2}''$ wide, and for a $3''$ face measure bottom rail a $2''$ wide tenon is usual.

The relish of the tenon is coped over the face edge of the stile and the shoulder is coped over the molding. Through mortise and tenon construction is common for all except casement sash in which the edges show when the sash is in an open position. For this reason some manufacturers use a blind mortise and tenon on casement sash.

Sash Bars. Unless specified in the order, it is optional with the manufacturer whether bars are mortised or coped (Fig. 2E). In the former case a blind mortise and tenon is usual, the mortise being made to the finish width of the bar.

Coped bars are cut to the net length of the glass opening, coped over the molding and edge, and nailed into place. Coped bars are common among most manufacturers of stock sash in ordinary sizes. Large sash with heavy bars should be mortised and tenoned.

Rabbeted Pairs of Sash. When two sash are hinged in the same frame using a rabbeted joint where the center stiles of the sash meet, they are called *a pair of casement sash* (Fig. 4). The width of the pair is equal to the width between the jambs of the frame. The height usually equals the standard sash or window height.

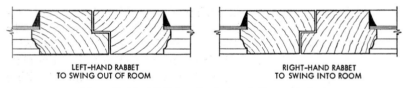

LEFT-HAND RABBET
TO SWING OUT OF ROOM

RIGHT-HAND RABBET
TO SWING INTO ROOM

Fig. 4. Rabbeted Joints for Pairs of Casement Sash

The width of each sash must include half the depth of a $\frac{1}{2}''$ rabbet. To illustrate: one pair of $3'0'' \times 3'0''$ casement sash means *two* sash each $1'6\frac{1}{4}'' \times 3'0''$. It is common practice to add $\frac{1}{4}''$ to each of the center or meeting stiles for a $\frac{1}{2}''$ rabbet or $\frac{3}{16}''$ for a $\frac{3}{8}''$ rabbet in order to allow for an even inch size glass.

When ordering rabbeted pairs of casements it is necessary to state whether the sash will swing in or out and whether the left or right hand sash will open first. See Fig. 4.

Storm Sash. As the name implies, storm sash are installed to provide additional insulation against cold weather. They are made like any other sash, except that the thickness is usually $1\frac{1}{8}''$, unless otherwise specified. The width of storm sash is standard. For height, $1''$ is added to the height of the regular window opening to accommodate the pitch of the sill and $1''$ more for the sub-sill if such is used. Storm sash are fastened in the *outside* window frame reveal by means of metal fasteners or hangers. This permits their easy installation and removal. When an order is received for storm sash, carefully check the height to be sure that it has either been taken on the job or that the pitch of the sill and the frame layout is standard.

The lights of storm sash are usually of the same size as on regular sash. The bottom rail is made wider to make up for the extra height of the sash.

LAYOUT FOR DOUBLE-HUNG WINDOWS

The details involved in the layout and construction of double-hung windows according to either Eastern or Western Standards of course vary. However, the basic principles are the same for either standard, and a mastery of one implies a mastery of the other. Significant differences in detail will be found in the following factors: depth of the rabbet for glass, construction and size of check rails, sizes of bars, glass, and other parts.

Fig. 3 shows a typical layout of the vertical section of a double-hung window which may be employed by manufacturers not adhering strictly to the standards, and on special orders. Figs. 3A and 3B show the manner in which the stiles of the top and bottom sash are laid out.

Check Rail Construction. Figure 3B shows an isometric view of the manner of joining the check rails to the stiles.

Lugs on Window Sash. Lugs (Fig. 3C) are usually made 3″ to 3½″ long and serve to strengthen the sash where the check rail joins the stiles. They are usually ogee-shaped. Making lugs on the top sash is standard practice with some factories while it is considered special with others. On special orders, especially on heavy or large windows, lugs may be made on bottom sash.

IRREGULAR AND SHAPED HEAD LAYOUT

Irregular Heads. Figure 5 shows some typical designs of *irregular* or *shaped heads*. The layout and construction described in the following examples should enable one to adopt a method which would serve for any type of irregular head.

Height and Spring Line Measuring Points. An order for an irregular head sash or window must specify the opening size and thickness of the sash together with the information regarding rise, radius, and shape, and is sometimes accompanied by a template. The height of the opening is understood to mean the over-all height including the rise from the spring line to the top.

The length of the straight stile up to the spring line is determined by subtracting the rise of the irregular head, from the over-all height, beginning at the spring line.

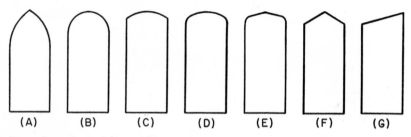

Fig. 5. Irregular and Shaped Heads for Windows and Sash. (A) Gothic Head (B) Circle Head (C) Segment Head (D) Elliptical Head (E) Tudor Head (F) Peak Head (G) Rake Head

Peak Head Layout. A peak head sash or window (Fig. 6) may be constructed by means of dowels and splines, or a slotted mortise and tenon. The rise and opening height being given, the length of the stile is found by subtracting the rise from the opening height. The length of the peak head sides can be found by making a full size layout of the

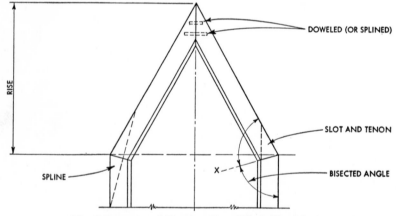

Fig. 6. Layout and Construction of Peak Head Sash

top or by measuring on a steel square the diagonal of the run and the rise.

Circle Head Layout. A circle head sash is semicircular, the radius in all instances being one-half the width of the sash (Fig. 7). The rise of the quadrant is necessarily the same as the outside radius. The joints are perpendicular to each other if two segments are used. The length of the chord of the arc forming the quadrant can be established by means of a steel square.

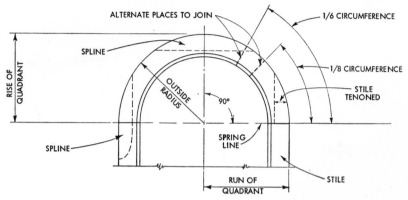

Fig. 7. Layout of Circle Head Sash

In large sash, three or four segments would be needed to complete the quarter circle. This problem may arise when the lumber available is not wide enough for a full quarter segment. It may also arise when

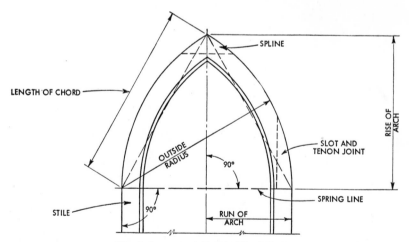

Fig. 8. Layout of Gothic Head Sash

a full quarter segment would result in too much cross grain at the ends of the segment. The solution is to lay out the segment in sixths or eighths of a circle.

Butt joints are usually splined as shown in Figure 7. On semicircular heads with small diameters the stile may be tenoned in a manner similar to that shown in Figure 9A.

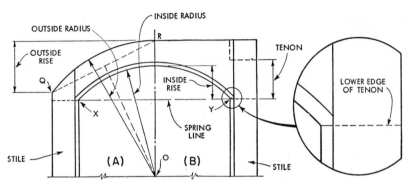

Fig. 9. Layout and Construction of Segment Head Sash

Gothic Head Layout. The radius of a Gothic head segment is not necessarily equal to the width of the arch (Fig. 8). However, the center of the radius in a Gothic head sash is always located on the spring line, thus making the outside edge of the stile tangent to the radius of the arch. The chord of the segment can be measured by making a full size layout or by measuring the rake of the chord. The rake is measured by setting the blade and the tongue of a steel square against the rise and run of the arch. The horizontal joint is located on the spring line and the vertical joint at the peak can be located by bisecting the angle formed by the chords of the segments. The construction is similar to that for semicircle head sash (Fig. 7), using either the slot or spline joint.

Segment Head Layout. A segment head may have a segment top as shown in Figure 9A or a square top as shown in Figure 9B. The outside rise and the width of the sash being given, the outside radius is found by drawing a perpendicular bisector to the line between points Q and R and extending it to intersect the center line at O. A full size layout is required to locate point X. The stile is slotted to this height and the rail is tenoned.

The square head segment shaped on the inside, as shown in Figure 9B, is laid out similarly except that either the inside radius or the inside rise must be given. The construction is usually by mortise and relished tenon, as shown. Point Y must be located by making a full size layout as in locating point X.

Elliptical Head Layout. Because of the many methods of laying out an ellipse, it is essential that an order for an elliptical head sash be accompanied by a template giving the exact shape of the ellipse desired (Fig. 10B). The head is usually made in one piece, but if it is to be made from two pieces, the segments are splined at the top. The elliptical head is slotted to receive the tenon, which is cut on the stile. The between-shoulders dimension must be accurately measured at the spring line.

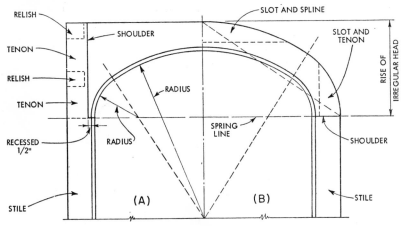

Fig. 10. Layout and Construction of Elliptical Head Sash

For a square head sash with an inside ellipse (Fig. 10A), the radius is based on one-half of the minor axis, which must be stated in the order. The stile is mortised to receive the tenon on the top rail, and the inside edge of the top rail is recessed ½″ into the stile.

Odd Size or Special Sash and Windows. On buildings which are finished on the exterior with brick the architect sometimes has to adjust the width of the window frames, in order that an even number of brick may be laid between windows. This avoids the cutting of the brick, but more important, it avoids the breaking of the brick bond which would result if partial bricks were used instead of whole ones. When this construction problem arises, window frame, window, and sash dimensions involving brick layout are predetermined by the architect during the drawing of the plans. A table of brick sizes and coverages is furnished to the architect by the brick manufacturer. Reasons for ordering special and odd size sash or windows may not always be due to special conditions in the design of the building.

SASH LUMBER

The lumber selected to make sash and windows is determined to some extent by the available supply native to the region where the sash are manufactured.

Cypress. In the Southern States cypress is extensively used for sash and window manufacture. It is highly decay-resistant and may be specified by architects in other sections of the country where this quality may be an important factor.

Pine. In the Southern States where it is native, the long leaf pine is used, although it is not as desirable as cypress or other pines grown in more remote regions.

The North Central States use northern white pine for sash as this wood is a close second to cypress for its decay-resisting quality.

In the Western States and particularly in California, sugar pine is most often the chosen wood, although Ponderosa and Idaho white pines are available.

In regions where cedar, fir, and spruce are native, these woods are often used for sash and windows.

Irrespective of kind, the lumber used in the manufacture of sash and windows is selected because of its relative toughness. This is necessary for making durable joints, and for withstanding dry or wet weather, rot or decay. In the United States as a whole the wood which is probably most used for the manufacture of sash is Ponderosa pine. This is due chiefly to its abundance and to its admirable qualities for the purpose.

Hardwood Sash. It is sometimes required that sash be made of hardwood to match the interior trim. Hardwood sash are usually veneered in a manner similar to that used for hardwood doors. Exposed edges are banded with the same hardwood as the face. Waterproof glue must be used unless the sash is for an interior wall or partition.

CONSTRUCTION STANDARDS

Standards. The term *construction standards* refers to the methods and standards for joining stiles, rails, bars, muntins, and other members into a complete sash.

The standards of manufacture and design that are published by the National Woodwork Manufacturers Association are referred to as Eastern Standards, and those published by the Southern California Retail Lumber Dealers Association are referred to as Western Standards. There are, however, many manufacturers not belonging to these associations who pursue their traditional methods of design and construction without varying a great deal from either of these published standards.

Standard Width. Both the Eastern and Western Standards specify that the width of a window or sash be even to the inch. The width of an even-inch size glass plus four inches equals a standard width. The four inches includes the width of the stiles plus clearance.

Height Measurement. On the height of a *window* 6″ of stock is required for the top and bottom sash combined. The Eastern Standard, being based on *even inch* glass sizes, determines the standard height of a window on increments of 4″ plus 6″ for sash stock. The Western Standard, being based on openings with increments of 6″ between stock sizes, specifies even-foot windows using odd-inch size glass.

Under both standards, a one-light casement *sash* requires odd-inch size glass since the sash frame allows five inches for the combined height of the top and bottom rails (two and three inches respectively.) The over-all or outside height is specified to the even inch to *equal the height* of the double-hung windows.

EASTERN STANDARD	WESTERN STANDARD

CONSTRUCTION OF WINDOWS AND SASH

At the option of the manufacturer, all windows and sash shall be constructed by what is known as *mortise and tenon* construction or *slot mortised* construction. Tenons shall not be less than three quarters of the rail width. Sash shall be well clamped together and all tenons carefully pinned with barbed steel pins set through tenons and countersunk. Stiles and rails shall have solid stickings. All joints shall be coped and well fitted.	Windows and sash may be of either *doweled* or *mortised and tenoned* construction. Check rails and top rails of double-hung windows may be slot mortised into the stiles. All mortised and tenoned assemblies shall be carefully pinned with barbed steel pins set through tenons and countersunk. Bars or muntins shall be either tenoned or coped and nailed to stiles and rails. The profile of all bars shall be uniform with the sticking profile of stiles and rails, and shall be precisely coped. All faces shall be smoothly sanded including the top of the bottom check rail.

LUGS

No specifications are given in the standards. It is assumed at that they	When applied to windows they indicate an extension of the stiles be-

would be considered extra and would make the window a special.

yond the meeting rails. Their purpose is to stop the upper sash from going all the way to the bottom when lowered, as well as for appearance.

Windows with lugs on both the top and bottom sash must be so specified as custom places them on top only.

WINDOW AND SASH THICKNESS

A tolerance of $\frac{1}{32}''$ less than the sanded or finished thickness shall be allowed.

Windows and sash shall not be less than $1\frac{3}{8}''$ thick after both faces are sanded. A tolerance of $\frac{1}{16}''$ is allowable.

GLASS RABBET MEASUREMENTS

The width of all wood parts shown in layouts are face measurements. Over-all widths for stiles, rails, and check rails are $\frac{9}{16}''$ greater than face measurements. For bars and muntins they are $\frac{3}{8}''$ greater.

Glass rabbets shall be at least $\frac{1}{4}''$ deep. The width of the glass rabbet shall be at least one-third of the sash thickness. Irregular head joints shall be either splined or tongued and these shall extend fully across the face of intersections.

CHECK RAIL CONSTRUCTION

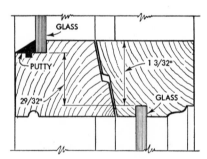

Fig. 11. Check Rails Construction, Eastern Standards

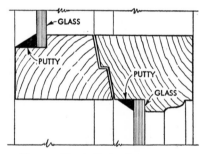

Fig. 12. Check Rails Construction, Western Standards

CHECK RAIL SIZES

Check rails shall be rabbeted and notched for a $\frac{1}{2}''$ parting stop or bead projection.

In the absence of instructions to the contrary, all $1\frac{3}{8}''$ check rail windows are made for a $\frac{3}{8}''$ parting bead, and all $1\frac{3}{4}''$ check rail windows are made for a $\frac{1}{2}''$ parting bead.

REVIEW QUESTIONS

1. Define the following terms: *opening, sash, double-hung window, check rail window, storm sash, open sash, glazed sash, transom sash, screen, lugs, meeting rails, bars, lights, face puttying, bedding, to-rabbet size, daylight opening.*

2. How deep should a sash rabbet be for receiving plate glass?

3. What is the best method for installing plate glass in a sash?

4. Name three kinds of lumber that are used in sash manufacturing.

5. State the order in which the dimensions of a sash or window should be given.

6. How much clearance is specified for pre-fit windows and sash?

7. Sketch a 12 light double-hung window 4 lights high.

8. What organizations publish standards of manufacture and design for windows and sash?

Window, Sash, and Door Frames

QUESTIONS CHAPTER XVI WILL ANSWER FOR YOU

1. *What are the basic types of frames that the cabinetmaker and millman are concerned with?*
2. *How are frame parts laid out and constructed?*
3. *How does the construction of door sills differ from that of window sills?*
4. *What are the less common types of frames?*
5. *How is the frame for a sliding door constructed?*

INTRODUCTION TO CHAPTER XVI

The construction and layout problems which pertain to window and door frames make a fascinating study because of the many variables which must be considered by the woodworker when preparing to make a frame. Among the factors which must be considered are the type of frame, the wall construction which it is to be set into, the shape of the different parts, and whether or not it is to be constructed as a single or multiple unit. Figure 1 shows a beautifully designed door frame.

Standard parts and moldings for stock frames are machined in large frame mills which wholesale them either as parts or complete frames to lumber yards and smaller woodworking shops. There are many cabinet and millwork plants which mill and assemble their own parts for custom or special work.

These mills and shops can manufacture frames that are more accurate than those made on the job, and at equal cost, if not less. Knocked-down or unassembled frames should be assembled by a skilled cabinetmaker or carpenter.

TYPES OF FRAMES

Basic Classification. Frames may be classified into three groups: door, sash, and window frames. Each of these types may be further specified as, for example, *exterior frames* or *interior frames.*

Frame Openings. A frame may have one or more openings for receiving doors, sash, or windows. A frame with one opening is called a *single frame;* with two openings it is called a *twin, double,* or *mullion* *frame.* Frames with three or more openings are called *triple, quadruple,* or *quintuple frames,* as the case may be. All multiple-opening frames have mullions separating the openings vertically.

Sidelights designate the sash at either side of a triple frame. Such a frame may have either one or three transom openings separated from the doors, sash, or windows by a horizontal *transom bar.*

Archway or *cased opening frames* are made for partition wall openings and do not require doors.

FRAME DESIGN

Frames are designed to meet the requirements of the owner and the conditions of the job. The design, size, and number of the members of a frame vary with the purpose and design of the door, sash, or window

Fig. 1. A Detail Front Entrance
Courtesy of Curtis Companies, Inc.

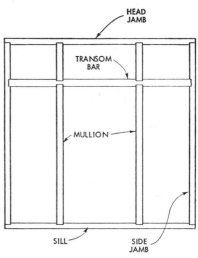

Fig. 2. Frame Terminology

which it is to receive, and with the type of wall into which it is to be installed.

Some of the basic factors which determine frame design are:

1. Swing of a door, whether in, out, or double acting.
2. Swing of a sash, if it swings, whether in or out.

3. Specified thickness of the sash, door, or window, whether standard or special.

4. Use of patented hardware, as in a casement sash frame.

5. Type of sash action for double-hung windows, whether by means of weights and pulleys, or by means of a sash balance.

6. Design of the interior trim of the frame and its effect on the design of the frame members, as in the window stool.

7. Type of wall to receive the frame, whether a *framed wall* with plaster, sheathing and plaster, shingle, or brick veneer exterior; or a *solid masonry wall* of either brick or concrete of varying thickness.

The basic parts of a single-opening frame are the *sides*, the *head*, and the *sill*. Multiple-opening frames will have at least one mullion, and may have a transom bar (Fig. 2).

Figure 3 of this chapter and Figure 20 of Chapter V are detail

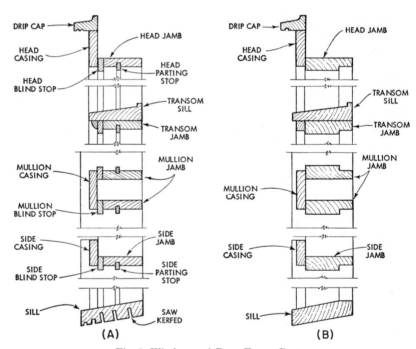

Fig. 3. Window and Door Frame Parts

drawings of double-hung window construction which will familiarize you with the names of the different parts and their construction. The chief advantage of drawings like these is that they permit one to visualize a sash and frame as a whole unit rather than just a number of parts.

FRAME PARTS

Jambs. Jambs are principal members of a window, sash, or door frame which form the sides and top of the frame and are known as side and head jambs respectively. With few exceptions, the head jamb should be made the same width and shape as the side jamb. Less common instances of the jamb are the back jamb which is used in box frames (Fig. 15), and the sub-jamb which is used in thick walls.

Window Jambs. The term *jamb* may refer to the whole side assembly of a window frame, including its sub-members, or it may refer specifically to the pulley stile against which the sash is fitted. In a double-hung window the jamb is often called a pulley stile whether the sash is built for pulley or sash balance action.

Note the construction of the pulley stile in Figure 3. The standard thickness of this part is $\frac{3}{4}''$ although it may vary according to the kind of lumber used, and may be $1\frac{3}{16}''$ or $\frac{7}{8}''$ thick for nominal 1″ lumber. In detail frames the thickness may vary between 1″, $1\frac{1}{16}''$, or $1\frac{1}{8}''$ for nominal $\frac{5}{4}''$ lumber.

The over-all width of the pulley stile plus the blind stop should equal the over-all thickness of the wall, which may include interior plaster and exterior sheathing. See Fig. 10.

The width of the space between the blind stop and the parting stop is the thickness of the sash plus $\frac{1}{16}''$ clearance.

Blind Stop. The function of the blind stop is to form one side of the sash groove, the other side being formed by the parting stop. The blind stop may need rabbeting to receive a storm sash (Fig. 4A), or building paper (Fig. 4B).

Parting Stop or Bead. The parting stop or bead separates the top and bottom sash, permitting them to slide freely. See Fig. 3.

Stucco Mold. The outside trim used with framed wall covered with lath and plaster is called a stucco mold. It is designed with a key or groove to receive and hold the plaster to prevent a plaster crack where the mold and stucco meet (Fig. 4C).

Brick Mold. Brick molding is used to finish a frame set in a concrete, brick, or brick veneer wall (Fig. 4D).

Outside Casing. The outside casing encloses the space between the jambs and the framed wall, serves as a finish trim, and makes a rabbet for a storm sash (Fig. 4A), or screen. Outside casings are either ¾″ or 1⅛″ thick. When the siding is fitted to the casing edge, the casing should be 1⅛″ thick (Fig. 4D). The width of the casing is determined by the width of the space to be covered. A window frame made for weight pockets requires a wide casing.

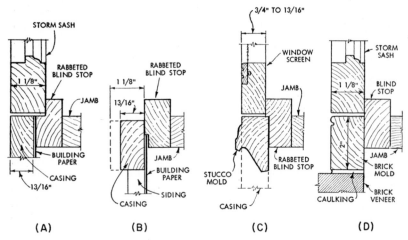

Fig. 4. Blind Stop Variations

Note that in Figure 4A the casing is only $1\frac{3}{16}$″ thick, since the blind stop is rabbeted to receive the 1⅛″ storm sash.

Drip Cap. Water tables are used on buildings to shed water and prevent seepage into the wall. A drip cap with a bed mold is shown in Figure 5. The groove serves to break the capillary flow of water, causing it to drip down.

Door and Sash Jambs. Sash jambs are discussed here together with door jambs because they are basically similar.

Exterior door and sash jambs may be either plain (Fig. 7A), or they may be rabbeted either on one edge (Fig. 7C) or on both edges (Fig. 7B). In the latter case, one rabbet receives the main door or sash, while the second receives a storm or screen door or sash. The rabbet for a door or sash is made ¹⁄₁₆″ to ⅛″ wider than the thickness of the door or sash to provide clearance between the door and the back edge of the rabbet. The standard depth of a rabbet for a door is ½″ for a jamb 1¾″ thick. This provides a thick stop and allows for the bevel on the door and for the shrinkage of the door. However, ⁷⁄₁₆″ and ⅜″ deep rabbets are often provided when jambs 1⅜″ thick are used.

An exterior door in a residence usually swings into the room, while schools and public buildings are required by law to have outward swinging doors to permit quick opening in case of emergencies. There-

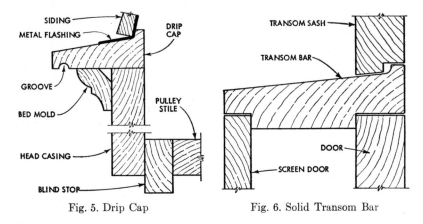

Fig. 5. Drip Cap

Fig. 6. Solid Transom Bar

fore the rabbet is made on the outside edge of the jamb, as shown in Figure 7C. Some doors in public buildings have "panic" hardware which opens the door when pressure is exerted against it.

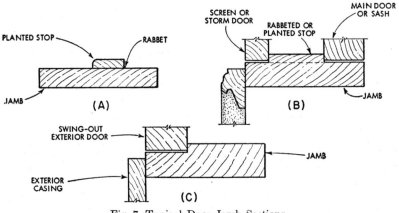

Fig. 7. Typical Door Jamb Sections

Figure 3B illustrates the basic plan and construction of an exterior door.

Transom Bar. The transom bar acts as a head jamb for an opening below, and as a sill for the transom. It may be milled as a solid piece (Fig. 6) or built up as in Figure 3B in a number of possible designs.

Sills. The sill of a sash, door, or window frame is the horizontal bottom member, usually a single piece of lumber.

Window Sills. A window sill is usually sloped at a standard angle of 3″ to 12″ to shed water, but a slope of 2″ to 12″ is sometimes used. The inside and outside edges are beveled so that they are parallel to the edge of the jamb. See Figure 8A which illustrates a plain sill. Note

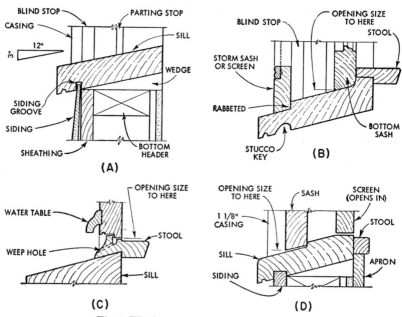

Fig. 8. Window and Sash Sill Constructions

in this figure that a siding groove is provided to receive siding material and building paper. Note also that this detail window sill is provided with a groove to aid the shedding of water.

Figure 8B shows how a detail sill is rabbeted to receive a screen or storm sash and is shaped to receive the bottom sash of a double-hung window.

Casement Sash Sill. Swing-in casement sash that effectively keep out water are difficult to construct. Figure 8C shows a swing-in casement sash sill with a molded stool and a weep hole for shedding water. Note the water table above the sill for the same purpose.

The swing-out casement sash shown in Figure 8D illustrates a rabbeted sill which is more effective than a plain sill. When economy allows, metal weather stripping may be used effectively on any casement.

An interior sash frame is usually full bound, that is, the horizontal bottom member or sill is made exactly the same as the side and head jambs as there is no problem of weatherproofing.

Door Sill. Fig. 9 shows a typical door sill for exterior frames. The pitch is standard. A bevel is formed on the top surface of the sill and parallel to the floor and should be equal in width to the door thickness.

The principal difference between an exterior and an interior door

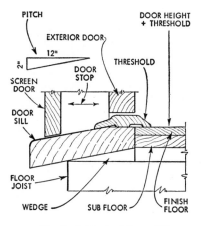

Fig. 9. A Typical Door Sill

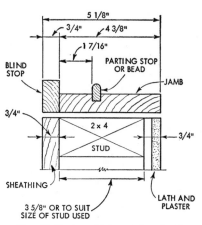

Fig. 10. Factors Determining Jamb Width

frame is in the sill, an exterior door frame usually having a hardwood sill. The interior door frame is usually set high enough so that the hardwood floor will exactly fit under the side jamb, and therefore requires no sill.

MODULAR COORDINATED STANDARDS FOR STOCK FRAMES

The stock window frames manufactured and sold wholesale by members of the National Woodwork Manufacturers Association are designed for modular coordination and are manufactured in basic units with adaptable parts for various wall thicknesses and types of wall construction.

CONSTRUCTION AND LAYOUT PROCEDURES

Width of the Jamb. The net width of a door, sash, or window jamb is determined by several factors. In laying out a frame the blueprints should be carefully studied, and any special construction features should be noted. For an ordinary residence standard wall construction permits the use of stock or standard window and door frames. These standards may vary in different regions.

Five basic factors determining the width of a jamb are:

1. The standard net size of the framing material and the width of the studs used, whether 2″ x 4″ or 2″ x 6″. See Fig. 10.

2. In double-hung windows, the thickness of the blind stop.

3. In stucco construction, the presence or absence of outside sheathing, and its thickness if present.

4. The thickness of the interior wall finish, whether it be drywall, lath and plaster, plywood, or paneled.

5. The thickness of the exterior wall whether it be brick, concrete, or frame. However, the box frame jamb should be of standard width (Fig. 15). Sub-jambs are sometimes required.

The thickness of a concrete wall is determined by engineering considerations, but the rules for determining jamb width apply as in the case of brick walls.

Frame Joints. The principal joints used in the construction of door, sash, and window frames are the dadoed, the mitered, the butted, and, less often, the coped joint. Combinations of these joints and their application to the design requirements of frame members may be many and varied.

The joining of the side jambs to the head and sill may be accomplished by dadoing the head and sill to receive the jambs (Fig. 15), by dadoing the jambs to receive the head and sill (Fig. 11A), or by a combination of the two methods (Fig. 11B).

Depth of Dado. In a pulley stile, the dado for the head and sill should be the same depth as the parting stop groove. For a rabbeted door or sash frame the dado should be as deep as the rabbet.

In situations where a jamb, head, or sill has detail contours, the corners may have to be mitered.

Multiple-opening frames may be constructed in two ways, as illustrated in Figures 11A and 11B. The method illustrated in Figure 11B permits greater strength for carrying overhead loads. The choice of method depends on such factors as shop practice and available equipment, convenience or efficiency in manufacture and assembly, and design and blueprint specifications.

Horns on Jambs.   The term *horn* refers to the extra stock extending beyond the sill and head of a jamb. See Fig. 13. The rough length of a jamb should be about 5″ greater than the frame height.

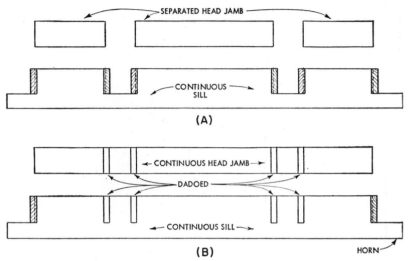

Fig. 11. Layout of Multiple-Frame Sill and Head Jamb

Horns on jambs have two advantages:

1. They permit the head and sill to be dadoed into the jamb. This gives a tighter, more solid joint than a rabbet.

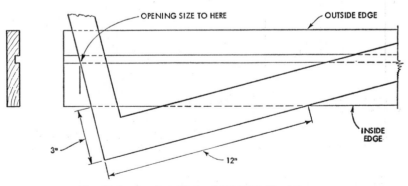

Fig. 12. Laying Out Pitch of Sill With Steel Square

2. They permit the handling of the frame before installation without much danger of the joints opening. The horns are sawn off just before installation.

Horns on Sills. Horns on sills (Fig. 11B) extend beyond the exact width of casings or moldings, and receive them when the frame is assembled. The horns are usually trimmed to finish frame size although in some cases they are allowed to project beyond the casing or mold. For box window frames or sash frames in masonry walls, the sill is made without horns when the outside edge is flush with the outside edge of the jamb or blind stop.

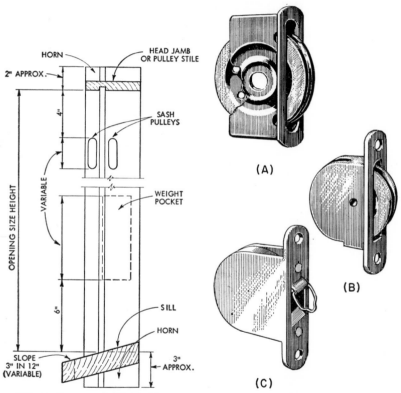

Fig. 13. Layout of Double-Hung Window Frame Pulley Stile

Fig. 14. Sash Pulleys (A) Pressed Steel Pulley (B) Cast Iron Pulley (C) Spring Sash Balance

Slope or Pitch of Sills. To determine the cutting line on a jamb so that it conforms to the slope or pitch of the sill, using a standard pitch of 3″ to 12″, place the steel square as shown in Figure 12. Adjust the square to the point which marks the bottom of the opening, then mark the angle across the face of the jamb. A T-bevel may then be set to the angle for making duplicate cuts, or for setting the angle on a power saw fence.

Opening Size. The opening size of a sash, door or window frame is established at the point where the unit to be fitted into the opening comes in contact with the frame as outlined below.

The width of a frame is measured between the faces of plain jambs, and between the rabbets of rabbeted jambs.

The measurement of opening height is more involved. On a double-hung window frame, the height is measured from the face of the head jamb to a point on the sloped sill which corresponds to the inside edge of the parting stop groove (Fig. 13).

When the side jambs are dadoed into the head and sill, as in twin double-hung windows, the depth of the dadoes should be allowed for when laying out the side jambs.

On a swing-out casement frame the height is measured from the outside edge of the rabbet on the head jamb to a corresponding point on the sill. See Figure 8D.

On a swing-in casement window frame the height is measured from the inside edge of the head to a corresponding point on the sill, with allowance for the stool if such is used. See Figure 8C.

On an exterior door frame the height is measured from the rabbeted edge of the head jamb to a corresponding point on the sill, with allowance for the threshold (Fig. 9). On an interior door jamb, which has no sill, make the side jamb the same height as the door plus ½" for rug clearance.

SASH PULLEYS, BALANCES, AND WEIGHT POCKETS

Sash Pulleys. Manufactured sash pulleys may be classified into two types:

1. The pressed steel type pulley, with thin flanges, which is inserted in a slot cut through the pulley stile. See Figure 14A.

2. The cast iron or bronze type with a face plate which must be routed through a slot into the side jamb to make it flush with the face of the jamb (Fig. 14B). The pulley is located approximately 4" from the face of the head jamb (Fig. 13).

Weight Pockets. The weight pockets in a double-hung window (Fig. 13) provide access to the sash weights in case repairs are necessary; otherwise repair work can only be done by removing the inside casing, which is impractical, since the casing would be marred and would require touch-up painting.

The size of a weight pocket is determined by the size of the window. The standard width of a weight pocket is 2″ to 2½″, since the weights are limited in diameter to the thickness of the sash plus ¼″. This allows a very limited clearance between the two weights when installed in the frame. The height of a weight pocket is determined by the length of the sash weight, which in turn is determined by the size of the window and the weight of the glass used.

The lower end of a weight pocket is located approximately 6″ above the window sill and may extend to midpoint between head and sill so that the pocket is covered by the lower sash when the latter is in a closed position.

Sash Balances. Various types of coil spring sash balances are available which eliminate the need for weights and pockets (Fig. 14C). Instructions for their installation accompany each sash balance.

BOX FRAMES

A special type of window frame, called the *box frame,* is required in a brick wall when weights are to be used for sash counterbalances.

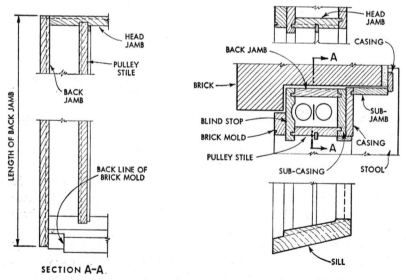

Fig. 15. Layout and Construction of Box Frame for Masonry Walls

A vertical box is constructed at each side of the frame to provide space for the weights (Fig. 15). The sill and head are dadoed to receive the pulley stiles and extended to provide support for the back jamb of the box. The sill is milled to receive the subcasing and is notched flush with the back edge of the brick mold. The back jamb extends the full length of the frame.

VERTICAL SLIDING SASH FRAME

Figure 16 shows the construction and layout of a vertical sliding sash frame.

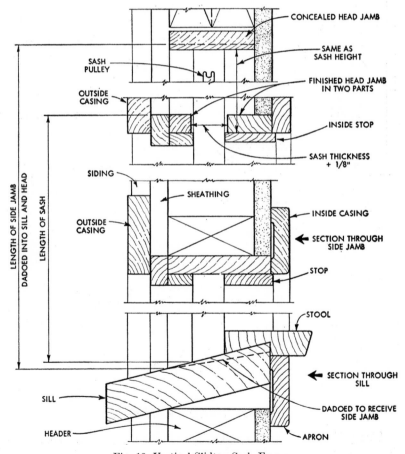

Fig. 16. Vertical-Sliding Sash Frame

INSIDE AND SLIDING DOOR FRAMES (JAMBS)

Plain Inside Door Frame. A plain inside door frame is simply two side jambs and a head wide enough to accommodate the thickness of the wall. The jambs may be dadoed into the head or vice versa.

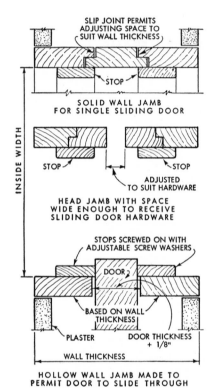

Fig. 17. Interior Sliding Door Frame

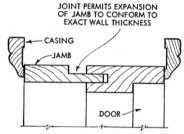

Fig. 18. Split Inside-Door Frame Construction

Sliding Door Frame. Figure 17 shows the layout and construction of a sliding door frame.

Split Inside Door Frame. Figure 18 shows a split jamb with casings attached. In high-grade work built-up interior frames with casings attached may be ordered. The casings may be mitered or splined, and glued at the corner joints and to the jambs. To accommodate variations in the thickness of a wall, the jambs are made in two parts, as shown in Figure 18. The jamb sections are made slightly under the wall thickness to permit the casings to fit tightly against the wall. The two sections are assembled by a carpenter or cabinetmaker when the jamb is installed.

DETAIL HEAD FRAMES

The principles of the layout of detail head frames are similar to those for detail head windows, sash, and doors. The spring line and radius centers are similarly determined. The layout of the sill end of a detail head frame is the same as that for a square top frame.

The usual procedure in constructing a detail or irregular head frame is to build up the head section with overlapping segments wide enough for band-sawing (Fig. 19A) and shaping the inside edge to the desired

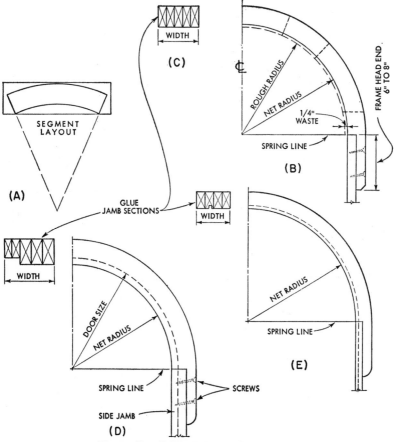

Fig. 19. Detail Head Frame Construction

(A) Bandsawed segment (B) built-up circular head showing rough cut net radius (C) built-up section (D) built-up circular head for rabbeted door frame (E) built-up circular head for double hung window frame.

radius (Fig. 19B). After being band-sawed to net radius the head is shaped to match the side jamb of the frame.

Each end of the frame head should be constructed as illustrated in Figure 19B to make a strong joint with the side jamb.

Figures 19C, 19D, and 19E show how the jamb stock should be built up for different types of frame heads.

The radius of the casing, blind stop, and other sub-members is based on the radius of the frame opening, usually the face of the jamb or the rabbet. In other words, the radius point remains constant.

REVIEW QUESTIONS

1. Name three types of frames according to the kinds of sash they take.

2. What are the terms for frames that have two, three, and four openings, respectively?

3. Name four types of exterior wall construction.

4. What is the name of the horizontal member that separates a door opening from an opening above the door?

5. Name five parts of a window frame.

6. What is the function of the blind stop?

7. What is the standard slope of a window frame sill?

8. What is the principal difference between an exterior and interior door frame?

9. Draw a sketch showing two methods of joining a side jamb with a head jamb.

10. What usually determines the depth of a dado joint on a double-hung window frame?

11. At what point is the height of a double-hung window frame measured?

12. What is a box frame?

13. What is a split inside door frame and why is it used?

Interior Trim and Exterior Woodwork

QUESTIONS CHAPTER XVII WILL ANSWER FOR YOU

1. *What are the most common types of exterior trim?*
2. *What are the most common types of interior trim?*
3. *How are the number and width of the staves in a column determined?*
4. *What are the classical orders of Greek and Roman architecture?*
5. *What are the basic parts and proportions of a classical order?*

INTRODUCTION TO CHAPTER XVII

The subject of interior trim and exterior woodwork is a broad one and includes a great variety of problems pertaining to high quality cabinetmaking and millwork.

Fig. 1. Mt. Vernon, Historic Residence of George Washington
Photograph by J. W. Stinchomb, Washington, D.C.

Mt. Vernon is an outstanding example of the use of exterior woodwork in architecture. The paneled columns blend with the dentil cornice just below the eaves to harmonize with the pediment above the main entrance and with the well-proportioned windows with their louvered shutters. The broken pediment (right elevation) supported by pilasters (relief columns) frame the tall circle-top window with its sidelight to enrich the broad space of this elevation. The circular arches on the decorated posts (extreme right) supporting the arcade add variety of detail. The four harmoniously spaced dormers shown on the roof, and the octagonal tower, with its curved roof and elegant finial at the summit, crown the work of artisans who probably had to fashion the detailed woodwork largely by hand. Today such items of architectural woodwork are economically made in the modern millwork plant.

The term *trim* as applied to the interior of a building includes all finish woodwork required to cover spaces around openings, the protective baseboards and shoe at the floor line, decorative cornice moldings at the ceiling line, wainscoting, picture molding, and other decorative moldings.

The term *exterior woodwork* refers to the various items required to give the exterior of a building a finished as well as decorative appearance (Fig. 1). Such items are usually not a part of the basic structure in the sense of giving support or carrying any weight. Therefore, they can be made to any dimension in conformity with good design or economy.

An understanding of the principles of the design of moldings and columns is valuable to the cabinetmaker or the millman for the following reasons:

1. It makes him appreciative of good woodwork design.
2. It stimulates him to a further study of architectural design.
3. It impresses on him the need for accuracy in quality detail woodwork.

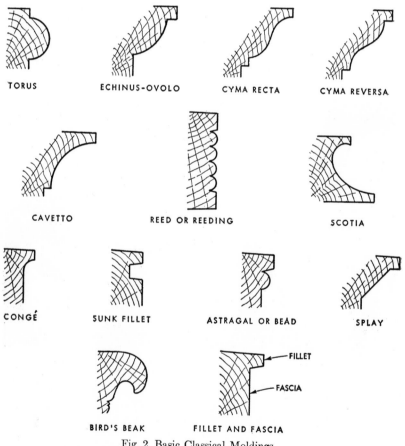

Fig. 2. Basic Classical Moldings

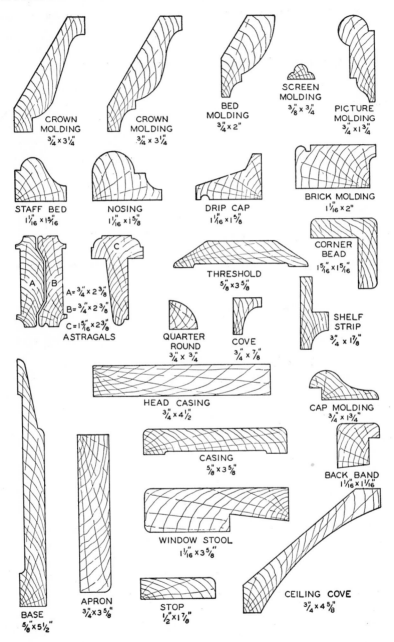

Fig. 3. Commonly Used Exterior and Interior Moldings

4. It prepares him for laying out detail woodwork on the basis of an architect's specifications and design.

MOLDING DESIGN AND TYPICAL MOLDINGS

The design of modern as well as classical moldings is based on the traditional orders of Roman and Greek architecture. Figure 2 illus-

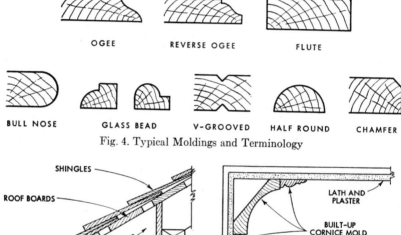

Fig. 4. Typical Moldings and Terminology

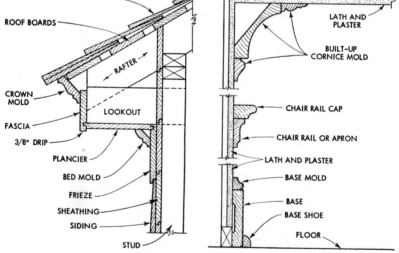

Fig. 5. Closed or Box Cornice   Fig. 6. Running Trim

trates several basic classical molding shapes which are designed to give pleasure to the eye as well as serving a useful purpose.

Moldings take their name either from their basic shape or from the purpose which they serve. Figures 3 and 4 show some basic moldings classified according to their use or shape. Figure 5 shows some basic *exterior* cornice members classified according to their structural use. The terms *crown molding* and *bed molding* refer to the use rather than the design of these moldings. Note their positions relative to the other members such as the frieze plancier and the fascia.

The term *cornice mold* usually refers to moldings for *interior* cornices sometimes found in living rooms and dining rooms. Figure 6 shows how a cornice mold may be built up of several members.

INTERIOR TRIM

Interior trim is classified under two general types, *standing trim* and *running trim*. Other kinds of interior woodwork such as paneling, cabinet work, etc., are *not* included in these terms.

Interior door jambs are parts of the interior trim and, as such, are

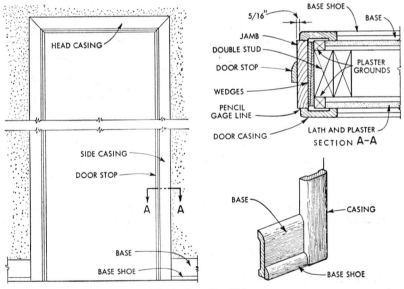

Fig. 7. Standing Trim

ordered with the trim. However, these jambs are often set prior to plastering at the time the exterior window and door frames are set. They are fully described in Chapter XVI.

Standing Trim. Standing trim consists of items which are used for trimming around door or window openings. Figure 7 of this chapter and Figure 3 of Chapter XV show how stools, aprons, casings, door and window stops, and plinth blocks are used. The designs shown in Figures 3, 4, 5, 6, and 7 are typical but there are numerous other variations in trim design.

Running Trim. Running trim consists of such items as the base (*baseboard* and *mop board* are alternate terms), base shoe, base mold, chair rail, picture molding, cornice molding and panel molding. All of these items are usually ordered in linear quantities, hence the term *running trim.* Figure 6 shows a sectional view of running wall trim.

EXTERIOR TRIM

To create decorative effects on the exterior walls of a house, and also to aid the shedding of water, several methods are used. Horizontal trim placed at the base of the exterior walls of a house (Fig. 8A) or at the second floor level of a two-story house is called a belt course (Fig. 8B).

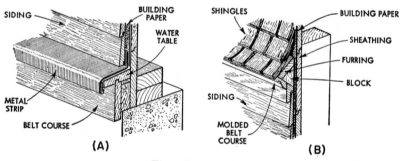

Fig. 8. Belt Courses

Cornices are constructed where the exterior walls of a building meet the roof to form an architectural finish (Fig. 5).

EXTERIOR WOODWORK

Exterior woodwork consists of such items as brackets, corbels, rafter ends, verge boards, door and window frames, porch stairs, columns, posts, railing, balusters, and beam casings.

Brackets, Corbels, and Bolsters. Fig. 9 shows a bracket which may be used to support a verge board, exposed rafter, or a flower box. Figure 10 shows a typical bracket used to support the hood over a door stoop.

A corbel is a fixture projecting from a wall, and used to provide support to overhead members (Fig. 11B).

In cabinet work a corbel is a solid or built-up projection which appears to be supporting weight but is used mainly for decorative pur-

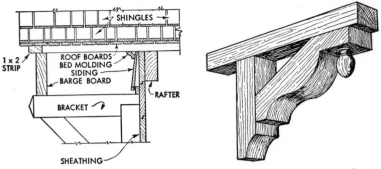

Fig. 9. Exterior Bracket to Support Gable Cornice

Fig. 10. Bracket for Hood or Stoop

poses. Such corbels are constructed according to the architect's design, using typical cabinetmaking methods.

A bolster is a top piece on a post used to lengthen the bearing of a beam (Fig. 11A).

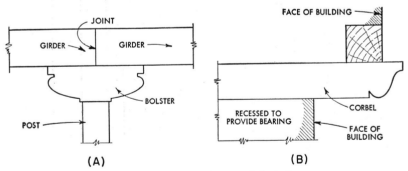

Fig. 11. Typical Bolster and Corbel

Verge Board (or Bargeboard). A verge board is an exposed roof member supporting the overhanging roof of a gable end open cornice (Fig. 9). Verge boards requiring band-sawing are furnished by a mill. Plain verge boards are usually selected from framing lumber and fitted to the roof by the carpenter. The term *bargeboard* is often used instead of *verge board*.

Rafter Ends.   Band-sawed rafter ends are not now in popular use (Fig. 9). However, they are used for the sake of conformity whenever an addition is made to a house which already has band-sawed rafters. See Chapter IX, pages 127, 155, 156.

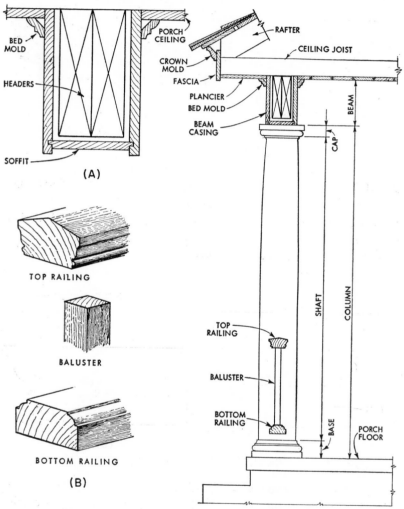

Fig. 12. Porch Millwork Construction and Terminology

Door and Window Frames.   Door and window frames are millwork items requiring considerable explanation concerning their types, construction, and layout. This information is given fully in Chapter XVI.

Exterior Stairs. The layout and construction of steps and stairs is fully described in Chapter XVIII.

Porch Work. A house porch is normally constructed by a carpenter although numerous millwork items may be required, such as beam casings, rails and balusters, posts or columns, and running trim (Fig. 12). In most cases stock finish lumber and dimension yard-stock

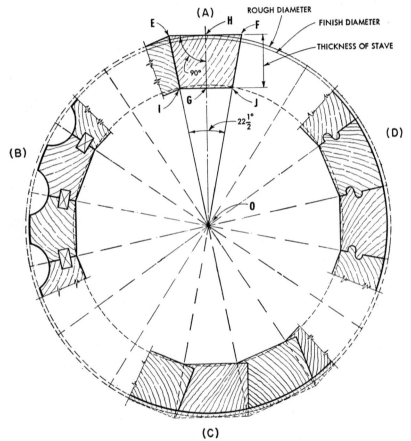

Fig. 13. Layout of Column Staves (A) Method of Determining Stave Width and Pattern (B), (C), (D), Typical Joints Used in Column Staves

are used. Exterior architecturally designed details must be made in a cabinet shop.

Beam Casings. The rough supporting beams of a porch are finished or cased with finish lumber forming two side casings and a soffit (Fig.

12A). The beam material dimensions should be specified on the plans.

Rails and Balusters. Figure 12B illustrates rail and baluster stock for porches. They may be ordered from stock designs or from the architect's detail drawings.

Posts and Columns. There are three basic ways for making posts and columns:

1. For a square column: Standard techniques for laying out and joining rectangular stock are employed.

2. For a small diameter circular column: A solid piece of lumber is turned, the base and cap being made separately. The cap is usually square and molded on the edges.

3. For a large diameter circular column: Since turning a solid piece of stock is impractical for this item, the column is built up by the assembly of a number of machined pieces called staves. The built-up stock is then turned to size. See Fig. 13.

LAYOUT OF COLUMN SHAFT STAVES

Number of Staves in a Column. The diameter of the shaft and the maximum width of a stave determine the number of staves a built-up shaft should have. The thickness of a stave is $1\frac{3}{8}''$ to $1\frac{3}{4}''$ depending on the specified diameter and height of the column shaft.

Problem. Find the number of staves required for a shaft with a specified diameter of $15\frac{1}{4}''$ and a maximum stave width of $3\frac{1}{8}''$. Remember that π equals 3.1416 and $3\frac{1}{8}''$ equals 3.125''.

Solution:

1. Allow $\frac{1}{4}''$ on the finish diameter for turning.

Thus: $15\frac{1}{4}''$ plus $\frac{1}{4}''$ equals $15\frac{1}{2}''$, or 15.5 in.

2. Divide the circumference by the maximum width of a stave, to get the number of staves required.

Thus: a. $15.5'' \times 3.1416 = 48.69''$ circumference

b. $48.69'' \div 3.125'' = 15.64$

3. Add 1 for any fractional or decimal part of the answer.

Thus: $15.64 = 15 + 1$ or 16 staves required.

Width of a Stave. The diameter of the shaft and the number of staves specified determine the width of a stave.

Problem. Find the required width of a stave if the specified shaft diameter is $15\frac{1}{4}''$ and the specified number of staves is 16.

Solution:

1. Lay out two concentric circles equal to the finish size and to the rough size $(15\frac{1}{4}'' + \frac{1}{4}'')$ of the shaft. See Fig. 13A.

2. Compute the number of degrees included in each stave.
Thus: 360° divided by 16 staves equals 22.5° per stave.

3. Lay off with a protractor two adjacent radii (OE and OF) at an angle of 22.5°.

4. Bisect the line EF with a radius (OH) so that line EF intersects OH at a right angle and tangent to the rough circle. The distance between E and F is the required width for a stave. The width is obtained by direct measurement.

5. To determine the exact shape of the stave, mark off the specified thickness of the stave (HG), then draw a line (IJ) through G and parallel to EF. Points E, F, J, and I determine the exact shape of the splined stave.

To check the accuracy of the layout, step off the stave width around the circle with dividers. The first stave and the last stave should coincide exactly.

If no protractor is available, the layout must be made by trial and error with a pair of dividers until the circle is divided into 16 equal parts.

The stave shape can be transferred to soft pine stock and bandsawed for use as a pattern. Great accuracy is necessary in this procedure to ensure that the built-up stock will be tightly jointed when glued. The angles may be checked for accuracy with a T-bevel.

TYPICAL STAVE JOINTS

Figures 13B, C, and D illustrate methods of joining staves for a column shaft.

COLUMN DESIGN

The columns of the classical orders of Greek and Roman architecture are particularly adaptable to the design of columns for modern residences. These orders are the Doric, Ionic, Corinthian, Tuscan (Fig. 14), and the Composite (Fig. 15). Figure 15 names the basic features of a classical order and gives some of the proportions of the column in relation to the shaft diameter as a basic unit of measurement.

REVIEW QUESTIONS

1. Name six millwork items which are included under the term *interior trim*.
2. Name four items of millwork which are included in the term *exterior woodwork*.

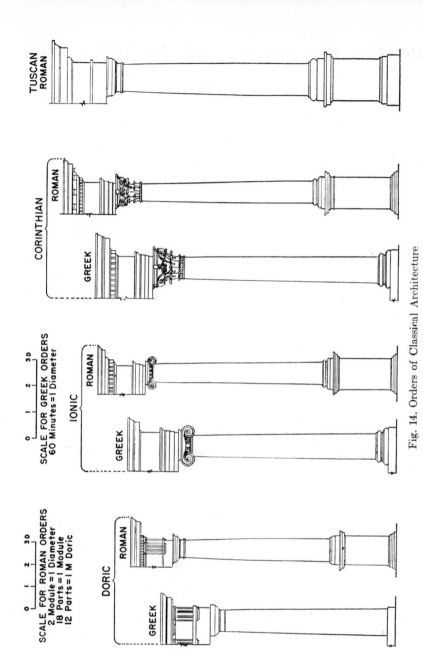

SCALE FOR ROMAN ORDERS
2 Module = 1 Diameter
18 Parts = 1 Module
12 Parts = 1 M Doric

SCALE FOR GREEK ORDERS
60 Minutes = 1 Diameter

0 1 2 3D

DORIC

GREEK   ROMAN

IONIC

GREEK   ROMAN

CORINTHIAN

GREEK   ROMAN

TUSCAN
ROMAN

Fig. 14. Orders of Classical Architecture

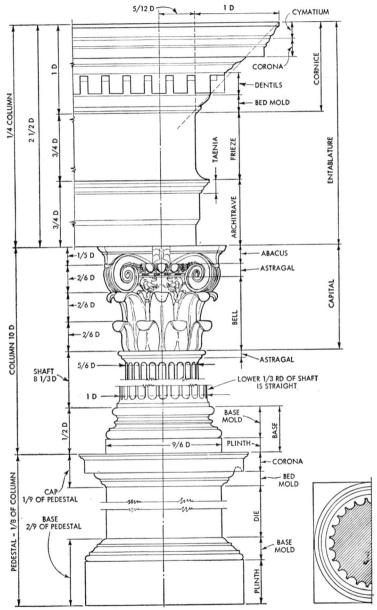

Fig. 15. Composite Column Proportions and Terminology

3. Sketch a crown mold and a bed mold
4. Name the four basic classical orders of architecture.
5. What is the difference between standing trim and running trim?
6. What is the function of a corbel on a piece of cabinet work?
7. What is a verge board?
8. Describe three ways in which a porch column or post can be constructed.
9. Define the term *stave*.

Stair Layout

QUESTIONS CHAPTER XVIII WILL ANSWER FOR YOU

1. *What are the basic terms used in stair building?*
2. *What are the main safety rules to observe in the layout and construction of a staircase?*
3. *What are the basic rules for determining the rise and run proportions of a stairway?*
4. *What are the basic methods of laying out stair horses, stringers, newels, and handrailing?*
5. *How is a stair rod used in stair building?*

INTRODUCTION TO CHAPTER XVIII

Stair building is a long recognized specialized trade carried on by expert craftsmen known as stair builders. This chapter provides sufficient information for an understanding of the basic principles of stair building.

Stairways vary from simple ladder-like affairs to beautiful curved staircases. Such stairways are often the center of interest in a large room or hall (Fig. 1).

GENERAL STAIR TERMINOLOGY

The following is a list of the more common trade terms relating to stair building that are used throughout the woodworking industry.

Staircase or Stairs. A complete flight of steps, with all its parts, leading from one floor to another floor of a building, and which may consist of two or more flights separated by landings.

Flight. An uninterrupted series of steps, consisting of treads, risers, etc., in a staircase.

Landing. A level platform between two flights of a staircase.

Stairway. The passageway of a staircase or stairs.

Open Stairway. A stairway not enclosed by walls on both sides.

Boxed Stairway. A stairway enclosed by walls on both sides.

Geometrical Stairway. A stairway which departs from straight flight design, especially a circular stairway.

Wellhole. The clear vertical space around which a stairway turns; also the framed opening for a stairway in the floor.

HORSE, STRINGER, TREAD, AND RISER

Horse or Carriage. The support for the members of a stairway during and after construction, made of rough stock and conforming to the rise and run of the risers and treads.

Fig. 1. An Interior Stairway
Courtesy of Curtis Companies, Inc.

Tread. The horizontal member of a step connecting the two risers.

Riser. The vertical member of a step connecting two treads.

Step. A riser and tread considered as a unit.

Nosing. That part of a tread which extends beyond the face of the riser.

Return or End Nosing. That part of a tread which is mitered and fastened to the end of the head in an open face stringer staircase.

Stringer. The finish sides of a staircase which support the risers and treads.

Wall or Closed Stringer. The stringer of a staircase against a wall or partition, usually housed.

Housed Stringer. A stringer grooved or dadoed to receive risers and treads.

Housing. Dadoes and grooves in a stringer for receiving risers and treads, the grooves usually being tapered to admit wedges behind the risers and treads.

Stair Wedge. Wedged stock driven and glued under treads and behind risers to ensure a tight joint with the stringer.

Open or Mitered Stringer. The stringer of an open staircase in which the ends of treads are exposed, also the outside member of a boxed stringer.

Boxed Stringer. A unit consisting of a housed and a face stringer connected by a shoe rail which receives the balusters.

Stair Bracket. A decorative fixture fastened under the treads of an open stringer.

Starting Step. The first tread-and-riser unit of a flight of steps, having either a rectangular or curved return end.

Winder. An angular tread of a winding staircase.

Landing Tread. A partial tread which forms the nosing of a landing, usually 4″ to 5″ wide and rabbeted to the landing floor.

RAILINGS AND RAILING PARTS

Balustrade. A railing consisting of a row of balusters connected by a rail and including all rail details.

Baluster or Bannister. An upright member of a railing or balustrade, often turned with decorative details.

Shoe Rail. The connecting member at the top of the stringers which is grooved to receive balusters.

Fillet. The member fitting between the balusters and filling the groove of a shoe rail.

Newel. A post which is anchored to a staircase and which supports the handrail.

Starting Newel. The first newel at the bottom of a stairway.

Angle or Landing Newel. The first newel on a landing or at the turn of a landing.

Stair Rail. The guard rail on the open side of a staircase.

Handrail. The guard rail on the wall side of a staircase.

Stair Rail Crook or Easement. A curved or twisted section of a stair rail to adapt the rail to a change in direction.

Gooseneck. An easement having the appearance of a gooseneck, generally used at the landing or head of a stairway.

Rosette. A turned decorative plaque made to receive the end of a handrail which is returned to the wall.

Finial. A turned decorative cap or top for a newel or a handrail.

Drop. A turned decorative base for a landing or angle newel.

Volute Wreath or Spiral. A geometrical easement for a handrail usually located at the bottom of a stairway and resting on a cluster of balusters surrounding a newel.

LAYOUT TERMINOLOGY

Total Rise. The vertical distance between finish floors connected by a stairway. See Figure 5.

Tread Rise. The vertical distance from one tread to the next one above. See Figure 5.

Total Run. The horizontal distance between the faces of the bottom and top risers of a stairway (Fig. 5).

Tread Run. The run of a single tread between the faces of two risers, exclusive of the nosing, or between the backs of two risers (Fig. 5).

Rake. The angle of a stairway based on the horizontal and formed by the rise and run of the stairway.

Headroom. The vertical distance between a step and the nearest obstruction above.

STAIR DESIGN

Architects are careful to design staircases that have a safe rake or slope and with balustrades and handrails to provide maximum safety. The basic dimensions of a staircase are therefore determined by the architect according to the local building code. Sufficient framing space must be allowed for the kind of stairway desired. The arrangement of the floors to be connected and the location of the stairway are factors which determine the type and direction of a staircase.

Safety Rules. The *Safety Engineering Department* of the *National Workmen's Compensation Service Bureau* has set up standards which should be adhered to when designing stairways. These are:

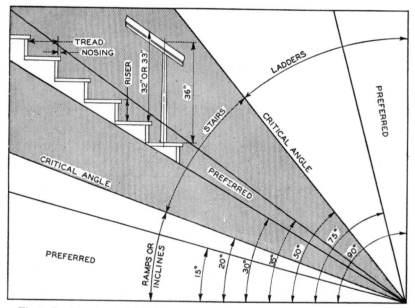

Fig. 2. Preferred and Critical Angles for Stairs, Ladders, Ramps, and Inclines
Courtesy Safety Department of National Workmen's Compensation Service Bureau

Stairways should be free from winders; the width of landings should be equal to or greater than the width of stairways between handrails or handrail and wall; landings should be level and free from intermediate steps between the main up flight and the main down flight; all treads should be equal and all risers should be equal in any one staircase. The sum of one tread and one riser, exclusive of the nosing, should not be more than 18 inches nor less than 17 inches. The nosing should not project to exceed 1¾ inches; all stairways should be equipped with permanent and substantial handrails 36 inches in height from the center of the tread; all handrails should have rounded corners and a surface that is smooth and free of splinters; the angle of the stairway with the horizontal should not be more than fifty degrees nor less than twenty degrees (Fig. 2). Stair treads should be slip proof, firmly secured, and have no protruding bolts, screws, or nails.

The above standards may be modified by specific limitations in the building code of a city, county, or state.

Rise and Run Proportions. The most satisfactory proportion between the rise and the run for an "easy" stairway is based on the following rule:

The sum of the tread rise and the tread run should equal approximately 17½″. Thus, a stairway with 10½″ of tread run for each step should have 7″ rise. (See safety rules above.) No exact rule can be followed, as rise and run dimensions must be adapted to the space into which the stairway is to be constructed.

BUILDING DIMENSIONS CHECK-UP

A foreman carpenter should follow very closely the architect's details as he constructs a building. When the stairway is constructed in a mill or cabinet shop, it is the stair builder's responsibility to check all job measurements. This checking should always be done before the building is plastered, and any errors found must be corrected.

STAIR CONSTRUCTION

To understand the layout of a stairway it is necessary to know how it is constructed. Figure 3 shows the cross section of a short flight of stairs using a housed wall stringer. Figure 4 shows other methods of constructing stairways on the job using framing materials to make the stair horses.

LAYOUT MATHEMATICS

The mathematics involved in laying out a stairway concern several factors, namely, total rise, tread rise, total run, tread run, rod layout, platform height, and length of stair horse or stringer. Review the section above on "Terminology" and see Figures 3 and 5.

Total Rise. It is very important to measure the total rise on the job because the connecting floors may have hardwood flooring of different thicknesses. The stair builder should compute the total rise ac-

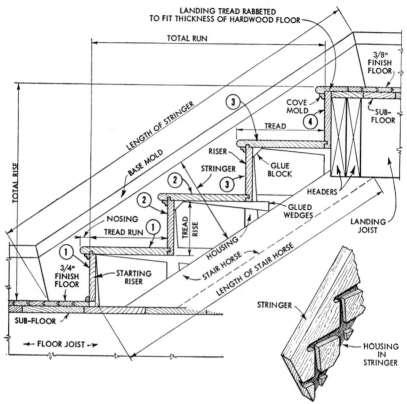

Fig. 3. Short Flight of Stairs Showing Housed Construction

cording to the finish floor thicknesses. The following procedure may be used in calculating the total rise:

1. Determine the *rough-to-rough* total rise measurement on the job.
2. Determine from the specifications any difference in the thickness of the two floors.
3. If the hardwood flooring is thicker downstairs, subtract the difference between the floor thicknesses from the rough-to-rough dimension.
4. If hardwood flooring is thicker upstairs, *add* the difference between the floor thicknesses to the rough-to-rough dimension.
5. If flooring is same thickness, the *finish-to-finish* dimension equals the rough-to-rough dimension.

Tread Rise. The tread rise is the next important measurement to be determined. It must be the same for each step in the stairway. To determine tread rise, divide the total rise by the number of risers.

Total Run. On most stairways the total run can be varied slightly from the plan measurements if necessary.

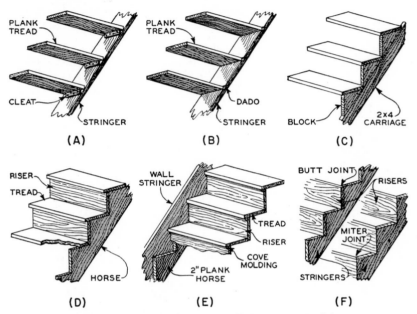

Fig. 4. Methods of Constructing Stairways on the Job
(A) Stringer with nailed cleats (B) dadoed stair stringer (C) stair blocks nailed to carriage (D) cutout horse (E) cutout horse with stringer (F) stringers with butted and mitered risers.

To determine the total run use a plumb bob to transfer the point of measurement of the top riser to a corresponding point on the floor below. Then measure the horizontal distance to the first riser.

If the total run is not given, determine the total run by multiplying the specified run of one tread by the specified number of treads. There is *always one less tread than risers* in a flight of stairs. See Figure 5.

Tread Run. The tread run is the exact length of each horizontal cut in a stair horse to form the tread supports.

If the tread run is not specified in the plans, it may be determined by dividing the total run by the number of treads.

Headroom. When the stair builder measures the framing layout, he must determine if enough headroom clearance will be available after the finish stair is installed.

The two kinds of headroom clearance which must be considered are the vertical distance permitting the passage of persons and the clearance to the obstruction measured at a right angle from the rake of the stairs (Fig. 5). This measurement becomes the maximum clearance for

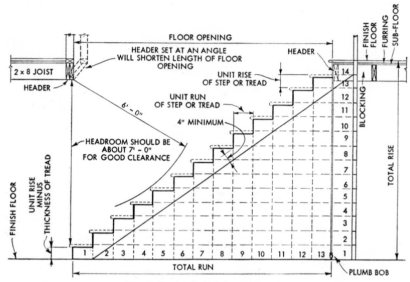

Fig. 5. Basic Stair Measurements

the movement of furniture. The vertical distance, however, is more important. This distance should be at least 6'8" and preferably 7'0".

Story Rod for Stair Layout. The quickest and most accurate method for determining the exact tread rise of a stairway is to use a story rod, usually a 1" x 1" or 1" x 2" rod. The procedure is as follows:

Place the rod vertically in the frame opening on top of a piece of finish flooring against the upper floor and mark off the upper floor level on the rod. Add to this mark the specified thickness of the upper finish floor. This is the total rise.

Divide the total rise dimension by the specified number of rises to get the rise per tread, and mark off the rise per tread on the rod by means of a pair of dividers.

Platform Height. The establishment of the height of a platform or landing in a stairway is a simple operation once a rod layout has been made (Fig. 6). Proceed as follows:

Read the blueprint to determine the number of the riser which is even with the landing. Locate and mark this riser on the rod to indicate the finish floor height of the landing. The platform is built to finish this height.

Length of Horse or Stringer Stock. The approximate length of a stair horse or stringer should be determined prior to selecting the stock. Use a steel square to represent the rise and run of one step and measure the diagonal. Multiply this figure by the number of treads to get the rake length of the horse or stringer. Convert this to a standard length of lumber.

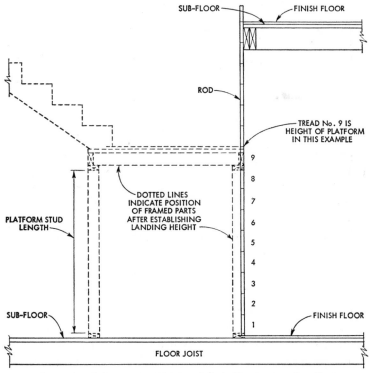

Fig. 6. Establishing the Height of Stair Platform or Landing

Finish wall stringers may need extra length to provide sufficient stock to meet the baseboard at top and bottom of the stairway. See Figure 5. Finish stringers housed into a post at top and bottom may be cut shorter and thus afford a saving in lumber. See Figure 13.

LAYOUT PROCEDURES

There are several layout procedures with which the stair builder must be familiar in laying out a stair horse, a stair stringer, a newel post, or a piece of handrailing.

Tread and Riser Thickness. The thickness of the risers and treads will vary according to specifications and must be determined before layout work can be started.

The tread and riser dimensions are calculated from the face side of the riser and tread. However, a stair horse is laid out to the *back side* of the riser and the *under side* of the tread (Fig. 7). On the other hand,

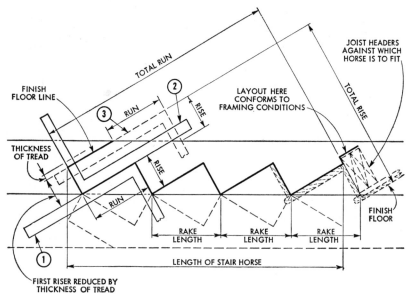

Fig. 7. Layout of a Stair Horse

a housed stair stringer is laid out to the face of the riser and tread (Fig. 3). In all cases the nosing is disregarded so far as the layout work is concerned.

Equalizing the First-Tread Rise. It has been established as a matter of safety that each step in a stairway should have the same rise. This rise may be obtained by calculation, as has been described.

In all stair layout, whether for a horse or stringer, the first or bottom tread requires a special procedure to equalize its rise with the rise of the other treads.

The problem arises from the fact that the distance between the finish floor and the face or top side of the first tread is affected by the thickness of the tread and the thickness of the finish floor. Other influencing factors depend on whether the horse or stringer rests on the sub-floor or the finish floor. See Figure 8.

Equalizing the first-tread rise *automatically adjusts* the top-tread rise to be the same as all others.

This equalizing procedure, known as *dropping the horse* can be reduced to two simple rules:

Rule 1. When the horse or stringer is set on a finish floor, cut off from the bottom of the horse or stringer an amount equal to the thickness of the tread. See Figure 8A.

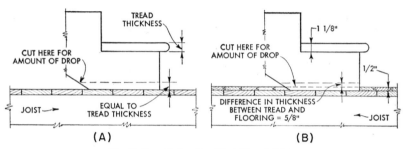

Fig. 8. Equalizing the First-Tread Rise

Rule 2. When the horse or stringer is placed on the subfloor before the hardwood floor is laid, cut off from the bottom of the horse or stringer the difference between the thickness of the hardwood flooring and the tread. See Figure 8B.

To illustrate: If the tread is $1\frac{1}{8}''$ thick and the hardwood flooring is $\frac{1}{2}''$ thick, the horse must be dropped $1\frac{1}{8}''$ minus $\frac{1}{2}''$ or $\frac{5}{8}''$.

Rake Length of Step. The rake length of a step is equivalent to the hypotenuse of the right triangle whose base and altitude are formed by the tread run and tread rise (Fig. 7). For accurate layout work, the rake length should first be determined. After the first rise and run are established, the rake length of each step should be *stepped off* and squared on the edges of the pair of stringers to assure uniformity and accuracy in locating each step.

Layout of a Sawed Stair Horse. Figure 7 shows a method of laying out a stair horse with a steel square.

1. Locate the determined tread rise on the tongue and the tread run on the blade of the steel square. Use stair gages for accurate work. See Figure 4 of Chapter III.

2. Place the square in position 1 and mark the rise and run.

3. Shift to position 2 and mark the first rise.

4. Determine the rake length and mark off the required number of steps.

5. Equalize the first rise, as in position 3, to determine the base or lower end cut.

6. Lay out the top end by methods similar to those employed at the bottom.

Built-up Stair Horse.   A built-up stair horse is constructed by nailing triangular blocks to a piece of 2″ x 4″ or 2″ x 6″ framing stock. The layout of the bottom and top depends on the framing conditions of the job. See Fig. 4C.

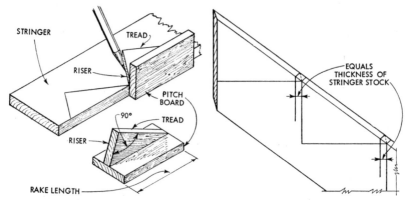

Fig. 9. Using a Pitch Board   Fig. 10. Laying Out a Miter Cut on a Stringer

Pitch Board Layout and Use.   A pitch board instead of a steel square is often used for laying out a stair stringer (Figs. 9 and 14).

Layout of an Open-Faced or Mitered Stringer.   An *open-faced* or *mitered stringer* is laid out in much the same manner as a stair horse except that the bottom and top ends must be fitted into the stair newels. The term *mitered stringer* refers to an open stairway in which one or both ends of the risers are mitered into the stringer, as in Figure 11. The tread ends projecting beyond the face of the stringer are known as *return ends* or *return nosings*. Balusters may be fitted to each tread as shown.

The stringer should be laid out from the top down and the marks should be made on the exposed face. The risers and treads are laid out in the same manner as for a stair horse except for the method of cutting the miter as illustrated in Figure 10:

1. The first set of riser marks should be made lightly with a pencil and need not be full length.

2. Only one miter cut need be laid out, the remaining miters being picked up with a bevel square. The miter is determined by marking off a distance in front of the riser mark equal to the thickness of the stringer,

squaring off both lines, and drawing a diagonal as in Figure 10. The diagonal represents the required miter which may be picked up with the bevel square and transferred to the other riser marks in the stringer.

A short cut method to determine the miter angle is to cut along the top tread line on the stringer. This leaves a horizontal surface on which a 45° miter may be directly laid out by means of a miter square.

Stringer-to-Newel Layout. Figure 12 shows the plan and elevation of an open-faced stair with a bull-nose starting step. Figure 13 shows the method of laying out the bottom and top ends of the same stringer. An additional piece of finish stock is glued to the stringer at the bottom

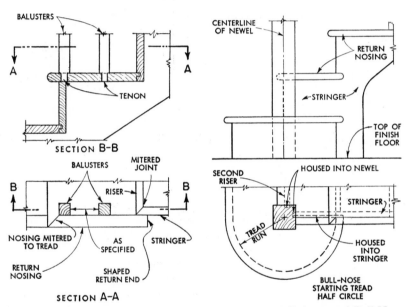

Fig. 11. Open-Faced Stringer Construction

Fig. 12. Newel, Stringer, and Bull-Nose Starting Step

end to provide a finish to the floor line and to provide stock to cut in the housing for the return end of the bull-nose step.

The *second riser* is housed into the newel with its face centered on the newel. At the *second rise*, the stair stringer is also housed into the newel. The *second tread* of the stringer is cut to fit around the newel, with allowance for the depth of the newel housing.

In the layout of the top end of the stringer, the face of the *top riser* is centered on the newel, and the *last tread* of the stringer is cut to fit around the newel, with allowance for the depth of the newel housing.

Layout of a Closed or Housed Stringer. The layout of a closed or housed stringer differs from that of an open-faced stringer in two basic ways:

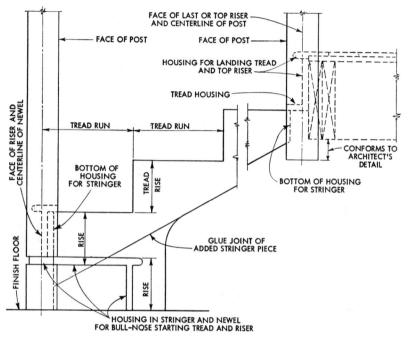

Fig. 13. Layout of Bottom and Top Ends of Open Stringer

1. In the closed stringer, the riser and tread are laid out to the face, as in Figure 14, rather than the under or back side.

2. The points of intersection of the rise and tread are laid out on a

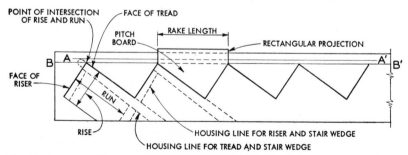

Fig. 14. Layout of Closed or Housed Stringer Using Pitch Board to Lay Out Tread and Riser Lines.

line drawn on the face of, and parallel to, the edge of the stringer, as shown in Figure 14.

The layout may be done in the following manner:

1. Draw line A-A′ about 1″ from the edge of the stock.
2. Make a full-size layout of the nosing at the proper angle to the rake and draw the line B-B′.
3. Make a pitch board conforming to the rise, run, and the distance of B-B′ from the edge of the stock.
4. Lay out the rake length of each step and complete the layout of the risers and treads, placing the pitch board as accurately as possible. Use a sharp knife for a scribe if the housing is to be done with hand tools.

Wedge Templates. In order to mark the bottom edge of the housing of each tread, a wedge-shaped tread template is made to the proper dimensions as shown in Figure 15. The template should be made long

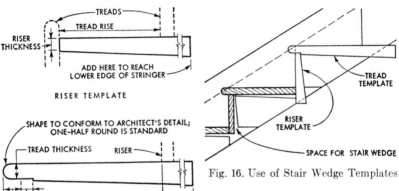

Fig. 16. Use of Stair Wedge Templates

Fig. 15. Stair Wedge Templates

enough to reach to the bottom edge of the stringer. The pitch of the stair wedge is determined by the stair builder and is applicable for all stairways, regardless of the tread rise and tread run dimensions. The riser template is made to the same angle as the tread housing to permit the use of stair wedges of the same pitch.

Figure 16 shows a tread template in position for the marking of the lower edge of the housing. If the treads are accurately molded, the nosing is projected the proper distance and marked.

On first-class work, the nosing of each tread is fitted individually and the tread housing marked and cut accordingly. The stair builder positions each appropriately numbered tread, keeping the back edge of the tread flush with the riser housing, and marking the exact shape of the nosing.

Boxed Stringer. A boxed stringer consists of two stringers connected by a shoe rail (Fig. 17). The inside stringer is similar to a wall stringer and is housed to receive the treads and risers. The face, or outside, stringer is plain or molded but *not housed* and forms the finish trim on the rake of the stairs.

The over-all, or face-to-face, dimensions of the box stringer are determined to some extent by the size of the balusters and the width of the shoe rail.

As a unit, the boxed stringer is necessarily centered on the newel post to permit the centering of the balusters and stair rail on the newel.

The face of the wall or panel below the boxed stringer is centered on the newel, and molding is placed under the face stringer to form a molded finish.

Several other factors may be noted:

1. The standard height of platform railing is 2′10″ to 3′0″.

2. The spacing of the balusters on a box stringer does not necessarily coincide with the tread run.

3. The standard height of the stair rail is 2′6″ to 2′8″ when measured from the top of the finished tread and parallel with the face of the riser.

4. The face of each riser that is housed into the newel is located on the center of the newel.

The layout for housing a boxed stringer is similar to that for a closed stringer. The layout for joining the boxed stringer to the newel is based on the same principle used for the layout of an open-faced stringer.

Layout of a Stair Newel. Figure 17 illustrates from four sides the layout of a stair newel for a boxed stringer. The stair builder usually places the newel horizontally on a bench when laying it out. The layout procedure is as follows:

1. Establish point A on the center line of side 1 of the newel where the top edge of the stair rail is to meet the newel.

2. Draw the rake line of the stair rail so that it passes through A and intersects the center line of the newel at B on side 2.

3. Lay out from B to C on side 2 the specified height of the stair rail (in this case 2′ 6″).

4. Lay out the housing for the edge and the nosing of tread #3 and riser #3 where they meet the newel on side 2 and on side 1.

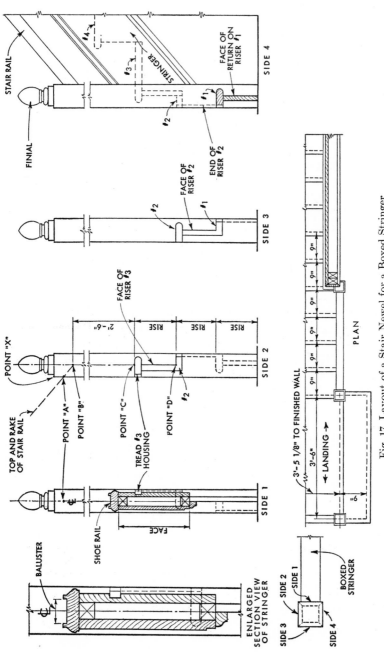

Fig. 17. Layout of a Stair Newel for a Boxed Stringer

5. Lay out the housing for the landing nosing (step #2) where it meets the newel on sides 2 and 3.

6. Lay out the housing for riser #2 where it meets the newel on side 3.

7. Lay out the housing for the edge and the nosing of tread #1 where it meets the newel on sides 3 and 4.

8. Lay out the housing for the return riser of the first step where it meets the newel on side 4.

9. Determine the face-to-face width and the vertical height of the boxed stringer where it meets the newel on side #1. These dimensions determine the layout of the stringer housing. See the enlarged section view.

Stair Rail Layout. In the layout of a straight rail between newels, the length and rake of the rail is determined by the layout of the stringer below it.

In the layout of a stair rail involving a gooseneck and easements (Fig. 18), a full size layout of the rake of the stair rail is necessary. The exact relationship between the center line and the height of a newel can be established by drawing an arc based on the radius of the stair rail easing tangent to the horizontal or vertical position, whichever is required.

The distance between the center of the newel and the vertical part of the gooseneck is determined by the size and design of the newel and the clearance desired between the stair rail and the newel.

The length of the straight run of stair rail is equal to the distance between the points of tangency of the easement and gooseneck. These points may be transferred to the stringer directly below and the distance between them measured to get the length of straight rail.

Figure 19 illustrates various types of stair rail crooks and easements. Each crook has to be tailored to the requirements of a given stairway according to rise, run, and direction. The layout of these crooks is not within the scope of this book, as a small volume could be devoted to this subject.

REVIEW QUESTIONS

1. Define the following terms: *staircase, flight, landing, wellhole, riser, tread, starting tread, nosing, return nosing, total run, total rise, tread run, headroom.*

2. What is the basic difference between a stair horse and a stair stringer?

3. What is a housed stringer?

4. What is the purpose of a stair wedge?

5. Why must the first or bottom riser of a stairway be equalized?

6. The sum of the tread run and the rise of one step, exclusive of the nosing, should be approximately how many inches?

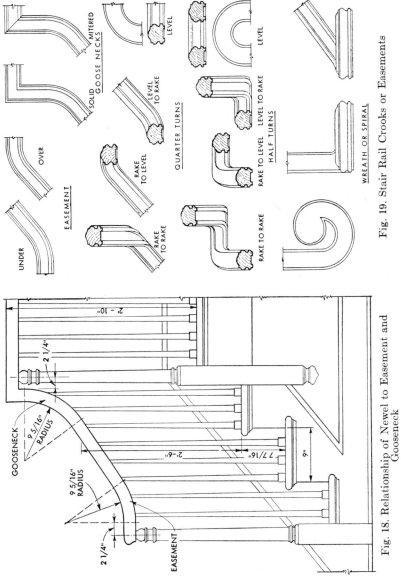

UNDER   OVER

EASEMENT

SOLID   MITERED

GOOSE NECKS

LEVEL

RAKE
TO LEVEL

LEVEL
TO RAKE

QUARTER TURNS

RAKE
TO RAKE

RAKE TO LEVEL   LEVEL TO RAKE

HALF TURNS

LEVEL

WREATH OR SPIRAL

Fig. 19. Stair Rail Crooks or Easements

GOOSENECK

9 5/16"
RADIUS

9 5/16" RADIUS

2 1/4"

2 1/4"

2'-10"

2'-6"

7 7/16"

9"

EASEMENT

Fig. 18. Relationship of Newel to Easement and
Gooseneck

APPENDIX

STANDARD CABINETMAKING ABBREVIATIONS

A

"A" face: First quality face
AD: Air dried
a.l.: All lengths
Amb.: Amber (glass)
Amb. Cath.: Amber cathedral (glass)
Apr.: Apron
Asb.: Asbestos

Astg.: Astragal
Att. Sh.: Attic sash
av.: Average
av. l.: Average length
av. w.: Average width
a.w.: All widths

B

Bal.: Baluster
B. & C.: Bead and cove
Basmt.: Basement
Bat.: Batten
Band M.: Band molding
Band. 1 S.: Banded one side
Band. 2 S.: Banded two sides
B.B.: Back band
BBS: Box bark strips
B. & Btr.: (quality) and better
B. 1 S.: Beaded one side
B. 2 S.: Beaded two sides
Bch. (Bir.): Birch
B. & C.B.: Beaded and center beaded
Bd. (bd.): Board
Bdl. (bdl.): Bundle
bdl.bk.s.: Bundle bark strips
bd.ft.: Board foot (feet) (measure)
B.F.: Board foot (feet) (measure)
B.F.M.: Board foot (feet) measure
Bd.Mldg.: Bed molding
Bd. & Pt.: Bed and point
Bet. Jbs.: Between jambs
Bet. Gl.: Between glass
Bet. S. (B.S.): Between shoulders
Bev.: Beveled
B. for G.: Bead for glass

Bev. Plt. (B.P.): Beveled plate glass
Bev.P.G. (B.Pl.G.): Beveled plate glass
Bev. Stkg.: Bevel sticking
Bk. Case: Back case
Bld.: Blind
B.R.: Bedroom
B.Sh.: Barn sash
Bs. Mldg.: Base molding
B/L: Bill of lading
Bld. St.: Blind stop
Bldg.: Building
b.m.: Board (foot) measure
B.M.R.: Beaded meeting rabbet
B.P.: Base plug
Bot. Rl. (B.Rl.): Bottom rail
Bot. Sh.: Bottom sash
Br. Opg.: Brick opening
Brkft. Nk.: Breakfast nook
Brkt.: Bracket
Br. Ven.: Brick veneer
Bs.: Base
Bs. Blox: Base blocks
B.S.: Both sides
Buf.: Buffet
B.W.: Black walnut (American)

C

c. (CL.), (₤): Center line
C.C.Sh.: China closet sash
C to C (C-C), (C/C): Center to center
C.C.Dr.: China closet door
C. & B.: Cove and bead
Cab.: Cabinet
Carvg.: Carving
cas.: Casing
Cas. Sh.: Casement sash
Casg.: Casing
Casmt.: Casement
Caswk.: Casework
Cat.: Catalogue
Cath.: Cathedral (glass)
Cel. Sh.: Cellar sash
C.F.: Cellar frame
Cham.: Chamfer
Ch. Cl.: China closet
Ch. Rl.: Chair rail
Cir. E.: Circle end
Cir. Hd.: Circle head
Cir. Top: Circle top
Ck.Rl.(Ck.R.): Check rail

Ck.R. Wds.: Check rail windows
Cl.: Carload
C1F.: Clear one face
Clg.: Ceiling
Clr.: Clear
CM.: Center-matched
C.M.: Crown mold
C.M.C.: Crown mold cap
C.O.: Cased opening
C.O.D.: Cash on delivery
Col.: Column
com. (Com.): Common
Comb. Dr.: Combination door
#1 combet: #1 common and better
Compo.: Composition
Cor. Bd.: Corner bead
Cop.: Copper
Cp. M.: Cap molding
Csg.: Casing
Ctg.: Crating
cu.ft.: Cubic foot
Cup.: Cupboard
Cyp.: Cypress

D

D.A.: Double acting
Dbl.: Double
Dbl. Bd.: Double-beaded
D&CM: Dressed and center-matched
D.C.: Drip cap
Dch. Dr.: Dutch door
Deld.: Delivered
Det.: Detail
D.F.: Douglas fir
D.H.: Double hung
Dia.: Diameter
Dim.: Dimension
Din. Rm.: Dining room
": Ditto
D&H: Dressed and headed
D&M: Dressed and matched
D.M.&B.: Dressed, matched, and beaded
Dn.: Down
Div.: Divided

Do.: Ditto
Dr.: Door (or doors)
Dres.: Dresser
Dr. Fr.,(Dr. Fra.): Door Frame
Dr. Jb.: Door Jamb
Dr. Tr.: Door Trim
Drw. (Drws.): Drawers
D.S.: Drop siding
D.S.: Downspout
D.S.: Double strength (glass)
D.S.A.: Double strength (glass) grade A
D&SM: Dressed and standard-matched
D2S&CM: Dressed two sides and center-matched
D2S&M (D2S&SM): Dressed two sides and center (or standard) matched
D.T.: Double thick

E

E.: Edge
E&CB1S: Edge and center bead one side
E&CB2S: Edge and center bead two sides
E&CV1S: Edge and center V (grooved) one side
E&CV2S: Edge and center V (grooved) two sides
E/B: Expense bill
ECM: Ends center-matched
E.D.F.: Edge (grain) douglas fir
EG (E.G.): Edge grain

El.: Elevation
Elev.: Elevator
Ellip. Hd.: Elliptical head
EM: End-matched (either center or standard)
Emb.: Embossed
Enc.: Enclosure
Ent.: Entrance
ESM: Ends standard-matched
Ex.: Extra
Exc.: Excavate
Ext.: Exterior

F

FAS: First and second
F.BD.: Full bound
f.bk.: Flat back
FBM: Feet board measure
Fch.Dr.: French door
Fch.Wd.: French window
fcty.: Factory (lumber)
Frt.: Freight
Feet b.m.: Feet board measure
feet s.m.: Feet surface measure
F.G.: Flat grain
F.G.: Fuel gas
Fig.: Figured
Fin.: Finish
Fin. S.: Finished size
Fl.: Floor
Fl.B.: Flour bin
Fl. Dr.: Floor drain
flg.: Flooring

Flor.: Florentine (glass)
Fl. Pan.: Flat panel
FM: Face measure
F.M.: Flush mold
F.M.1 S.: Flush molded one side
F.M.2 S.: Flush molded two sides
' Foot (feet)
F.O.B.: Free on board
f.o.k.: Free of knots
F-p.: Fireproof
Fra.: Frame
F.R.G.: Figured red gum
Frm.: Frame (framing)
Frt. Dr.: Front door
ft.: Foot (feet)
Ftgs.: Footings
Ft. Sh.: Front sash
Ft. Wd.: Front window (transom window)

G

Galv.: Galvanized (wire)
Gar. Dr.: Garage door
G.I.: Galvanized Iron
G.L.: Grade line (ground line)
Gl.: Glass (glazed)

Goth.: Gothic
G1S: Good one side
Goth. Hd.: Gothic head
G.R.: Grooved roofing
G.S.: Glass size

H

H.bk.: Hollow back
Hdl.: Handle
Hdwd.: Hardwood
Hept.: Heptagon (seven-sided)
Hex.: Hexagon (six-sided)

H. or M.: Hit or miss
H.P.: High point
Hrt.: Heart
Hrtwd.: Heartwood

" Inch (inches)
in.: Inch (inches)
Ins.: Inside
Insul.: Insulation

Jb.: Jamb

Kd.: Kiln dried

Lam.: Laminated
Lat.: Lattice
Lav.: Lavatory
lbr.: Lumber
L-d.: Leader drain
Lgr.: Longer
lgth.: length
L.G.: Leaded glass
Lin.: Lineal

M.: Thousand (thousands)
M. & B.: Matched and beaded
Mat.: Material
M. & V.: Matched & V'd
M.B.F. (MBF): Thousand board feet
M.b.m.: Thousand (feet) board measure
M.C.: Medicine cabinet
MC.: Moisture content
M.C.Dr.: Medicine cabinet door
Mch.Sand.: Machine sanded
MCO.: Mill culls out
M.D & V.: Matched, dressed & V'd.
Meast.: Measurement
Merch.: Merchantable
Mhgy.: Mahogany
Millwk. (Mlwk.): Millwork

Number
No.: Number

O.A.: Over-all
Obs.: Obscure (glass)

I

Int.: Interior
Irg.Bd.: Ironing board
Is.F.Scr.: Inside full screen
Is.S.Scr.: Inside sliding half-screen

J

K

k.d.: Knocked down

L

Lin. ft.: Linear foot (feet)
Liv.Rm.: Living room
Lng.: Lining
L.P.: Loose pin
L.P.: Low point
L.R.: Lock rail
Lt.: Light (lights)
Lth.: Lath

M

Mir.: Mirror
Mir. Dr.: Mirror door
m.l.: Mixed lengths
Mldg.: Molding
Moss: Moss (glass)
Mort.: Mortise
Mpl.: Maple
MR. (M.R.): Mill run
M.R.: Meeting rail
M.s.m.: Thousand (feet) surface measure
Mt.Rl.: Meeting rail
Mty: Empty or unglazed
Mull.: Mullion
Munt.: Muntin
m.w.: Mixed widths
M.W.L.: Mixed widths (and) lengths

N

N.P.: Nickel plate
Nwl.: Newel

O

o.c.: On center
O.Csg.: Outside casing

Octg. (oct.): Octagon (eight)
O.F.S.: Outside full screen
O.G.: Ogee (sticking)
Opg.: Opening
1/S: One side
Ord.: Order

Orn.: Ornament
O/S: Outside
O.S. Opg.: Outside opening
O.S.S.: Outside sliding (half) screen
Ovo.: Ovolo

P

P.: Planed
Pan.: Panel
Para Hd.: Parabola head
Pat. (P.): Pattern
lb. (#): Pound
P.&B.: Plowed and bored
P. & P.: Pockets and pulleys
P.B.S.D.: Panel bottom screen door
Pc.: Piece
Pct.Mo.: Picture mold
Ped.: Pedestal
Perg.: Pergola
Phil.: Philippine
Ph.Mhgy.: Philippine mahogany
Pil.: Pilaster
Pky.: Pecky
Pl. (Plas): Plaster
Pl.: Plate (glass)
Pl.Gl.: Plate glass
Pl. Gum: Plain gum
Pln.: Plain (sawn)
Pl.P.Gl: Plain plate glass
Pl. Plt.: Plain plate (glass)
Pl.R. (Pl.Rl.): Plain rail
Pl.R.O.: Plain (sawn) red oak
Pl.R.Wds.: Plain rail windows
Pl.W.O.: Plain (sawn) white oak

Pn.: Partition
Pol.P.: Polished plate (glass)
P.O.C.: Port Orford cedar (white)
Pop.: Poplar
Po.Wire: Polished wire (glass)
P.P.: Plain plate (glass)
P.P.: Ponderosa pine
P.P.Mir.: Plain plate mirror
Pr.: Pair
Pr.Blds.: Pair (of) blinds
Pr.CC Drs.: Pair of china closet doors
Pr.CC Sh.: Pair of china closet sash
Pr.Csmt.: Pair (of) casement
Pr.Fch.Drs.: Pair (of) French doors
Pr.Is.F.Scr.: Pair of inside full screens
P.R.Oak: Plain (sawn) red oak
Pr.Os.F.Scr.: Pair (of) outside full screens
Pr.Scr.Drs.: Pair (of) screen doors
P.S. (P.St.): Pulley stiles
P.Stp.: Parting stop
Pt.: Point
Ptg.Bd.: Parting bead
P.W.O. (P.W.oak): Plain (sawn) white oak

Q

Q.R.G. (1/4 R.G.): Quarter (sawn) red gum
Q.R.O. (1/4 R.O.): Quarter (sawn) red oak
Qr.Rd.: Quarter-round
Qr.S.: Quarter-sawn

Qtd. Quartered (quarter-sawn)
Quad.: Quadruple (four)
Quan.: Quantity
Quin.: Quintuple (five)
Q.W.O. (1/4 W.O.): Quarter (sawn) white oak

R

R.: Radius
R.: Rail (rails)
R.: Riser
Rab. (Rabt.): Rabbet (rabbeted)

rad.: Radiator
r.c.: Round corner
R.C.: Rotary cut
R.D.F.: Random (grain) Douglas fir

rdm.: Random
reg.: Register
Rel.Arch: Relieving arch
res. (RS): Resawn
Rev.: Revision
rfg.: Roofing
R.G.: Red gum
rip.: Ripped
Riv.: Riveted
r.l.: Random lengths

S.: Stile (stiles)
S.: Sink
S.: Switch
sap.: Sapwood
Scr.: Screen
Scr.Dr.: Screen door
sdg.: Siding
Sh.: Shorts
S&CM: Surfaced one or two sides and center-matched
S&SM: Surfaced one or two sides and standard-matched
SB.: Standard bead
sd.: Seasoned
S.D.: Sash door
Sdbd.: Sideboard
Sd.Lt. (Sd.lts): Side light (sidelights)
Sec.: Section
Seg.Hd.: Segment head
sel.: Select (grade)
Seg.Top: Segment top
Sept. (Hept.): Septagon (seven)
S.E.Sdg.: Square-edge siding
Set Blds.: Set of blinds
Sex. (Hex): Sextet (six)
s.f.: Surface foot
S4S.: Surfaced four sides
S4SCS: Surfaced four sides with a calking seam on each edge
Sftwd.: Softwood
S.G.: Sap gum
Sgl.: Single
Sh.: Sash
Sh.D.: Shipping dry
Sh.Dr.: Sash door
Shlp.: Shiplap
Shtrs.: Shutters

R.M.O.S.: Raised mold outside
R.M.1 S.: Raised mold one side
R.M.2 S.: Raised mold two sides
rnd.: Round
Ro.: Rough
R.Sdg.: Rustic Siding
r.w.: Random widths
Rwd.: Redwood
RWL.: Random widths (and) lengths

S

Sldg.: Sliding
S&M: Surfaced and matched
S.M.: Solid mold
S.M.: Standard-matched
sm.: Surface measure
sm.: Solid molding
smkd.: Smoked (dried)
smk. stnd.: Smoke stained
snd.: Sound
SND: Sap no defect
Snd2Sds.: Sound two sides
S1E.: Surfaced one edge
S1S.: Surfaced one side
S1S1E.: Surfaced one side and one edge
S.P.: Soil pipe
S.P.: Sugar pine
Spl.: Special
Spl.: Spline
Spr.: Spruce (Sitka)
sq.: Square
Sq.E.&S.: Square edge and sound
Sq.Ft.: Square foot (feet)
Sq. (Sqrs.): Squares
Sq.Hd.: Square head
S.R.: Steam riser
S. & R.: Stile and rail
S.Rt.: Steam return
ss: Short shorts (12″ to 23″)
S.S.: Single strength (glass)
S.S.Blds.: Stationary slat blinds
St. (Stl.): Stile
St.: Stone
Sta.Sl.: Stationary slat
std.: Standard
St.Dr.: Storm door
St.Gr.: Straight grained

Stk.: Stock
Stkg.: Sticking
Stl.: Stool
stnd.: Stained
St.P.: Stand pipe
stp.: Stepping
Stp.: Stop (stops)
St.Sh.: Storm sash
S2E.: Surfaced two edges
S2S: Surfaced two sides

S2S&CM: Surfaced two sides and
center-matched
S2S&SM: Surfaced two sides and
standard-matched
S2S&M: Surfaced two sides and
center (or standard) matched
Stud.: Studding
S.U.: Set up
SW: Sound wormy
Syc.: Sycamore

T

T.: Thread
TB&S: Top, bottom, and sides
T. & G."V": Tongued and grooved V
(Joint)
Ten.: Tenon
Th.: Thick
Toil. Dr.: Toilet door
T.R.: Top rail
Tr. (Trans.): Transom
Tr.: Trim
Tr.Br.: Transom bar
Thres.: Threshold

Trd.: Tread
Trel.: Trellis
Trip.: Triple (three)
Tr.Sh.: Transom sash
Tr.Wd.: Transom window
T.C.: Terra cotta
Tbrs.: Timbers
T&G: Tongued and grooved
T.R.C.: Tennessee red cedar
Tud.Hd.: Tudor head
Twin: Two (openings in unit)

U

U.: Universal
Uns.: Unselected
Unsl.Gum: Unselected gum

Uns.Bir. (Unsl. Bch): Unselected
birch

V

V.: Vent. or ventilator
V: V grooved
VCV: V grooved and center grooved
Ven.: Veneer (veneered)
Vest.: Vestibule
V.G.: Vertical grain

V.G.D.F.: Vertical grained Douglas
Fir
Vit.: Vitrified
V1S: V grooved one side
V2S: V grooved two sides

W

W.: Waste
Wains.Cap: Wainscot cap
w.a.l.: Wider, all lengths
W.C.: Water closet
Wd.: Window (windows)
Wd.Fr.: Window frame
Wdr.: Wider
W.Gl.: Wire glass

WHAD: Worm holes a defect
WHND: Worm holes no defect
W.I.: Wrought iron
Wk.T.: Work table
Wp.: Waterproof
W.P.: White pine
Wt.: Weight
Wts. & C.: Weights and cord

X

x: By, as 2 x 4

X Pan.: Cross panels

Y

Yd.: Yard

Y.P.: Yellow pine

INDEX